REVISE HUMAN BIOLOGY

A COMPLETE REVISION COURSE FOR
GCSE

Morton Jenkins BSc C.Biol MIBiol

Section Leader in Science, Coleg Glan Hafren, Cardiff

Chief Examiner GCSE Biology, WJEC

EDUCATIONAL

BPP Letts Educational Ltd

First published 1983
Revised 1987, 1989, 1992

Illustrations: Chartwell and Tek Art

© Morton Jenkins 1983, 1987, 1989, 1992
© Illustrations: BPP (Letts Educational) Ltd 1983, 1987, 1989, 1992
© BPP (Letts Educational) Ltd
Aldine House
Aldine Place
142–144 Uxbridge Road
London W12 8AW

British Library Cataloguing in Publication Data

Jenkins, Morton
  Revise Human Biology: a complete revision
  course for GCSE.—4th ed.—(Letts
  study aids)
  1. Human biology
  I. Title
  599.9   QP36

  ISBN 1 85758 010 9

Printed and bound in Great Britain by
Staples Printers St Albans Ltd

PREFACE

The aim of this text is to help students of Human Biology to attain their highest level of achievement at one of the most important tests in their careers. Students often find it useful to plan their revision according to some predetermined pattern, during which weaknesses can be recognized and eliminated so that confidence can grow, and so the primary consideration has been to present main principles on which study can be based.

A sound knowledge of facts and an understanding of principles are prerequisites in attempting any examination and can be antidotes to 'examination nerves' which, in many instances, result from a fear of not being adequately prepared. There is no substitute for hard work of the right kind on the part of the student. Indeed, it can be said that a person does not really know a certain fact unless it is more difficult to forget the fact than it is to recall it. The lay-out is intended to help students to arrange factual knowledge according to a logical pattern and to understand biological concepts as applied to man.

The author has written the text using his experience as a Chief Examiner in GCSE Biology and, as a member of the teams of writers, responsible for the National Criteria for Biology and Grade Related Criteria for Biology. The author was also appointed as Subject Leader for Wales in GCSE Biology to train Heads of Biology Departments throughout Wales in the initial developments of GCSE Biology.

Acknowledgements

In preparing this book I have been assisted by the constructive criticism of Dr G. Frith, Mr J. Haddow, Mrs L. Hajdukiewicz, Mr L. Bender and Mrs P. Rowlinson. I am also grateful to the London Express News and Feature services for permission to use their reference for the illustration on page 93, and to the Examination Boards within the following Examining Groups, Northern Examination Association, Midland Examining Group, London East Anglian Group, Southern Examining Group, Welsh Joint Education Committee and Northern Ireland Schools Examination Council, who gave their permission to reproduce questions from their examination papers.

Please note that the Examination Boards accept no responsibility for the accuracy or method of working in the answers given to sample questions.

Thanks are due also to Bruce Coleman for the photographs used for Fig. 3.49 and Fig. 5.65 and to Philip Harris Biological Ltd for the photographs used for Fig. 3.36(a) and Fig. 5.52.

Morton Jenkins 1989

CONTENTS

INTRODUCTION AND GUIDE TO USING THIS BOOK

This revision guide has been prepared for those who need help in reaching a standard of work appropriate to a GCSE examination in Human Biology. It has been written for the requirements of all the British Examination Boards. Information is given concerning:

—learning and remembering
—devising a revision programme
—syllabus requirements
—the GCSE system
—topics to be learned and understood
—advice on answering examination questions
—types of examination questions to be expected
—acceptable answers to examination questions
—advice on experimental skills and coursework assessment.

Learning and Remembering

The best way to learn about any science is through an investigatory approach, and most teachers would agree that students remember most facts if they have learned and understood them via experiments which they have carried out themselves. Unfortunately, there are some topics in Human Biology which cannot be learned in this way and one has to use second-hand data and certain well-known aids to memory. Repeated reading of notes and texts is one way of remembering certain facts. The construction of simple flow diagrams using key words is another commonly used method. Topics are summarized by using key words, linked logically with arrows. But whichever method you use, none is a substitute to *understanding*. This book is structured in such a way that it can be used to learn, understand and revise Human Biology in a simple and straightforward manner.

Devising a Revision Programme

The importance of beginning your revision well in advance of your examination cannot be overemphasized. You will obtain a fair idea of your memory capacity by reading a part of a text which is new to you and, after 40 minutes, writing out how many of the facts you can remember. The average person will recall about 50%, then after an interval of 10 minutes, 25% of the original material will be remembered. After two days you will probably recall no more than 15%. These are average figures, of course, so do not be depressed if your scores are lower, or complacent if they are higher. Your capacity for retention will be influenced by the amount of sleep that you have had, what other matters are on your mind, and your interest in the topic. Even 15% of the original information may seem to be a very small amount but the percentage can be dramatically increased by revising the original text after one week, and then again after two weeks. By this time, the facts will now be retained by your so-called long-term memory store and up to 80% of the original material may be recalled in this way. Bearing in mind that the time each student can maintain concentration will vary considerably, there are certain revision principles which can be followed:

1 Make a realistic estimate of how much you can revise each week over a period beginning perhaps three months before your examination.

2 Divide your revision time into 30-minute periods separated by intervals of about 10 minutes.

3 Use the revision notes and summary tables in this text to help you.

Table of analysis of GCSE syllabuses

	Welsh Joint Education Committee	London and East Anglian Group	Midland Examining Group	Southern Examining Group	Northern Examination Association	Northern Ireland
Number of papers	1	2	2 or 3	1 or 2	2	2 or 3
Number of hours for each paper	Paper 1 — 2; Paper 2 — 2½	Paper 1 — 2; Papers 2 or 3 — 1½	Paper 1 — 40 min; Paper 2 — 1⅓; Paper 3 — 1¼	Paper 1 — 2; Paper 3 — 1½	Paper 1 — 2; 2P — 1½; 2Q — 1½	Paper 1 — 1; Paper 2 — 1¼; Paper 3 — 1¼
Teacher assessment %	20	20	20	20	30	20
Differentiation model	Papers 1 or 2	Papers 1+2 or 3	Papers 1+2 or Papers 1+2+3	Papers 1 or 1+3	Papers 1+P or Q	Papers 1+2 or Papers 1+2+3
Available grades	Paper 1 G–C; Paper 2 E–A	Papers 1+2 G–C; Papers 1+3 E–A	Papers 1+2 G–C; Papers 1+2+3 E–A	Paper 1 G–C; Papers 1+3 E–A	Papers 1+P G–C; Papers 1+Q E–A	Papers 1+2 G–C; Papers 1+2+3 E–A
Theme 1						
1.1 The cell as a unit of life	●	●	●	●	●	●
1.2 The importance of enzymes	●	●	●	●	●	●
1.3 Comparison of green plants and animals	●	●	●	●	●	●
1.4 Distinction between cells, tissues and organs	●	●	●	●	●	●
1.5 Characteristics of living organisms	●	●	●	●	●	●
1.6 Conditions necessary for all forms of life	●	●	●	●	●	●
1.7 Man as a mammal	●	●	●	●		●
1.8 Man as a product of an evolutionary process		●	○			○
Theme 2						
2.1 Interdependence						
2.1.1 The interdependence of plants and animals	●	●	●	●	●	●
2.1.2 Decomposition cycles	●	●	●	●	●	●
2.1.3 Plants as the ultimate source of man's food	●	●	●	●	●	●
2.1.4 The world food problems	●	○		○	●	●
2.1.5 Growth of populations	●	○	○	●	●	●
2.1.6 Population control	○	●	●	●	●	●
2.2 Disease						
2.2.1 Bacteria	●	●	●	●	●	●
2.2.2 Culture of bacteria					●	
2.2.3 Bacteria and disease	●	●	●	●	●	●
2.2.4 Some diseases caused by bacteria	○	○	○	○	○	○
2.2.5 Food preservation	●	●	●	●	●	●
2.2.6 Hygienic preserving, handling and distribution of milk	○	○	○	○	○	○
2.2.7 Microbial production processes		●		●	●	●
2.2.8 Some diseases caused by viruses	○	○	○	○	○	
2.2.9 Notifiable diseases	○	○	○	○	○	
2.2.10 Antibiotics	●	●	●	●	●	●
2.2.11 Antimicrobial methods	●	●	●	●	●	●
2.2.12 Immunity	●	●	●	●	●	●
2.2.13 Protozoa and disease	○	○	○			○
2.2.14 Nematodes				○		
2.2.15 Diseases caused by fungi	○	○	○		○	○
2.2.16 Vectors	○	○	○	○	○	○
2.2.17 Inherited diseases	○	○	○	○	○	○
2.2.18 Occupational diseases	○	○	○	○	○	○
2.2.19 Environmental diseases	○	○	○	○	○	○
2.2.20 Deficiency diseases	○	○	○	○	○	○
2.2.21 Cancer	○	○	○	○	○	●
2.3 Personal health and hygiene						
2.3.1 Care of skin, hair and teeth	●	○	○	○		●

	Welsh Joint Education Committee	London and East Anglian Group	Midland Examining Group	Southern Examining Group	Northern Examination Association	Northern Ireland
Number of papers	1	2	2 or 3	1 or 2	2	2 or 3
Number of hours for each paper	Paper 1 — 2; Paper 2 — 2½	Paper 1 — 2; Papers 2 or 3 — 1½	Paper 1 — 40 min; Paper 2 — 1⅓; Paper 3 — 1¼	Paper 1 — 2; Paper 3 — 1½	Paper 1 — 2; 2P — 1½; 2Q — 1½	Paper 1 — 1; Paper 2 — 1¼; Paper 3 — 1¼
Teacher assessment %	20	20	20	20	30	20
Differentiation model	Papers 1 or 2	Papers 1+2 or 3	Papers 1+2 or 1+2+3	Papers 1 or 1+3	Papers 1+P or Q	Papers 1+2 or 1+2+3
Available grades	Paper 1 G–C; Paper 2 E–A	Papers 1+2 G–C; Papers 1+3 E–A	Papers 1+2 G–C; Papers 1+2+3 E–A	Paper 1 G–C; Papers 1+3 E–A	Papers 1+P G–C; Papers 1+Q E–A	Papers 1+2 G–C; Papers 1+2+3 E–A
2.3.2 Characteristics of good posture	○	●	○	●		
2.3.3 Need for exercise	●	●	●	●	●	●
2.3.4 Need for sleep	●		○			
2.3.5 Drugs and the nervous system	●	●	●	●	●	●
2.3.6 Alcohol	●	●	●	●	●	●
2.4 Public health						
2.4.1 Water supply	●	○	●	●	●	●
2.4.2 Sewage disposal	●	●	●	●	●	●
2.4.3 Refuse disposal		○	●	●	●	●
2.4.4 Pollution of the environment	●	●	●	●	●	●
2.4.5 Conservation	●	○	○	●	●	●
2.4.6 The Public Health Service	○				○	●
2.4.7 International health control	○				○	○
Theme 3						
3.1 The skeleton and movement	●	●	●	●		●
3.1.1 Functions of the skeleton						●
3.1.2 The skeletal system		●	●	●		●
3.1.3 Axial skeleton		●	●	●		●
3.1.4 Appendicular skeleton	○	●	●	●	○	●
3.1.5 Joints	●	●	●	●	●	●
3.1.6 Principles of levers applied to the skeleton		○		●		
3.1.7 Bone		●	●	○		
3.1.8 Cartilage		●	●	○		
3.1.9 Muscles		●		○	○	○
3.1.10 The antagonistic action of pairs of muscles	●	●	●	●	●	●
3.1.11 The physiology of muscle action	○	●	●		●	○
3.2 The respiratory system						
3.2.1 The respiratory system and exchange of gases	●	●	●	●	●	●
3.2.2 Respiration and the provision of energy	●	●	●		●	●
3.2.3 The respiratory organs	●	●	●	●	○	●
3.2.4 The mechanism of breathing	●	●	●	●	●	●
3.2.5 The difference between inspired and expired air	●	●	●	●	○	●
3.2.6 Smoking and its effects on the respiratory system	●	●	●	●	○	●
3.3 Food and nutrition						
3.3.1 Classes of food	●	●	●	●	●	●
3.3.2 Basic food requirements	●	●	●	●	●	●
3.3.3 Vitamins	●	●	●	●	●	●
3.3.4 The importance of a balanced diet	●	●	●	●	●	●
3.3.5 Daily energy requirements	●	●	●	●	●	●
3.3.6 Food tests	●	●	●	●	●	●
3.4 The digestive system						
3.4.1 Principles of digestion	●	●	●	●		●
3.4.2 Teeth	●	●	●	●	●	●

	Welsh Joint Education Committee	London and East Anglian Group	Midland Examining Group	Southern Examining Group	Northern Examination Association	Northern Ireland
Number of papers	1	2	2 or 3	1 or 2	2	2 or 3
Number of hours for each paper	Paper 1 2 Paper 2 2½	Paper 1 2 Papers 2 or 3 1½	Paper 1 40 min Paper 2 1⅓ Paper 3 1¼	Paper 1 2 Paper 3 1½	Paper 1 2 2P 1½ 2Q 1½	Paper 1 1 Paper 2 1¼ Paper 3 1¼
Teacher assessment %	20	20	20	20	30	20
Differentiation model	Papers 1 or 2	Papers 1+2 or 3	Papers 1+2 or 1+2+3	Papers 1 or 1+3	Papers 1+P or Q	Papers 1+2 or 1+2+3
Available grades	Paper 1 G–C Paper 2 E–A	Papers 1+2 G–C Papers 1+3 E–A	Papers 1+2 G–C Papers 1+2+3 E–A	Paper 1 G–C Papers 1+3 E–A	Papers 1+P G–C Papers 1+Q E–A	Papers 1+2 G–C Papers 1+2+3 E–A
3.4.3 The alimentary canal	●	●	●	●	●	●
3.4.4 The liver	●	●	●	●	●	●
3.4.5 The chemistry of digestion	●	●	●	●	○	●
3.4.6 Investigations with digestive enzymes	●	●	●	●	●	●
3.4.7 The fate of the products of digestion	●	●	●	●	●	●
3.5 The cirulatory system						
3.5.1 The need for a blood system	●	●	●	●	●	●
3.5.2 Passage of blood through the heart	●	●	●	●	●	●
3.5.3 The pulse	●	●	●	●	●	●
3.5.4 Structure, function and action of the heart	●	●	●	●	●	●
3.5.5 Differences between arteries and veins	●	●	●	●	●	●
3.5.6 Structure and function of blood	●	●	●	●	●	●
3.5.7 Blood groups	○	●	○	●	●	●
3.5.8 The Rhesus factor		●	○			●
3.5.9 The lymphatic system	●	●	●	●	●	●
3.6 Regulation/homeostasis						
3.6.1 Excretion	●	●	●	●	●	●
3.6.2 The kidneys	●	●	●	●	○	●
3.6.3 Formation of urine	●	●	●	●	●	●
3.6.4 An artificial kidney	●	●	●	●	●	●
3.6.5 Skin	●	●	●	○	●	●
3.6.6 Organs concerned with homeostasis	●	●	●	●	●	●
3.6.7 Temperature regulation	●	●	●	●	●	●
3.7 Coordination						
3.7.1 Nervous coordination	●	●	●	●		●
3.7.2 The central nervous system	●	●	●	●		●
3.7.3 Reflex actions	●	●	●	●	●	●
3.7.4 Comparison of a typical spinal reflex action and a voluntary action	○	●	●	●	○	○
3.7.5 Nerves	○	●	●	●	○	
3.7.6 Nerve impulses	○	●	○	○		
3.7.7 The autonomic nervous system			○	○		
3.7.8 The eye	●	●	●	●	●	○
3.7.9 The ear	●	●	●	●	●	
3.7.10 Taste and smell	●	●		○	○	
3.7.11 Chemical coordination	●	●	●	●	●	●
3.7.12 Interaction of nervous and chemical coordination	○	○	●	○	○	○
Theme 4						
4.1 Reproduction and development						
4.1.1 Sexual reproduction	●	●	●	●	●	●
4.1.2 The reproductive system	●	●	●	●	●	●
4.1.3 The fate of an egg	●	●	●	●	●	●
4.1.4 Stages of development of an embryo	●	●	●	●	●	●
4.1.5 Care of the mother during pregnancy	●	●	●	●	●	●
4.1.6 Use and abuse of drugs during pregnancy	●	●	●	●	○	●

	Welsh Joint Education Committee	London and East Anglian Group	Midland Examining Group	Southern Examining Group	Northern Examination Association	Northern Ireland
Number of papers	1	2	2	1 or 2	2	2 or 3
Number of hours for each paper	Paper 1 2 Paper 2 2½	Paper 1 2 Paper 2 or 3 1½	Paper 1 40 mins Paper 2 1⅓ Paper 3 1¼	Paper 1 2 Paper 3 1½	Paper 1 2 2P 1½ 2Q 1½	Paper 1 1 Paper 2 1¼ Paper 3 1¼
Teacher assessment %	20	20	20	20	30	20
Differentiation model	Papers 1 or 2	Papers 1+2 or 3	Papers 1+2 or 3	Papers 1 or 1+3	Papers 1+P or Q	Papers 1+2 or Papers 1+2+3
Available grades	Paper 1 G–C Paper 2 E–A	Papers 1+2 G–C Papers 1+3 E–A	Papers 1+2 G–C Papers 1+3 E–A	Paper 1 G–C Papers 1+3 E–A	Papers 1+P G–C Papers 1+Q E–A	Papers 1+2 G–C Papers 1+2+3 E–A
4.1.7 Birth	●	●	●	●	●	●
4.1.8 Parental care	●	●	●	●	●	●
4.1.9 Growth of the individual	●	●	●	●	●	●
4.2 Genetics						
4.2.1 Mendel's First Law	○	○	○	○	○	●
4.2.2 Sex determination	●	●	●	●	●	●
4.2.3 Sex linkage	○	●	●		●	●
4.2.4 Variation	●	●	●	●	●	●
4.2.5 Chromosomes as carriers of hereditary factors	●	●	●	●	●	●
4.2.6 How proteins are made in cells		○				○
4.2.7 Cell division		●	○			●
Mitosis	○	○	○	○	○	○
Meiosis	●	○	●	●	●	●

Key   ●   Stated as a requirement
      ○   Required as a limited study
Blank   Section not required

Examination Boards: Addresses

Northern Examination Association (NEA)

JMB	Joint Matriculation Board Devas Street, Manchester M15 6EU
ALSEB	Associated Lancashire Schools Examining Board 12 Harter Street, Manchester M1 6HL
NREB	Northern Regional Examinations Board Wheatfield Road, Westerhope, Newcastle upon Tyne NE5 5JZ
NWREB	North-West Regional Examinations Board Orbit House, Albert Street, Eccles, Manchester M20 0WL
YHREB	Yorkshire and Humberside Regional Examinations Board Harrogate Office – 31-33 Springfield Avenue, Harrogate HG1 2HW Sheffield Office – Scarsdale House, 136 Derbyshire Lane, Sheffield S8 8SE

Midland Examining Group (MEG)

Cambridge	University of Cambridge Local Examinations Syndicate Syndicate Buildings, 1 Hills Road, Cambridge CB1 2EU
O & C	Oxford and Cambridge Schools Examination Board Purbeck House, Purbeck Road, Cambridge CB2 1PU and Elsfield Way, Oxford OX2 7BZ
WMEB	West Midlands Examinations Board Mill Wharf, Mill Street, Birmingham B6 4BU
EMREB	East Midland Regional Examinations Board Robins Wood House, Robins Wood Road, Aspley, Nottingham NG8 3NR

London East Anglian Group (LEAG)
(now known as University of London Examinations and Assessment Council)

London office	Stewart House, 32 Russell Square, London WC1B 5DN
Colchester office	The Lindens, Lexden Road, Colchester CO3 3RL

Southern Examining Group (SEG)

AEB	The Associated Examining Board Stag Hill House, Guildford GU2 5XJ
OSEB	Oxford School Examinations Board Ewert House, Ewert Place, Summertown, Oxford OX2 7BZ
SEG	Southern Regional Examinations Board Unit 23, Monksbrook Industrial Park, Chandlers Ford, Eastleigh SO5 3RA
	South-East Regional Examinations Board Beloe House, 2-10 Mount Ephraim Road, Tunbridge Wells TN1 1EU
	South-Western Examinations Board 23-29 Marsh Street, Bristol BS1 4BP

Wales

WJEC	Welsh Joint Education Committee 245 Western Avenue, Cardiff CF5 2YX

Northern Ireland

NISEAC	Northern Ireland Schools Examinations and Assessment Council Beechill House, 42 Beechill Road, Belfast BT8 4RS

Scotland

SEB	Scottish Examination Board Ironmills Road, Dalkeith, Midlothian EH22 1LE

THE GENERAL CERTIFICATE OF SECONDARY EDUCATION (GCSE)

Before the development of GCSE syllabuses it was possible to obtain an 'O' level grade in twenty-five different ways for many subjects offered by examination boards. The users of examination certificates questioned the comparability of standards. For example, was a Grade C from Board X the same as a Grade C from Board Y? Could you be certain that someone with a Grade C knew and understood a particular body of facts? In order to answer these questions, the Secretary of State for Education invited the GCE and CSE boards' Joint Council to submit recommendations for 16+ National Criteria.

It was recognized that there was a need to produce standardization for syllabuses with common

- Aims
- Objectives
- Content
- Assessment pattern

By September 1982 work had begun on writing the National Criteria. Early in 1983 a wide range of interested groups were invited to comment on the first drafts. They included schools, colleges, further education and higher education establishments, Schools' Council, HM Inspectorate and certain professional associations. By March 1985, after certain modifications of the original drafts, the Secretary of State for Education and the Secretary of State for Wales approved the National Criteria. They believed that the goal of having guidelines for the GCSE, agreed nationally by all parties concerned, had been achieved.

Aims

In Biology (and Human Biology) the aims describe the educational purposes of following a course for the GCSE examination. They are:

1 To develop an interest in, and enjoyment of, the study of living organisms.

2 To encourage an attitude of curiosity and scientific enquiry.

3 To promote an appreciation of the importance of experimental and investigatory work in the study of Biology (and Human Biology).

4 To promote respect for all forms of life.

5 To develop knowledge and understanding of fundamental biological concepts and principles.

6 To develop an awareness of:

(a) relationships between living organisms,

(b) relationships between living organisms and their environment,

(c) the effect of human activities on these relationships.

7 To develop a range of manipulative and communicative skills appropriate to the subject.

8 To develop an ability to use these skills to identify and solve problems.

9 To promote an awareness and appreciation of the development and significance of biology in a personal, social, economic and technological context.

10 To provide:

(a) a worthwhile educational experience for all, whether or not they are intending to study biology beyond GCSE level;

(b) a suitable preparation for careers which require a knowledge of biology;

(c) a suitable foundation for further studies in biology and related disciplines.

Objectives

These reflect the aims that are measurable.

1 Knowledge and understanding. Candidates should be able to:

(a) demonstrate knowledge and understanding of biological facts and principles, practical techniques and safety precautions;

(b) demonstrate knowledge and understanding of the personal, social, economic and technological applications of biology in modern society;

(c) use appropriate terminology in demonstrating this knowledge.

2 Skills and processes. Candidates should be able to:

(a) make and record accurate observations;

(b) plan and conduct simple experiments to test given hypotheses;

(c) formulate hypotheses and design and conduct simple experiments to test them;

(d) make constructive criticisms of the design of experiments;

(e) analyse, interpret and draw inferences from a variety of forms of information including the results of experiments;

(f) apply biological knowledge and understanding to the solution of problems, including those of a personal, social, economic and technological nature;

(g) select and organize information relevant to particular ideas and communicate this information cogently in a variety of ways;

(h) present biological information coherently.

Assessment

In assessing whether candidates have achieved these objectives, certain criteria will be used in assisting grading. These are called Criteria Related Grades. Examination boards will have statements in their syllabuses which clearly describe the performance expected for the award of certain grades. To gain a grade, candidates will have to demonstrate mastery of skills or competences described by the Criteria Related Grades. The criteria are defined so that they

(a) are expressed in positive terms and must reflect what the candidates know and can do (they are not expressed in terms of failure);

(b) refer to the positive attainments of candidates gaining A, C and F grades in the GCSE examination which will grade candidates from A to G.

The least able candidates will be given credit for what they know, rather than be penalized for what they do not know. In an assessment, questions will be set by examination boards which will be able to be completed by the very good, the average and below average. Motivation of pupils through positive achievement is one of the aims of the Criteria Related Grades.

WHY CRITERIA RELATED GRADES?

For a number of years it has been recognized that the users of examination certificates wanted to know more than just a grade. This was particularly true of employers and admission officers for further education. In other words, a mere symbol, e.g. A, B, or C, does not give enough information on the 'likely levels of competence' of a prospective employee or student. In 1983 educationalists began to look at the possibility of defining criteria which could be applied to the examination performance of candidates. The grade obtained should then reflect a degree of mastery of certain skills. For example, in all subjects which have 'Biology' in their title, the skills are under three 'Domain' headings:

1 Knowledge with understanding.

2 Handling information and solving problems.

3 Experimental skills and investigations.

Each candidate could have a certificate which could show not only an aggregate grade but also a grade in each of the domains. The user of the certificate could therefore have a more complete picture of the abilities of a candidate. But what do the 'Domains' mean?

1 Knowledge with understanding. Candidates should be able to demonstrate their knowledge and understanding of:

(a) biological terminology,

(b) biological facts, principles and concepts,

(c) practical techniques and safety precautions,

(d) everyday uses of biology,

(e) personal, social, economic, technological and environmental applications of biology.

2 Handling information and solving problems. Candidates should be able to demonstrate their ability, within a biological context, to:

(a) locate, select, organize, translate and present information (diagrammatic graphical, numerical, written and oral),

(b) use information to draw inferences and report trends,

(c) use knowledge to present reasoned explanations for phenomena, patterns and relationships and to propose hypotheses,

(d) make predictions,

(e) solve problems including some of a quantitative nature.

3 Experimental skills and investigations. Candidates should be able to demonstrate their ability, within a biological context to show:

(a) observational skills,

(b) procedural and manipulative skills,

(c) measurement skills.

The expectations of a Grade F, C, and A candidate will be defined so that their performance in each domain can be measured.

THEME 1 MAN'S POSITION IN THE LIVING WORLD

1.1 The Cell as a Unit of Life

A cell is the simplest organized unit of living matter and can maintain itself at a higher energy level than its surroundings, grow and reproduce. For this reason, cells are recognized as the basic units of life. All cells are enclosed in a thin membrane that surrounds a fluid with a consistency of the white of an egg, the **cytoplasm**. With the notable exception of the red blood cells of mammals, cells have a nucleus which acts as a control centre. The cytoplasm, together with the nucleus, is called **protoplasm**. Electron microscopes provide the most detailed pictures of cell structure and reveal the contents of cells as a collection of **organelles**. Each organelle has a particular function to perform and uses special chemicals, **enzymes**, to help it carry out the chemical reactions which go on inside it.

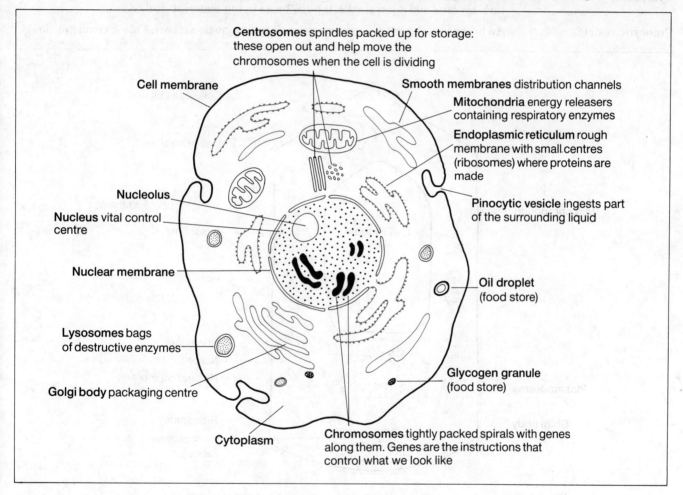

Fig. 1.1 Section of a generalized animal cell as seen with an electron microscope

Table 1.1 Summary of cell structure and function

Organelle	Structure and function
Cell membrane	Thin 'skin' of a cell. This gives the cell its characteristic shape. It **controls the entry and exit** of all materials
Mitochondria (—singular, mitochondrion)	Sausage-shaped bodies, with a highly folded interior. These are the **power houses** of the cell. Within mitochondria most **energy is released** during the process of respiration
Ribosomes	The small centres where **proteins** are made by the cell. The proteins may be used inside the cell for growth or they may be transported out of the cell, e.g. digestive enzymes

Organelle	Structure and function
Lysosomes	Spherical bodies which **store** certain enzymes for use within the cell
Endoplasmic reticulum	A series of membranes continuous with the cell membrane. It **increases the surface area** for the attachment of ribosomes and may help in the exchange of materials between the inside and outside of the cell
Golgi body	A collection of flattened sacs. The **packaging department** of the cellular factory. It is here that enzymes and other materials are packaged in 'envelopes' of endoplasmic reticulum for transport to the exterior
Nucleolus	Spherical body within the nucleus. It contains large numbers of ribosomes and is concerned with the **manufacture of proteins**. There may be more than one present
Centrosomes	These are paired rod-shaped structures at right angles to one another near the nucleus. They help in **spindle formation** during cell division and are found in animal cells only
Nucleus	This is the **control centre** of the cell. It is surrounded by a porous double membrane which allows exchange of materials and is made largely of nucleo-protein
Cytoplasm	A complex mixture of chemicals of which 80% is water. The main constituents are proteins, fats, carbohydrates and mineral salts. It is the **basic living material** of all cells
Pinocytic vesicle	An infolding of the cell membrane concerned with **ingestion** of part of the surrounding liquid

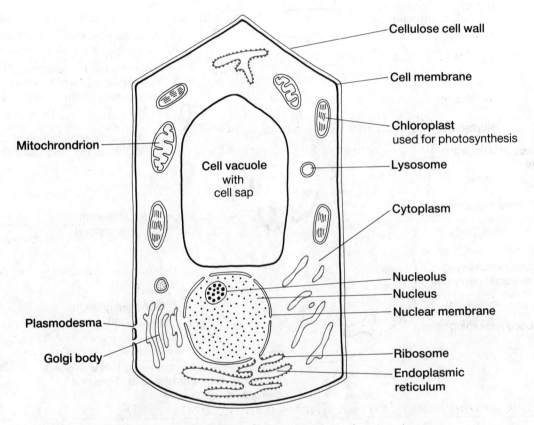

Fig. 1.2 Section of a generalized plant cell as seen with an electron microscope

1.2 The Importance of Enzymes

Enzymes are chemicals produced by living cells which have the power of altering the rate of chemical reactions occurring in the body.

Properties of enzymes

1 They are all **proteins**.
2 They all require **water** before they are able to function.
3 They are only produced by **living cells**.
4 They are **specific** in their action, one enzyme speeding up one reaction only.
5 The enzyme molecule is only **temporarily changed** during its action and can be used repeatedly. Large quantities of enzyme are not necessary.

6 They work within only a **narrow range of acidity or alkalinity**.

7 They work within only a **narrow range of temperature**.

8 As they are proteins, **high temperatures** will coagulate or denature them.

NB NEVER SAY THAT HEAT KILLS ENZYMES AS THIS IS INACCURATE

It is unfortunate that many students have the incorrect idea that enzymes are concerned only with digestion or breaking down materials. Most enzymes have nothing whatsoever to do with digestion. One group only is concerned with the breakdown of large molecules of food to smaller soluble molecules.

Investigating the action of the enzyme, catalase

Every living cell contains catalase which acts on certain chemicals to release oxygen. This process is often necessary to change harmful waste products into harmless substances.

Procedure

1 Place 10 cm^3 of hydrogen peroxide in a test tube.

2 Add a small piece of fresh liver to the hydrogen peroxide and note the result.

3 Expected observation: vigorous bubbling in the liquid.

4 Test the gas being evolved by using a glowing splint. It should re-light when inserted in the test tube near the bubbles.

5 Repeat stage 1 but add a small piece of *boiled* and cooled liver.

6 Expected observation: no bubbling of the liquid.

Deduction

(a) The enzyme in fresh liver (catalase) can break down hydrogen peroxide into water and oxygen:

$$2H_2O_2 \xrightarrow{\text{Catalase}} 2H_2O + O_2$$

(b) Boiling denatures catalase.

Summary of enzymes used in detergents

The following enzymes are all produced by bacteria:

Table 1.2

Name	Acts on	pH	Use
Alcalase	Protein	7–10	Soaking preparations and general purpose detergents
Esperase	Protein	7–12	General purpose and heavy duty detergents in liquid form
Savinase	Protein	7–12	Liquid detergents
Termamyl	Starch-containing foods	7–9.5	At high temperature (up to 90°C). Dishwashing machine detergents for removing starchy food remains.

1.3 Comparison of Green Plants and Animals

Cells

A typical plant cell	*A typical animal cell*
Cellulose cell wall	No cellulose cell wall
Chloroplasts	No chloroplasts
Large vacuole	No single large vacuole
No centrosomes	Centrosomes present

Organisms

Plant	*Animal*
Photosynthesis takes place	No photosynthesis
Body is often branched	Body is compact rather than branched
Chlorophyll is present	No chlorophyll present
Does not move in search of its food	Moves in search of its food at some stage during its life
Stores protein	Protein is not stored

1.4 Distinction Between Cells, Tissues and Organs

A cell is a basic unit of all living organisms consisting of cytoplasm bounded by a membrane and usually with a nucleus.

A tissue is a collection of similar cells subject to the same laws of growth and development, e.g. muscle tissue, bone tissue.

An organ is part of a living organism which acts as a functional unit and is composed of a collection of tissues, e.g. kidney, liver, heart.

An organ system is a group of organs which combine to perform certain functions, e.g. the digestive system, endocrine system and nervous system.

1.5 Characteristics of Living Organisms

MERRING

1 Movement *The ability to move* as a result of expenditure of energy released by cells is present in all living things. All animals move in search of food at some stage of their lives. All plants move towards or away from certain stimuli such as light or gravity.

2 Nutrition *The ability to obtain food* is present in both plants and animals but the methods by which they do this form a basic difference between them.

3 Growth This is *the irreversible increase* in size by incorporation of new cytoplasm. It occurs when the rate of manufacture of living material is greater than the rate of breakdown.

4 Respiration This is *the release of energy from glucose sugar* present in all living cells of the body. *It does not mean breathing.* Breathing is just the exchange of gases at the respiratory surface, e.g. the air sacs of the lungs.

5 Excretion This is *the elimination of waste material* which has come from chemical reactions taking place in the cells of the body. *The elimination of faeces via the anus is NOT excretion—it is egestion.*

6 Reproduction This is *the ability to produce new individuals* resembling the original parents. It ensures the continuity of the species.

7 Sensitivity This is *the ability to react to changes* in the surroundings—stimuli—and to changes within the organism.

If you read the above definitions carefully you will see that none of them can be applied to non-living things, e.g. movement of inanimate objects will only take place if energy is applied to them in some form. It is never released within themselves. In chemistry, growth of crystals does not involve the manufacture of new protoplasm and it is reversible.

1.6 Conditions Necessary for All Forms of Life

1 A suitable temperature DO NOT USE THE TERM 'WARMTH' BECAUSE THIS IS A RELATIVE TERM.

2 A source of energy In other words, a means of obtaining food.

3 Water This is necessary **in order for enzymes to work** and **as a solvent** for all the chemical reactions taking place in the body.

NOTE THAT OXYGEN IS NOT A CONDITION NECESSARY FOR ALL FORMS OF LIFE. MANY BACTERIA DO NOT REQUIRE IT. INDEED SOME BACTERIA CANNOT LIVE IN THE PRESENCE OF OXYGEN.

1.7 Man as a Mammal

Characteristics of mammals in general and man in particular

Mammals are **warm-blooded vertebrates** that possess **hair, sweat glands**, a **four-chambered heart**, a **diaphragm** and **external ears**. A **hard palate** separates the nasal from the food passage, allowing simultaneous breathing and chewing, and the **teeth are differentiated** into four distinct types (see p. 58). Most mammals **do not lay eggs**. Instead, the young develop inside the mother's body in *the uterus* until they are ready to be born. The exceptions are members of a group of mammals, the *monotremes*, which includes the *duck-billed platypus* and the *spiny anteater.*

All mammals **suckle their young on milk** and show some degree of **parental care** after the young have been born. This reaches its most developed form in humans. Finally, mammals have a **more developed brain** than other animals, and in man the brain reaches a level of development not found in any other creature.

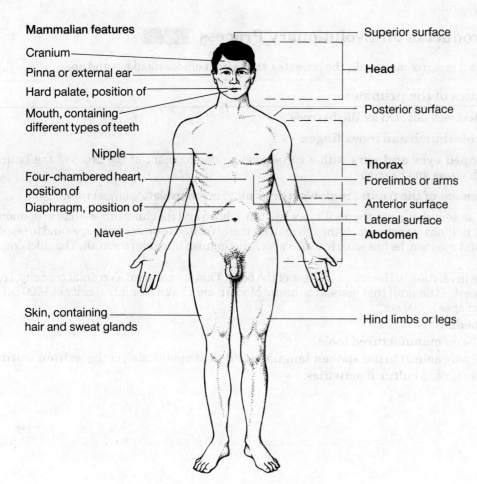

Mammalian features

Cranium

Pinna or external ear

Hard palate, position of

Mouth, containing
different types of teeth

Nipple

Four-chambered heart,
position of

Diaphragm, position of

Navel

Skin, containing
hair and sweat glands

Superior surface

Head

Posterior surface

Thorax

Forelimbs or arms

Anterior surface

Lateral surface

Abdomen

Hind limbs or legs

Fig. 1.3 Mammalian features of man

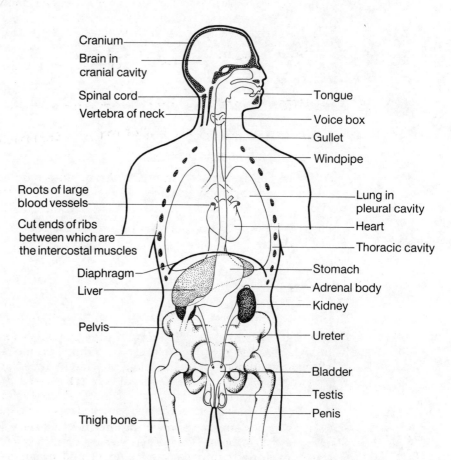

Cranium

Brain in
cranial cavity

Spinal cord

Vertebra of neck

Roots of large
blood vessels

Cut ends of ribs
between which are
the intercostal muscles

Diaphragm

Liver

Pelvis

Thigh bone

Tongue

Voice box

Gullet

Windpipe

Lung in
pleural cavity

Heart

Thoracic cavity

Stomach

Adrenal body

Kidney

Ureter

Bladder

Testis

Penis

Fig. 1.4 Some of the more important cavities and body structures of man

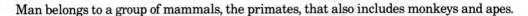

1.8 Man as a Product of an Evolutionary Process

Man belongs to a group of mammals, the primates, that also includes monkeys and apes.

Characteristics of the primates

1 Hands and feet well adapted for **life in trees.**

Prehensile hands. ✗ 2 An **opposable thumb and index finger.**

3 **Well developed eyes and ears** with a corresponding development of the areas of the brain concerned with vision and hearing.

4 **An enlargement of the frontal region of the skull** to accommodate a large brain.

Both man and present-day apes—the gorilla, orang-utan, gibbon and the chimpanzee—had a common ancestor many millions of years ago. Although man is closely related to present-day apes and to fossil forms of apes and ape-men, he has some features which distinguish him from them all. The chief ones are:

(a) **Brain size** in relation to the size of the rest of the body. This is expressed as cranial capacity, i.e. the size of the part of the skull that houses the brain. Modern man has a cranial capacity of 1600 cm^3 whereas that of apes is 600 cm^3.

(b) Man is **bipedal.**

(c) Man has always **manufactured tools.**

(d) Man is the only animal to use **spoken language** and to communicate via the **written word.**

(e) Man devotes time to **cultural activities.**

THEME 2
MAN AND HIS ENVIRONMENT

2.1 Interdependence

2.1.1 THE INTERDEPENDENCE OF PLANTS AND ANIMALS
People feed at the end of food chains

e.g. grass→grasshopper→frog→trout→man

If man were to live on trout alone, to survive, he would have to eat approximately one every day, and he would require about *300 trout* to support him for a year. Each trout would similarly require a frog every day. Therefore the 300 trout needed to support the man for a year would themselves have to eat *90 000 frogs* annually. In turn, each frog would require a grasshopper every day, so the frog population would eat *27 million grasshoppers* in a year. A herd of grasshoppers that large would require *1000 tons of grass*. So we can draw a food pyramid that looks like this:

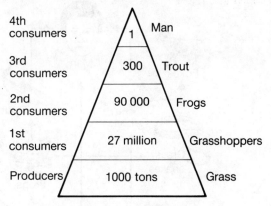

Fig. 2.1 Pyramid of numbers

The large numbers of organisms towards the base of the pyramid are required to support the smaller numbers of organisms near the apex because none of the organisms is very efficient at *converting food into body tissue*. Only about **1%** of the solar energy striking the field is converted into grass via photosynthesis. The grasshoppers are able to convert only about **10%** of the grass into grasshopper tissue: most of the grass is uneaten, undigested, or used to provide energy for hopping, chewing and other activities. Similarly, the man, trout and frogs are able to convert only about **10%** of their food into man, trout, and frog tissue, respectively. It is apparent that the *number of animals* that can be supported at the top of the pyramid is directly related to the *number of layers within the pyramid*.

We can support more people on this food chain simply by *shortening* it. Eliminate the trout and the land will yield 90 000 frogs for human consumption. Assuming each person could survive on 10 frogs per day, the frogs would support *30 people for a year.*

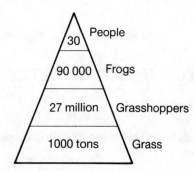

Fig. 2.2 Pyramid of numbers

But who likes frogs? Let us consider grasshoppers instead and assume that 100 a day would satisfy you. Now the 27 million grasshoppers would support *900 people for a year.*

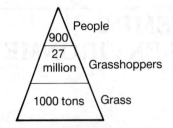

Fig. 2.3 Pyramid of numbers

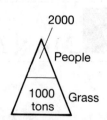

Fig. 2.4 Pyramid of numbers

If we eliminate the grasshoppers and eat the grass ourselves, the land would support even more people. In fact, about 2000 people, each eating about 1 kg of grass per day, could live on the land that supported the one fish-eating man we met at the beginning of this argument.

The conclusion is that, theoretically, the *shorter* the food chain, the *more efficient* it is at energy conversion. In practice, however, the anatomy, physiology and behaviour of man make it impossible for him to be a primary consumer of grass, apart from cereal crops. The feeding relationships of man and plants are rarely, if ever, as simple as the food chain quoted. Usually, several food chains are interconnected forming **food webs**. A complete food web for any habitat is impossible to illustrate because of the vast variety of feeders and their food. A simplified version of one which incorporates the food chain mentioned above is as follows:

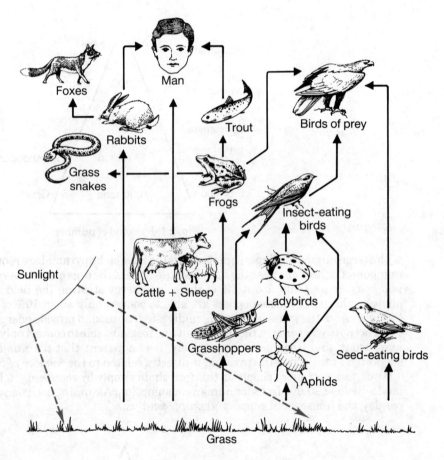

Fig. 2.5 A typical food web

2.1.2 DECOMPOSITION CYCLES

The Nitrogen Cycle

The cycle can be divided into a 'building up' part and a 'breaking down' part. Each part uses a different set of bacteria.

'Building up' bacteria

1 **Nitrifying:** These build up molecules of nitrates from nitrites and ammonium salts.

2 **Nitrogen fixing:** These take nitrogen from the air and change it into a form which can be used by

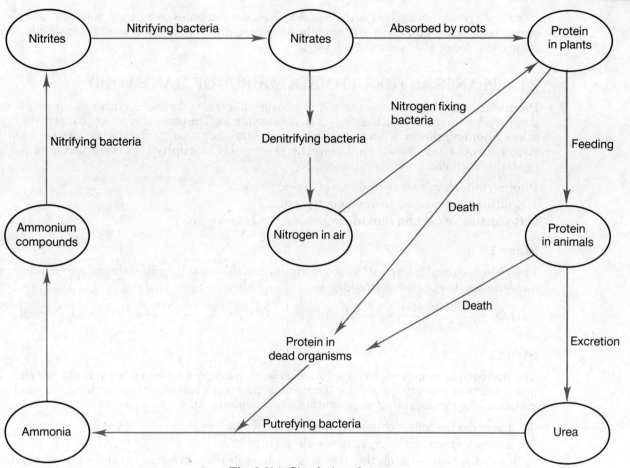

Fig. 2.6(a) Circulation of nitrogen

plants to make proteins. They are found in the soil and inside the roots of pod-bearing plants (legumes), e.g. peas, beans, clover.

'Breaking down' bacteria

1 Denitrifying: These break down nitrates into nitrogen and oxygen which then pass back into the air.

2 Putrefying: These cause the decay of dead things. They break them down into carbon dioxide and ammonia. Ammonia quickly reacts to form ammonium salts in the soil.

The Carbon Cycle

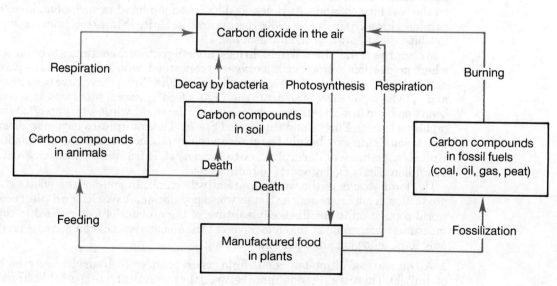

Fig. 2.6(b) The carbon cycle

It ensures a constant supply of carbon dioxide to plants and relies on animals putting it into the air during respiration. Plants take it out of the air during photosynthesis. It is added to the air during respiration, decay, and burning fossil fuels.

2.1.3 PLANTS AS THE ULTIMATE SOURCE OF MAN'S FOOD

Plants (and some bacteria) are the only organisms that can *make food*. Animals either *eat plants* or they *eat other animals* which themselves have eaten plants. The process by which plants make food is called **photosynthesis**. Plants use inorganic materials, in particular *carbon dioxide* from the atmosphere and *water* from the soil, and in the presence of **chlorophyll** and *energy* (in the form of sunlight) they manufacture carbohydrates.

Photosynthesis can be divided into *two* basic stages:
1 **Splitting water** using energy from the sun.
2 **Reduction of carbon dioxide** by the addition of hydrogen.

Stage 1

Energy from sunlight, trapped by the green pigment, chlorophyll, splits water molecules into *oxygen* and *hydrogen*, the process of **photolysis**.

$$4H_2O \xrightarrow[\text{Chlorophyll}]{\text{Sunlight}} 4[OH]+4[H] \qquad 4[OH] \longrightarrow 2H_2O+O_2 \text{ (by-products)}$$

Stage 2

The hydrogen is combined with carbon dioxide in a complex series of **reduction** reactions. The product acts as a starting point for the manufacture of all carbohydrates, proteins, fats and most vitamins. The significance of photosynthesis to *animals* is thus:

(a) It provides the source of their dietary requirements.
(b) It provides them with oxygen (given off in Stage 1).
(c) It uses the carbon dioxide that they produce as waste during respiration and releases oxygen into the atmosphere.

2.1.4 THE WORLD FOOD PROBLEM

There is a growing fear of a **world food crisis**. More than half the human population suffers from *hunger* or *malnutrition*, and worldwide the number of people is increasing faster than the food supply. Some authorities have produced statistics of food and population growth which show that a *food crisis* is imminent. But throughout history there has been insufficient food for all the people of the world; *population size* has always tended to *increase faster* than the *food supply*. Periodic **famines**, reducing the population of a region to what the available food could support, have occurred in every part of the world, including Europe. However, starting in the 17th century, developments took place which eventually freed Europe from recurring famines. First, from about 1650 to 1900 more than 60 million people left Europe for the sparsely populated continents of America and Australasia, and then these regions exported food back to Europe. By 1900, two-thirds of the food consumed in Britain was imported. A second, and an even more important development, was the **application of science to agriculture**. In the past 300 years this has produced nearly a tenfold increase in the yield per hectare on the best farmed lands. At times, food has been produced in such abundance that unmarketable surpluses have arisen. In the 1930s Britain and the United States took measures to control production to adjust the supply to economic demand.

In countries of the **Third World**, in most areas agriculture continues to be largely primitive (except where production of crops such as *sugar* is concerned, which is exported to western industrialized nations), and famines continue to occur. Since 1800, in China there have been more than 400 famines, and in India today there is an acute shortage of food in several provinces. In recent years hunger has been a problem in most of the poorer countries of the world, while a surplus of food has caused economic problems in both Europe and the United States. These surpluses have now disappeared: the Soviet Union and China have bought the grain and dairy product 'mountains' of Canada and Australia. The United States has sent its surplus food to a variety of Third World countries. From 1951 to 1966 it sent 52 million tons of food products to India alone.

The **food stocks** of the world are relatively small. In spite of the efforts of some nations, food production is not increasing as fast as world population. A **world food plan** needs estimates of the world population in the foreseeable future, of the amount of food needed to support it, and of the measures which could be taken to produce this. Modern science can increase production enormously only if the following are taken into account:

1 All human food ultimately comes from **green plants** which survive and grow by fixing the energy of sunlight. There is a vast difference between the theoretical rate of plant food production and the best rates achieved by present-day agriculture.

2 One can only generalize about **human dietary requirements**; even the amounts of different foods required to *prevent crippling disease* or *produce optimal health* are very imprecisely known. Yet such knowledge is vital if malnutrition is to be prevented.

3 Farm animals sometimes compete directly with man for food, but more often they provide the most practical means—and occasionally the only way—of providing **essential protein**. In the future, more animals, husbanded more efficiently, will be needed to improve the quality of human diets throughout the world.

4 We know technically, or can find out, **how to produce enough food for mankind**, but to actually achieve this cannot be done without far-reaching changes in the social, economic and agricultural structure of the hungry nations. To learn how to bring about these changes is more urgent than any technical discovery.

5 Plant protein in oil-seeded meal until recently was not normally used for human consumption, but it is now available commercially for use in foods, often being mixed with other proteins. If fully expanded, this development could meet almost the entire present world protein deficit.

6 Salt water has been used successfully to irrigate plants grown on sand. Such experiments indicate that very large *desert areas* can be reclaimed for food reproduction.

7 Management of commercial **marine fish stocks** and an increasing exploitation of the less known varieties of fish can yield vast quantities of food.

8 The world shortage of protein could be alleviated by new foods obtained from cultivated **bacteria, algae, yeasts, protozoans** and **fungi**. Protein from these single-celled organisms is now being produced in many countries of the world.

2.1.5 GROWTH OF POPULATIONS

The population of the world as a whole has been *growing steadily*, though in individual countries there have been *fluctuations* in population size as people have migrated to newly discovered territories or have gone off in search of new food and mineral sources. Malthus, in 1798, suggested that because the population *increases faster* than food production there should be some sort of **birth control**. The growth of the world's population is now much faster than it has been in the past for the following reasons:

1 The **increased effectiveness of medical science in saving lives** and virtually wiping out many formerly fatal diseases, such as *diphtheria, smallpox* and *tuberculosis.*

2 Practically all mothers and babies survive childbirth because of **improved pre- and post-natal medical care.**

3 Increased lifespan in the Western industrial countries due to a **better diet** than that enjoyed by our ancestors.

4 Agricultural development (see Section 2.1.4).

5 Industrial development due to technological advances leading to greater potential for trade and greater affluence.

Consequences of an increasing population growth rate

1 Shortage of food (see Section 2.1.4).
2 Pollution (see Section 2.4.4).

Methods used to calculate population growth

1 Crude birth rate: This is the number of *births per 1000 of the population per year* and is calculated as follows:

$$\frac{\text{Number of births in a year}}{\text{Total population of that year}} \times 1000$$

2 Fertility rate: This is the number of *live births per 1000 women of child-bearing age per year.* It is used for forecasting population trends and is calculated as follows:

$$\frac{\text{Number of births in a year}}{\text{Number of women aged between 15 and 45 in that year}} \times 1000$$

3 Infant mortality rate: This is the number of *deaths of children under 1 year of age per 1000 live births per year.* It is an indication of standards of hygiene and medical care in a community and is calculated as follows:

$$\frac{\text{Number of infant deaths in a year}}{\text{Number of live births in that year}} \times 1000$$

4 Crude death rate: This is the number of *deaths per 1000 of the population per year.* It is an indication of the relative health of a community and can be calculated as follows:

$$\frac{\text{Number of deaths in a year}}{\text{Total population of that year}} \times 1000$$

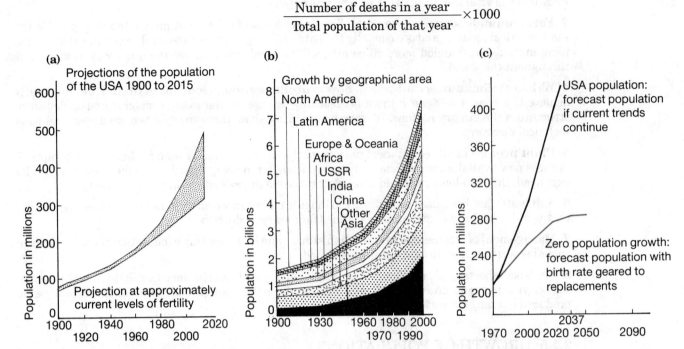

Fig. 2.7 Within 70 years the population of the world has doubled and it is expected to double again by the end of the century. The graphs illustrate the problem of the population explosions. **(a)** The population of the USA with a projection to AD 2015 based on current fertility rate data. **(b)** The rise in population up to the year AD 2000 for the major areas of the world. **(c)** A comparison between the anticipated population growth of the USA and what it would be if kept in check by birth control.

2.1.6 POPULATION CONTROL—CONTRACEPTION

Table 2.1 Methods of contraception

Method	How it is used	Reasons why it might fail
1 Contraceptive pills taken by women	As prescribed by a doctor; usually taken orally, one every day	Not following the instructions or forgetting to take the pill at the prescribed time
2 A contraceptive sheath (condom, Durex, French letter, rubber)	Put on the erect penis before intercourse	Not put on before any contact with the vagina. Not carefully removed after intercourse.
3 The intra-uterine device (IUD) (coil or loop) worn by women	Put inside the womb by a doctor	Fails in a proportion of women. Reasons not understood. Can cause pain and heavy bleeding
4 The diaphragm (Dutch cap) worn by women	Inserted by the woman at the cervix prior to intercourse. Removed 8 hours later	Not put in place properly. Not used with a spermicide
5 Spermicides (sperm killers). As a cream; used by men and women	The woman puts the spermicide high up in the vagina. The man puts the cream inside a contraceptive sheath before use	Impossible for the cream to reach every part of the folded inner wall of the vagina
6 The 'safe' period calculated by the woman	No sexual intercourse after the egg is shed and is in the oviduct	Very difficult to be accurate with the timing of egg release (ovulation). Women vary in the length of their menstrual cycles. Sperms can remain active in the female reproductive tracts for some time after intercourse
7 Withdrawal of penis by man (coitus interruptus)	The man removes his penis from the vagina before ejaculation	A very high risk of pregnancy as any sperms left in the reproductive tract can swim to the egg
8 Sterilization of men and women	In men, the vas deferens are cut and tied. In women, the oviducts are cut and tied	This never fails if the operation has been carried out properly

2.2 Disease

2.2.1 BACTERIA

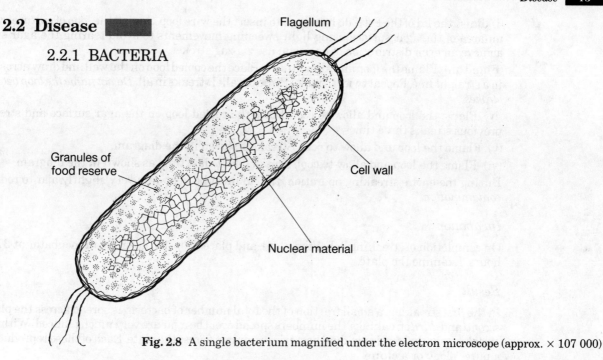

Fig. 2.8 A single bacterium magnified under the electron microscope (approx. × 107 000)

Minute *acellular* organisms that lack both mitochondria and a distinct nucleus. They can be **saprophytic** (feeding on dead material), **parasitic** (feeding on living organisms), **photosynthetic** (capable of using light energy and inorganic materials to make food) or **chemo-autotrophic** (capable of using energy from chemical compounds to manufacture food). Their shape can be: spherical—**coccus**; rod-like—**bacillius**; spiral—**spirillum**; comma-like—**vibrio; filamentous;** or corkscrew-like—**spirochaete.**

Those which infect humans are parasitic and feed using *extracellular digestion*. Their life cycle involves:

(a) Secretion of digestive enzymes

(b) Extracellular digestion

(c) Absorption

(d) Metabolism

(e) Excretion

(f) Growth and reproduction

Most bacteria are killed by temperatures above 70°C. However, certain species can form resistant spores which can remain alive in boiling water for periods varying from a few minutes to several hours. Reproduction in bacteria involves simple cell division and in ideal conditions can occur every ½ hour.

2.2.2 CULTURE OF BACTERIA

The streak plate method is one of many methods which is useful for isolating *pure colonies* of bacteria from a *mixed culture*. The materials needed are: source of bacteria (e.g. mixed culture of soil bacteria); nutrient agar plate; wire loop; and a Bunsen burner.

Procedure (for results within 24 hours)

Taking the bacterial sample

Hold the tube of bacterial culture in the left hand, the wire loop in the right hand. Flame the loop and allow to cool. Remove the cotton wool plug of the tube with the little finger of the right hand. Flame the mouth of the tube. Insert the loop and remove one loopful of culture. Flame the mouth of the tube, replace the plug and return the tube to its rack.

Streaking the plate

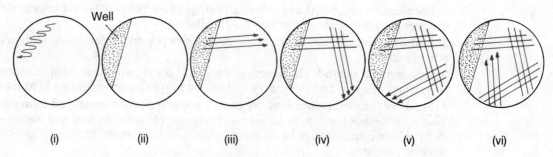

Fig. 2.9 Diagrammatic representation of the stages of streaking an agar plate

(i) Raise the lid of the Petri dish enough to insert the wire loop. Spread the loop of culture evenly over an area of the agar surface using light sweeping movements to avoid tearing the agar surface. To achieve an even distribution of bacteria, use zig-zag strokes.

(ii) and (iii) Flame the loop and allow to cool. Place the cooled loop on the well and draw across the agar in a straight line. Repeat twice to make three parallel streaks in all. *Do not flame the loop between these strokes.*

(iv) Flame the loop and allow to cool. Place the cooled loop on the agar surface and streak across previous streaks three times.

(v) Flame the loop and allow to cool. Streak as shown in the diagram.

(vi) Flame the loop and allow to cool. Streak for the last time as shown in the diagram.

During the entire streaking operation, the lid must be kept only very slightly ajar to reduce *aerial contamination.*

Incubation

On completion of streaking, label the plate, and place it upside down in an incubator at 37°C for 24 hours. Examine the plate.

Result

In the *first* streaking, a small fraction of the total number of bacteria is spread across the plate. In the *second* and *third* streakings, the numbers spread over the agar are very much reduced. With the *fourth* streakings, only a few individual bacteria are drawn across the plate. Each of these reproduces to form a pure colony or a **clone**.

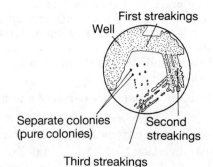

Fig. 2.10 Typical appearance of a streaked plate after incubation

2.2.3 BACTERIA AND DISEASE—PATHOGENS

If a *parasitic* bacterium gets into human tissue, establishes itself, reproduces and produces a *disease*, it is classed as a **pathogen**.

Body defences

1 Skin—acts as a barrier, preventing entry into the body of micro-organisms, dust particles and most chemicals.

2 Lachrymal glands—secrete tears containing a bactericidal chemical.

3 Blood clotting—provides a temporary barrier before a wound heals.

4 Phagocytes—special white blood cells which ingest micro-organisms that have invaded the body.

5 Antibodies and antitoxins—produced by lymphocytes (see Section 3.5.9).

6 Stomach—produces hydrochloric acid which sterilizes food.

Important terms to understand when studying all infectious diseases are:

1 Incubation period: During this early stage of an infection the pathogen multiplies rapidly and the person begins to show symptoms of the disease.

2 Isolation period: The length of time that a sick person is infectious and should be kept away from other people.

3 Quarantine period: The length of time that people who have been in contact with an infected person and who may therefore carry and spread the pathogen should avoid mixing with other people.

4 Mode of transmission: How organisms causing disease are spread from one person to another. The main methods are: (a) by air-borne droplets; (b) by infected food and water; (c) by insect vectors; (d) by objects contaminated by micro-organisms; (e) by human carriers; (f) by direct contact with the infected person.

5 Prevention of spread: How to stop or reduce the spread of micro-organisms to healthy people.

How bacteria cause disease

Like all living organisms, bacteria produce *waste products*. Unfortunately for the infected host, these act like **poisons** and are harmful to its cells. If the bacteria are able to establish themselves and thrive within the hosts, overcoming its *defence mechanisms* (even if only temporarily), there occurs a rapid increase in the amount of bacterial waste products in the host's tissues. This produces the symptoms of a disease. The nature of the disease depends on the particular kind of bacterium: some bacteria thrive in blood, some in nerve tissue, and some in bone tissue, etc. The following is a summary of the effects of some types of harmful bacteria.

2.2.4 SOME DISEASES CAUSED BY BACTERIA

Table 2.2 Characteristics of some bacterial diseases

Disease	Incubation period	Isolation period	Quarantine period	Mode of transmission	Prevention of spread	Symptoms and course of disease	Treatment
Diphtheria	4 days	Until tests show the patient is free from infection	No definite period, but all contacts should be tested for immunity and immunized if necessary	By air-borne droplets and by carriers	Isolation of infected person and contacts. Used handkerchiefs should be burned because the mucous fluid from the nose contains bacteria. Immunization of contacts	Bacteria infect membranes of the respiratory system, releasing a poison. Fever and sore throats are followed by damage to the heart and the nervous system	Injection of antitoxin. Antibiotics
Tuberculosis	Variable	Until all evidence of infection has disappeared	None	By air-borne droplets; in milk	Vaccination. Mass X-ray programme to detect carriers	Many organs may be infected by the bacteria but lungs are the prime targets. General weight loss occurs. Sputum often contains blood. A persistent cough develops	Antibiotics
Pneumonia	Variable	None	None	By air-borne droplets	Avoid low temperatures. Treat infections following from colds and influenza with antibiotics for a year after an attack of pneumonia	Coughing, fever, chest pains. Fluid in the lungs	Antibiotics and sulphonamide drugs
Typhoid	7–21 days	Until tests show faeces and urine free from the bacteria	21 days	By contaminated water and food	Vaccination lasts up to 1 year	Fever, abdominal pains, constipation followed by diarrhoea. Ulceration of the intestine often occurs	Antibiotics
Dysentery	1–7 days	Until tests show the person is free from infection	14 days	By contaminated water and food. Insects can carry bacteria	Strict hygienic handling of food	Fever, abdominal pains, vomiting and diarrhoea	Antibiotics, also fluids to replace loss
Food poisoning	1 day	1–2 days	1–2 days	By contaminated water and food	Strict hygienic handling of food	Abdominal pains, vomiting, diarrhoea and possibly fever	Antibiotics, also fluids to replace loss

Disease	Incubation period	Isolation period	Quarantine period	Mode of transmission	Prevention of spread	Symptoms and course of disease	Treatment
Scarlet fever	5 days	28 days	10 days	By air-borne droplets, food, or by insect vectors	Isolation of infected person and contacts. Strict hygiene. Contaminated handkerchiefs should be burned and bedding and utensils disinfected	Scarlet rash—white around mouth. Skin peels	Antibiotics
Cholera	5 hours to 3 days	Until tests show the person is free from infection	21 days	Contaminated water	Purification of water supply and treatment of sewage. Vaccination gives protection for 3–12 months	Inflamed intestine. Severe diarrhoea. Massive loss of body fluids which may prove fatal	Injection of saline. Antibiotics and sulphonamide drugs
Whooping cough	8–14 days	42 days	21 days	Air-borne droplets	Vaccination	Severe coughing with a 'whoop' sound as air is inspired	Antibiotics
Bubonic plague	36 hours to 10 days	As for typhoid	As for typhoid	Rat flea	Eradication of rats. Storage of food in rat-proof containers	High fever. Swollen lymph nodes in groin and armpits. Haemorrhages in capillaries leading to a darkening of the skin (hence the name, Black Death)	Antibiotics
Yaws	3–4 weeks	21 days	21 days	Direct contact with infected sores	Strict hygiene. Prevention of overcrowding	Open sores spread over the body, particularly in children under 16. Bones become affected	Antibiotics

Venereal (sexually transmitted) diseases

1 Gonorrhoea (caused by a coccal bacterium)
Symptoms: Itching and burning sensation when passing urine. Pus may occur in the urine. The untreated condition leads to eventual arthritis, heart disease and blindness.
Incubation: Normally 2–3 days but can be up to 10 days.
Mode of transmission: As a result of direct contact between sex organs during intercourse. It can also be passed from mother to baby during birth via the mother's vagina.
Treatment: Sulphonamide drugs and antibiotics.
Prevention: Avoiding sexual intercourse with infected persons and identification and treatment of carriers.

2 Syphilis (caused by a spirochaete bacterium)
Symptoms: A sore appears where the infection has taken place. It may appear as a blister or as an open sore. After 3–6 weeks a body rash, sore throat and fever usually occur. The hair may fall out in patches. Ulcers develop on the lips or in the mouth and, in the female, in the vulva. If the disease remains untreated it may attack the heart, blood vessels and brain.
Incubation: 10–90 days.
Mode of transmission: Sexual contact, as with gonorrhoea, but also through skin wounds and scratches. The bacterium can also pass from an infected pregnant woman to her foetus across the placenta, resulting in the disease being present in the newborn.
Treatment: Antibiotics or arsenical drugs.
Prevention: As for gonorrhoea.

2.2.5 FOOD PRESERVATION

In order to prevent the decay of food, one must provide and maintain conditions that are unsuitable for the growth of bacteria, i.e. dryness or a temperature which either kills the bacteria or prevents their reproduction.

Table 2.3 Methods of preserving food from bacterial attack

Technique	Preparation of food	Effect on bacteria	Foods preserved
Deep freezing	Reduction of temperature below 0°C	Low temperature prevents reproduction or is fatal	All types, but certain fruits have their flavour altered
Salting	Addition of salt	Removes water by osmosis thereby preventing growth	Meat and fish
Bottling	Food sealed in airtight jars then boiled	High temperature and pressure kills them	Fruits
Freeze-drying	In a desiccator at very low temperature	Removes water and lowers the temperature so that reproduction is impossible	Most foods
Pickling	Pre-soak in strong salt solution, then store in vinegar	Vinegar, which is an acid, kills or prevents the growth of most bacteria	Vegetables
Curing	Hang the food over charcoal fires	Formaldehyde in smoke kills most bacteria	Meat and fish
Canning	Strongly heat the food to drive out air from the can which is then sealed	Kills them in a similar fashion to bottling	Most foods
Sterilization	Very high temperatures or exposure to gamma rays	High temperature or radiation kills them	Milk and cream (high temperature), fish and pork products (radiation)
Vacuum packing	Air is sucked out of containers by a vacuum pump. The container is then sealed completely	Bacteria and their spores cannot survive in the absence of oxygen	Meat and cheese

2.2.6 HYGIENIC PRESERVING, HANDLING AND DISTRIBUTION OF MILK

Milk is an excellent, highly nutritious food for *bacteria* as well as for *humans* and so it is essential to prevent its *contamination* at all stages in its production. The bacterium which causes **tuberculosis** can spread in milk taken from an infected cow. Milk can also be contaminated with those bacteria responsible for *diphtheria, scarlet fever, food poisoning* and *epidemic diarrhoea*, those being introduced when present on the hands and clothing of anyone concerned with the collection and transport of milk.

Collection

Laws governing the hygiene of milking methods are strict. *Udders* and *hind legs* must be washed before the animal is attached to the milking machine. The machine and the building itself must be regularly *disinfected*. Cows must be regularly *inspected* for disease (especially bovine tuberculosis). After being collected from cows, milk is cooled, filtered, tested for contamination, then collected in sterilized stainless steel tankers. It is pasteurized before bottling.

Pasteurization

This is a process that kills pathogenic bacteria. There are two methods:

1 The high temperature, short time (HTST) method in which milk is heated to 72°C, held at that temperature for 15 seconds, then cooled to about 10°C.

2 The milk is heated to a temperature between 63°C and 66°C, held at that temperature for 30 minutes, then cooled rapidly to about 10°C.

To test whether the milk has been correctly pasteurized, one of two procedures is carried out:

(a) **The phosphatase test:** Phosphatase is an enzyme produced by pathogenic bacteria. If it is found to be present in the milk, pasteurization has not been successful.

(b) **Methylene blue test:** This dye changes colour based on the amount of oxygen in the milk. If the test proves positive, there is a danger of there being sufficient oxygen for the growth of bacteria.

Sterilization

Milk can also be preserved by subjecting it to very high temperatures, which kill all bacteria present. Unfortunately, the flavour of the milk is altered by this treatment.

2.2.7 MICROBIAL PRODUCTION PROCESSES

Yoghurt

Bacteria used

Lactobacillus bulgaricus and *Streptococcus thermophilus*

Stages

1 Milk is pasteurized and homogenized.

2 2.5% starter culture is added at 45°C.

3 It is packed into containers and fermented at 45°C for 4 hours. Lactose is changed to glucose which in turn is changed to lactic acid.

4 After cooling, the yoghurt will keep for up to 3 weeks. If fruit is added it reduces the shelf life of the yoghurt.

Cheddar cheese

Bacteria used

Streptococcus thermophilus

Stages

1 Rennet is used to coagulate the milk.

2 Starter cultures of *S. thermophilus* are added to pasteurized milk. The rennet produces the curd.

3 After cooking for 45 minutes at 38°C the cheddaring process begins. This consists of cutting the warm curd into blocks and stacking them on each other. The pH falls to 5.2−5.3 and the harmful bacteria are killed.

4 Bacteria or fungi are added to ripen and flavour the cheese. The bacteria or fungi produce enzymes during maturation. Protein and fat are acted on by a series of enzymes to produce chemicals with the distinctive flavours of the various types of cheese available in shops.

Table 2.4 Various micro-organisms are used for various types of cheese:

Type of cheese	Micro-organism
Limburger and Bel Paese	*Brevibacterium linens*
Gorgonzola, Stilton, Roquefort	*Penicillium roqueforti* and *P. glaucum*
Camembert	*P. camemberti*
Brie	*Brevibacterium linens* and *P. camemberti*

Vinegar

Summary

1st reaction: glucose $\xrightarrow[\text{(yeast)}]{\text{fermentation}}$ ethanol + carbon dioxide

2nd reaction: ethanol + oxygen $\xrightarrow[\text{(bacteria)}]{\text{fermentation}}$ acetic acid (vinegar) + water

Micro-organisms involved

1st reaction: *Saccharomyces cerevisiae var elipsoides* (yeast)
    Anaerobic (without oxygen)

2nd reaction: *Acetobacter* (bacterium)
    Aerobic (with oxygen)

Stages

Slow

1 Yeasts present on grapes are added to 11−13% ethanol to form a low grade wine.

2 The alcoholic solution is then put in barrels and a culture of *Acetobacter* is added.

3 It is left for up to 3 months to produce vinegar.

Quick

This relies on actively moving the liquid over a large surface for good oxygenation.

1 The alcoholic solution is sprinkled over wood shavings with *Acetobacter* growing on them.

2 The ethanol is changed into acetic acid.

2.2.8 SOME DISEASES CAUSED BY VIRUSES

A virus is a minute particle that is capable of reproduction only within *living cells*. Viruses are often classed as non-living. Each consists of a **nucleic acid core** and a **protein coat**.

Table 2.5 Characteristics of some viral diseases

Disease	Incubation period	Isolation period	Quarantine period	Mode of transmission	Prevention of spread	Symptoms and course of disease	Treatment
Common cold	3 days	1–2 days	1–2 days	By air-borne droplets	Avoiding large gatherings, stuffy rooms especially in winter, or contact with infected persons	Irritation of the respiratory tract, coughing and sneezing	None, but aspirin may relieve discomfort
Measles	10 days	14 days	16 days	By air-borne droplets	Keep young babies away from the infection because the disease can have serious consequences for those under 3 years of age. Strict hygiene. Handkerchiefs should be burned because of contamination with virus-filled mucus	Sore throat, runny nose, cough and fever. Small white spots (Koplik's spots) on the inside of mouth. Rash on scalp, neck and ears. Mainly a disease of children. Occasionally, the virus can damage the heart, kidneys and brain	Injection of gamma globulin protein
Rubella	18 days	7 days	21 days	By air-borne droplets and saliva	Vaccination, particularly of girls aged 11-14 because women during the first 4 months of pregnancy can pass on the virus to the foetus: there is a 20% chance of the baby being born blind and deaf as a result of this	Fever and body rash which disappears after 3 days	None, but aspirin can relieve discomfort. Pregnant women are injected with gamma globulin
Poliomyelitis	10 days	21 days	14 days	By air-borne droplets, contaminated water and food	Isolation of the infected person and contacts. Strict hygiene. Handkerchiefs must be burned and all faeces disinfected before flushing away. Bed pans should be disinfected immediately after use. Vaccination	Fever, stiffness of muscles, followed by paralysis and wasting of muscles. Respiratory movements may have to be performed by an 'iron lung' if the virus affects intercostal muscles and the diaphragm	No known successful treatment
Smallpox	14 days	Varies but should continue until scabs have gone	21 days	Direct contact or insect carriers	Vaccination	High fever, rash on the face which spreads all over the body. Secondary bacterial infection causes permanent scars. The disease is believed to be eliminated throughout the world	None, but antibiotics to control secondary bacterial infections

Disease	Incubation period	Isolation period	Quarantine period	Mode of transmission	Prevention of spread	Symptoms and course of disease	Treatment
Influenza	1–3 days	7 days	7 days	By air-borne droplets	Vaccination may give immunity for 1–2 years. Avoiding contact with infected persons	Fever and headache. Sore throat and muscular pains. Secondary infection by bacteria can lead to pneumonia	Aspirin to relieve discomfort. Antibiotics against secondary infections
Mumps	14–21 days	21 days	21 days	By air-borne droplets and saliva	Vaccination	Fever and swelling of paratid salivary glands lasting about 10 days. Testes and ovaries may be affected in those who have reached puberty	Aspirin to reduce fever and relieve discomfort
Chickenpox	14 days	Until all sores have disappeared	21 days	Direct contact and droplets from sores	Isolation. Strict hygiene. Disposal of any materials which have come into contact with the patient's infected blisters	Most common in young people. Fever, headache, sore throat and rash all over body. Blisters may become infected by bacteria, leading to secondary infection	Antibiotics to treat secondary infection

Acquired Immune Deficiency Syndrome (AIDS)

AIDS is a disease which interferes with the body's normal immunity to disease. The spread of the disease has become one of the most serious medical problems in recent history. The director of the World Health Organization stated, in 1986, that 100 000 people throughout the world suffer symptoms of AIDS and that a staggering 10 million carry the virus in their blood. Methods of controlling its spread depend on prevention because a cure has not yet been found.

AIDS is transmitted via blood and semen. A few weeks after infection, the virus causes an illness similar to influenza or glandular fever. Next follows a period of months or even years when no symptoms are shown, then weight loss, fever, diarrhoea and infections such as TB or pneumonia. As the white cells of the immune system have been destroyed by the virus, death follows these more serious illnesses. AIDS can also infect brain cells as well as the blood cells in the lymph nodes and spleen.

2.2.9 NOTIFIABLE DISEASES

Highly infectious diseases must be reported immediately to your local doctor who may then, if necessary, notify the local Environmental Health Officer. The aim is to trace the *source* of the infection and thus *minimize the spread* of the disease. Some notifiable diseases are: *cholera, diphtheria, food poisoning, malaria, measles, poliomyelitis, smallpox, tetanus, tuberculosis, typhoid, whooping cough* and *yellow fever.* Various countries have their own laws governing notifiable diseases. In Britain, gonorrhoea and syphilis, though highly infectious, are not notifiable (as they are in many other countries), neither are the common cold, influenza, pneumonia, chickenpox, German measles and mumps.

2.2.10 ANTIBIOTICS

These are substances produced naturally by organisms such as fungi which *prevent the growth* of bacteria, e.g. *Penicillium* is a fungus that makes the antibiotic **penicillin**. This prevents the growth of pathogenic bacteria such as *streptococci* and *staphylococci.*

Production of antibiotics

Penicillin

A mutant form of the fungus, *Penicillium*, has been developed under laboratory conditions. It produces far more of the antibiotic, penicillin (up to 100 000 units per cm^3 culture) than normal *Penicillium.* Tanks of 90 000 litre volume are used and the culture conditions are computer controlled.

Semi-synthetic penicillins are produced using enzymes. Ordinary penicillin made by fermentation is treated with an enzyme (acylase) which produces the starting material for semi-synthetic penicillin.

Neomycin

This is produced by *Streptomyces fradiae*. It grows best at 28°C in the presence of oxygen at a pH of 7.0–7.5.

Two growth phases occur:

1 In the presence of a high concentration of oxygen, carbohydrates are broken down and this results in a drop in pH.

2 In the presence of low oxygen concentration, nitrogenous compounds are released resulting in a rise in pH. The body of the fungus breaks down and neomycin is produced.

2.2.11 ANTIMICROBIAL METHODS

Sterilization is the *elimination* of live micro-organisms. Hospital clothes and equipment, for example, are sterilized in a steam-pressure chamber or autoclave at 121°C.

Disinfection is the *reduction in the number* of live micro-organisms and usually involves subjecting material to chemical treatment.

Antisepsis is the *prevention of the reproduction* of micro-organisms.

Asepsis is the *prevention of contamination* by micro-organisms.

2.2.12 IMMUNITY

The ability of the body to resist the possible dangers of invading organisms.

When micro-organisms enter the body, they stimulate the production of antibodies within certain cells, the **lymphocytes** (see Section 3.5.9). Antibodies are able to counteract the effects of the invading organisms. There are two main forms of immunity, *natural* and *acquired*.

Table 2.6 Natural immunity

Form A—Specific	Form B—Genetic	Form C
One species of animal (or plant) may be immune to diseases from which other species suffer, e.g. *myxomatosis* in rabbits does not affect man	Some people inherit immunity to a disease, e.g. many people are not affected by the *chickenpox* virus even after contact with the disease	By suffering once from a disease, e.g. with *whooping cough* the body produces antibodies during the first attack. Immune persons will resist a second invasion by the same micro-organism

Table 2.7 Acquired immunity

Form A—Passive (short term protection)	Form B—Active (long term protection)
Obtained by injecting **serum** (plasma without clotting agents) of an animal which has previously been subjected to a mild infection of the disease. The serum contains antibodies for that disease and these retain their effect after injection into man. The serum may be given in an emergency, e.g. a person with *diphtheria* is given antitoxin at the beginning of the infection to boost his own supply. *Antitetanus serum* works in the same way	The body makes its own antibodies over a long period. There are three methods: *(i)* By inoculating with a vaccine containing a **weakened** micro-organism, e.g. *smallpox* or *poliomyelitis* *(ii)* By inoculating with a vaccine containing **dead** micro-organisms, e.g. *whooping cough* *(iii)* By inoculating with **modified toxins** produced by harmful micro-organisms. This makes the body produce antitoxins which give protection against a more virulent attack

Interferon

Interferons were discovered in 1957. They are hormone-like proteins that are part of the body's defence against viruses and other disease-causing agents. Until 1970 human white blood cells were the only source of interferon and the world's supply for medical use was no more than a few milligrams. Now bacteria can be used to make more than a milligram of interferon per litre of culture.

For certain types of leukaemia, treatment with interferon has been very successful. Cancer of the breast, intestine and lungs do not generally respond to treatment with interferon. There are some side effects of its use including fever, tiredness and muscle pain. High doses may lead to hallucinations and coma. Interferons act directly on cells, not on the viruses that infect them. They limit the course of virus infection. They may not cure virus-caused diseases but they may prevent them. Hepatitis, herpes virus and shingles respond to interferon treatment.

2.2.13 PROTOZOA AND DISEASE

The malarial parasite

The organisms that cause malaria belong to the genus *Plasmodium*, which is a member of the phylum of one-celled animals, the **Protozoa**. They share a common life cycle, part of which takes place in the **mosquito** and part in **man**. If a person suffering from malaria is bitten by a mosquito of the right type, the parasite passes with the blood into the mosquito's **stomach**. Here it undergoes a series of changes and becomes capable of *sexual reproduction*, which results in the production of more individuals. These pass to the **salivary glands** of the mosquito. If the mosquito bites another person, the parasites are passed into that person's **bloodstream**. The parasites then pass to the **liver** and undergo *asexual reproduction*, resulting in a massive increase of numbers. They then invade **red blood cells**, from which they obtain their food. At this stage, *poisons* are released into the bloodstream, causing the **fever** which is a characteristic symptom of malaria. The fever usually develops 10 days after the entry of the parasite. It may be *continuous, irregular* or occur *twice a day*, depending on the species of *Plasmodium* injected by the mosquito.

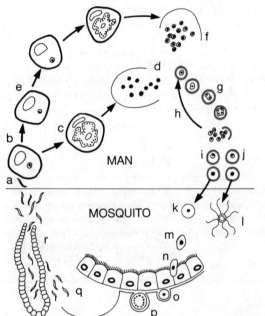

a. The parasite is injected into the blood vessels of man by a female mosquito and passes into the liver cells.
b. The parasite divides in the liver cells.
c. Many thousands of individuals are formed.
d. Some of the parasites enter red blood cells.
e. Others remain in liver cells and invade red blood cells several months later.
f. The parasites feed on the blood cell's cytoplasm.
g. Asexual reproduction continues in red blood cells.
h. A massive build up of asexual stages.

i. Sexual stages develop.
j. These are taken up by a mosquito when it feeds.
k. Gametes form inside the mosquito's stomach.
l. Fertilization occurs.
m. A zygote forms.
n. The zygote bores into the gut wall.
o. A cyst forms in which division occurs.
p. Large numbers of parasites are formed in the cysts.
q. These break out and move to the salivary glands of the mosquito.
r. They are injected into a human when the mosquito feeds on blood.

Fig. 2.11 Life cycle of the malarial parasite, *Plasmodium vivax*

Control of malaria ideally should be aimed at elimination of the mosquito vector but the parasites can be killed when they are inside man using the drugs *chloroquine* and *quinine*. Other drugs, for example *paludrine* and *daraprim*, are used to prevent infection. They must be taken regularly during, and for a month after, a stay in a malarial area.

Entamoeba histolytica

This protozoan causes **amoebic dysentery**. The symptoms of the disease are *severe diarrhoea* with loss of blood, *fever* and *vomiting*, the combination of which can lead to death. The parasite can live in the human **intestine** and can pass out in the *faeces* to contaminate anything with which it comes in contact. Therefore, unhygienically prepared food may be a source of the parasite. The *housefly* and other insects may carry the parasite and spread the disease. The disease is controlled by strict hygiene, especially in the handling and storing of food. Antibiotics and sulphonamide drugs can be used as effective treatments.

2.2.14 NEMATODES

Enterobius vermicularis (Pinworm)

This is a nematode worm which lays its eggs near the anus. They cause severe itching and the infected person, often a child, cannot resist scratching the area. The eggs on the fingers are often transferred into the mouth and are subsequently swallowed to cause a reinfection or a new infection.

Intestinal worms are killed with drugs called anthelmintics. Proper hygiene will prevent the spread of this species of worm. Faeces should be deposited where flies, food or bare feet cannot be contaminated.

Ascaris lumbricoides

Just like *Enterobius*, this roundworm (nematode) lives as an adult in the intestine. It is much larger than *Enterobius* and causes diarrhoea, pain in the abdomen, or even blockage of the intestine.

Life history

The egg is swallowed in food or drink. The cyst covering the egg dissolves and the larvae escape. They burrow through the wall of the small intestine and enter the blood stream, eventually reaching the lungs. These larvae are then carried up to the trachea to the throat when they are swallowed. They pass to the small intestine where they become adults. The eggs of the adults pass out in the faeces and may contaminate food or drinking water.

2.2.15 DISEASES CAUSED BY FUNGI

Ringworm

Caused by several species of the fungus *Tinea*, each of which infects a different part of the body, for example, the *feet* (**Athlete's foot**), the *groin* (**Dhobies itch**), the *scalp* (**true ringworm**), the *nails* or the *trunk*.
Symptoms: Irritating blisters and reddened areas from which the skin eventually peels.
Mode of transmission: By spores carried on pets, by contact with infected people or their contaminated clothing or, with athlete's foot, via showers.
Treatment: Use of fungicidal ointments or powders. Keep infected region covered to prevent scratching and to prevent spores spreading. All combs, brushes, towels, underclothes and bedding should be discarded if they have come into contact with badly infected skin. With athlete's foot, do not use public swimming baths and gymnasia while the symptoms are present: to avoid contracting the disease, wash the feet daily and dry well between the toes. Air shoes after use and change socks, tights or stockings daily. Do not use swimming baths unless there are special disinfectant footbaths provided for use before and after bathing.

Thrush

Caused by a yeast-like organism. It affects the *mouth*, *intestine* and *vagina*.
Symptoms: Irritating reddened patches of tissue. The disease is particularly obvious when it occurs on the inside of the cheeks.
Mode of transmission: Spores are spread by contact with infected people. After a course of antibiotics, the disease may re-establish itself because some of the bacteria that normally defend the body from fungal attack may have been killed along with the thrush organism.
Treatment: The fungicide *Nystatin* is used as a cream. The most important point is to establish the source of the infection and eliminate it.

2.2.16 VECTORS (CARRIERS OF DISEASE)

Housefly

Life history

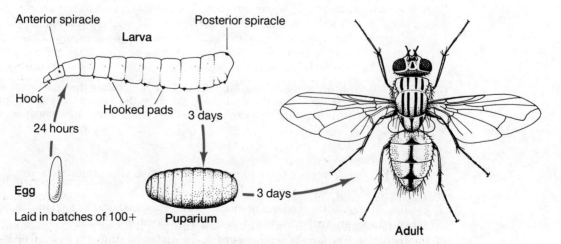

Fig. 2.12 Life cycle of a housefly (*Musca domestica*)

Habits

1 Diet. Decaying organic material, e.g. faeces, sweet substances, meat.

2 Feeding. Sucks up liquids. It releases digestive enzymes on to its food and sucks up the dissolved nutrients. It then regurgitates the food by vomiting and sucks it up again after mixing it with more digestive enzymes.

3 Egestion. It frequently passes out faeces on to its food.

4 Reproduction. A rapid rate of reproduction: several thousand eggs are laid by each female during her lifespan. The pupae can remain dormant in winter.

5 It cleans its body using a brushing action of its legs.

Factors relevant to the spread of disease

1 Has a hairy body and sticky pads on its feet to which micro-organisms readily become attached.

2 Transmits pathogenic bacteria from faeces and decaying refuse to food.

3 Its regurgitated food and its faeces contain those micro-organisms that are present in its gut.

The most common pathogenic bacteria carried by houseflies cause **dysentery** and **diarrhoea**, particularly in summer.

Control

1 Elimination of breeding places, for example, by burning refuse and using disposable polythene waste sacks inside dustbins which, when full, are sealed to prevent entry of flies.

2 Elimination of the adult insect by the use of insecticides.

3 Prevention of contamination of food (e.g. keeping foodstuffs in refrigerators or in sealed containers) and of cooking utensils, crockery and cutlery.

Mosquito

Life history

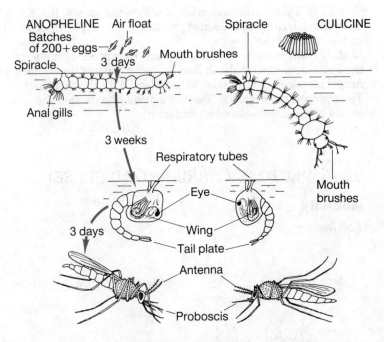

Fig. 2.13 The life history of mosquitoes. The drawings on the left show the eggs, larva, pupa and female imago of the anopheline mosquito and those on the right show the same stages of the culicine mosquito. The anopheline mosquito is responsible for carrying the single-celled animal, *Plasmodium*, which causes malaria

Habits

1 Diet. The *female* mosquito requires *blood* because this contains a protein essential for the manufacture of egg cases. The *male* feeds on *plant juices*.

2 Feeding. It inserts its needle-like mouth part (proboscis) into its food and sucks up the liquid. The female produces an **anti-coagulant** to stop the blood from clotting.

3 Reproduction. The female lays her eggs on the surface of stagnant water. The larval and pupal stage are aquatic (see Fig. 2.13).

Control

1 Elimination of the adult mosquito by the use of insecticides such as DDT.
2 Prevention of reproduction by draining the insect's stagnant water breeding sites.
3 Elimination of larvae by spraying oil on the breeding sites, which reduces the surface tension of the water, thereby interfering with larval breathing.
4 Elimination of larvae by *biological control*, e.g. introducing to breeding waters fish that eat the larvae.

Lice

Life history

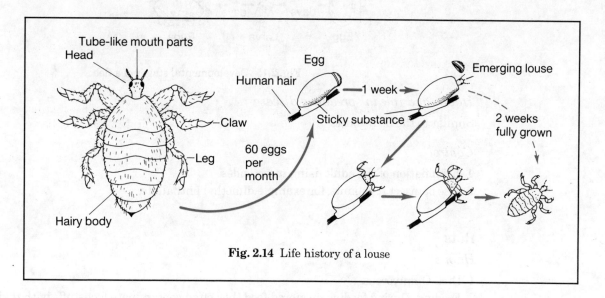

Fig. 2.14 Life history of a louse

Habits

1 Diet. Blood.
2 Feeding. Mouthparts are adapted for piercing the skin and sucking blood.
3 Reproduction. **Head lice** lay their eggs (*nits*) in the hair of the scalp. **Body lice** lay their eggs in clothing, usually around seams and buttonholes. Crab lice lay their eggs in pubic hair (see Fig. 2.14).

Factors relevant to the spread of disease

1 Irritation caused by a bite leads to scratching and the sores become infected by bacteria.
2 The body louse can spread in its faeces the virus which causes *typhus*.

Control

The use of an insecticide such as gamma benzene hexachloride in shampoos and as a powder dusted on to clothing.

Bed bug

Life history and role in spreading disease

Similar to the body louse.

Habits

1 Diet. Blood.
2 Feeding. Mouthparts are adapted for piercing skin and sucking blood. Feeding occurs at night; during the day bed bugs remain in crevices in walls, furniture and in mattresses. A bed bug can survive several months on a single blood meal.

Control

1 Elimination of the adult using insecticides.
2 In severe cases fumigation of homes with hydrogen cyanide gas to eliminate the eggs. This gas is extremely poisonous but milder toxins are unable to kill the eggs.

Human flea

Life history

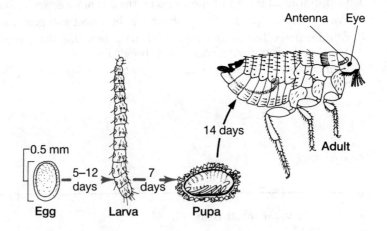

Fig. 2.15 Developmental stages of a flea

Habits and role in spreading disease

Similar to the body louse.

Control

1 Elimination of the adult using insecticides.

2 Use of insect repellants, for example dimethyl phthallate.

Rats

Habits

1 Diet. Omnivorous.

2 Feeding. During feeding on stored food they often contaminate foodstuffs with their urine. Many obtain their food in sewers.

3 Reproduction. A very high reproductive rate. A typical female starts to breed at 4–6 months old and produces 4–5 litters, each of 6–10 offspring, per year.

Factors relevant to the spread of disease

The *rat flea* can carry *bubonic plague* and *typhus*. **Scrub typhus** is spread by *rat mites*. **Salmonella food poisoning** and **Weil's disease** are caused by *bacteria* carried by rats. The latter can be contracted as a result of contact with contaminated rat urine; it is an occupational hazard of *sewage workers*. Symptoms include serious disorders of the liver and kidneys.

Control

1 Trapping and killing rats.

2 Using poisons such as *Warfarin* although some populations have developed immunity to this particular chemical.

2.2.17 INHERITED DISEASES

Haemophilia

An inherited disease that is characterized by **uncontrolled bleeding**. It usually affects *males* although women can be carriers, transmitting the disease to future generations. (A female carrier usually has blood that clots normally but she may give birth to sons in whom the condition is expressed.)

Normal people possess substances in the blood that rapidly stop bleeding by an efficient clotting mechanism. The *haemophiliac*, however, has no such mechanism and spontaneous bleeding, usually into *joints*, occurs. As a result, the joints become swollen and stiff. Internal bleeding can often be more serious than external bleeding, for example it may cause pressure on the windpipe resulting in asphyxiation. The severity of the disease is highly variable. There is no cure for haemophilia, only treatment to stop haemorrhaging.

The condition is a classic example of a **sex-linked disease** in man. In the nucleus of every human cell (except sperm and eggs) there are *23 pairs* of chromosomes one of which is concerned with *sex* *determination* (the X and Y chromosomes). In females the sex chromosome pair consists of two Xs, and in males, of an X and a Y. These chromosomes differ in size:

X Y

The *inheritance of sex* can be followed:

		MALE	
	gametes	X	Y
FEMALE	X	XX	XY
	X	XX	XY

OFFSPRING
50% male, 50% female

The *gene for haemophilia* is carried on the *non-pairing segment* of the X chromosome and is inherited as follows:

		NORMAL MALE	
	gametes	X	Y
CARRIER FEMALE	X^h	XX^h	X^hY
	X	XX	XY

OFFSPRING (F_1)
normal males XY
normal females XX
carrier females XX^h
haemophiliac males X^hY

Down's syndrome

An inherited disability caused by the presence of an **extra chromosome** in the number of cells (see Section 4.2.5). Affected children are of *short* stature for their age and are *mentally retarded*. The head is *smaller* than normal, the face *round*, the eyes *slanted* and there is a *fold of skin* across the inner corner of the eyes. The hands are *short* and *stubby*, often with a curved little finger. The feet have a large *gap* between the first and second toes. *Abnormal development of internal organs* such as the heart and intestine may also occur.

The internal abnormalities and an above-average tendency to catch infectious diseases used to cause early death in Down's syndrome children but survival has improved with advances in medical treatment. The *incidence of Down's syndrome* is approximately 1 in 600 births. However, the risk of giving birth to a Down's syndrome child depends on the mother's age. For women in their 20s, the chances are 1 in 2000, and the figure rises sharply at the age of about 35, reaching a maximum of 1 in 50 for women giving birth at the age of 45 or more. In rare cases, Down's syndrome is caused by **fusion** of one chromosome with another. The fused chromosome can be carried by clinically normal people, who run the risk of having further affected children. There is no cure for Down's syndrome. Parents of Down's syndrome children who are contemplating having further children should discuss the problem with a *genetic counsellor.*

2.2.18 OCCUPATIONAL DISEASES

Pneumoconiosis

A general term for a group of **lung diseases** caused by **inhalation of dust**. The diseases are occupational hazards of *miners, stone masons, quarrymen* and workers in *asbestos* and *metal-finishing factories*. Normally, the cilia of cells lining the respiratory system carry dust away from the *bronchioles* in mucus. Continued exposure to dust causes this natural cleansing system to become inefficient. Air flow is obstructed by blockages in the air passages. Thus less **oxygen** is delivered to the alveoli for gaseous exchange (see Section 3.2.3). Furthermore, the **abrasive action** of the dust particles leads to *infection, accumulation of secretions* and *destruction of lung tissue*. The latter, in turn, leads to increased resistance to the flow of blood through the lungs at each cycle. This places a stress on the **heart**, which may fail.

Symptoms include **breathlessness** and a **dry cough**. An X-ray examination generally shows the presence of **scar tissue**, with the destruction of air spaces. **Bronchitis** often results, and further complications include *pulmonary tuberculosis* and *lung cancer.* Treatment consists of early diagnosis of lung damage and prevention of the above complications, if necessary by cessation of working in a dust-laden environment. **Smoking** should be discouraged as it heightens the symptoms. Preventive measures including the wearing of *helmets* and *face masks, damping down dust* with water sprays and the use of *ventilation systems* to remove dust from the air.

Asbestosis

A type of **pneumoconiosis** caused by continuous inhalation of the dust and fibres of **asbestos**. It often develops among workers in asbestos factories (even after only a few weeks' exposure to the dust) and used to be a hazard in the *building industry* before safety regulations restricting the use of asbestos materials in houses were introduced. In serious cases, lung cancer is a complication.

Silicosis

A type of pneumoconiosis caused by continuous inhalation of **silica dust**, generally from *fine sand* or *crushed rock*. It is a hazard of stone masonry and quarrying.

Emphysema

This is a condition of the **lungs** in which there is *overdistension* of the **air sacs**; some of which *rupture* and fuse together to form abnormally large air spaces. The efficiency of the lungs in *gaseous exchange* is greatly reduced. Symptoms include *breathlessness* and *cyanosis* (blueing of the skin). The most common cause of emphysema is **bronchitis**, which in turn is caused by *irritative particles* in the bronchial tubes leading to the invasion of *bacteria*. Destruction of the air sacs makes it more difficult for the heart to circulate blood through the lungs and this often leads to **heart failure**. There is no real cure for emphysema because it occurs as the final consequence of damage. **Smoking** must be avoided because this aggravates the condition. A certain amount of relief can be obtained by giving *antispasmodic* drugs which dilate the bronchial tubes and minimize the resistance to air flow.

2.2.19 ENVIRONMENTAL DISEASES

Stress

Today, in overcrowded cities, people work in an atmosphere of intense competition. If this is allowed to get out of hand, it can upset the natural rhythms of life and the body's reaction shows itself in physical and mental disturbance.

Causes of stress

1 Overcrowding—aggravation in commuting to and from work.
2 Noise—from traffic.
3 Pollution of the environment—from traffic and factories.
4 Competition with others—'Keeping up with the Joneses'.
5 Crises of everyday life—having to work long hours, not having time to eat regularly and well, etc.
6 Major disasters—such as death of a close relative or unemployment.

Forms that stress takes

1 Mental breakdown.	6 Asthma.
2 Withdrawal from society.	7 Migraine.
3 Anxiety.	8 Eczema.
4 High blood pressure.	9 Constipation.
5 Ulcerated digestive tract.	10 Diarrhoea.

Coping with the problem

Sympathy and understanding can help to reduce the harmful effects of stressful situations. Wherever possible, stress should be avoided. The person who is prone to high blood pressure should avoid unnecessary anxiety and control his or her *smoking, eating* and *drinking* habits. Parents of children who seem *anxious, shy* or *aggressive* should encourage the children to talk about their worries and to feel less afraid of the world outside the home environment.

Radiation sickness

The results of exposure to **radioactivity**. Chemical elements above *atomic number 83* emit subatomic particles as the nucleus of the atom disintegrates. The emissions damage molecules in cells, including those from which *genes* are composed. The genes can become altered (mutations) and if they are in gametes can give rise to abnormalities in future generations.

When a human is exposed to large doses of radiation (above 1000 roentgen units) death is inevitable. Doses over 200 roentgen units can produce symptoms of radiation sickness. The body starts to show disturbances in its most rapidly dividing tissues. The first tissue to be affected is the **gut lining**. Within 24 hours, there is *nausea, vomiting* and *diarrhoea*, and these symptoms may prove fatal. Intravenous fluid replacement is essential at this stage. On about the 6th day there is failure to produce the normal number of *white blood cells*. *Gamete production* can be affected by doses of 400 roentgen units, leading to temporary or permanent *sterility.*

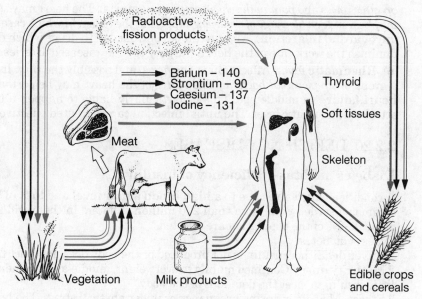

Fig. 2.16 Routes of radioactive substances affecting man

Leukaemia (inability to produce blood cells in the correct proportions) and other forms of **cancer** have been linked with the effects of radiation. **Radioactive fall-out** from nuclear reactions has an indirect as well as a direct effect on man. The indirect effect may be more widespread and longer-lasting. Figure 2.16 shows how some radioactive materials get into plants, then via food into man.

Hypothermia

Low body temperature generally resulting from prolonged exposure to cold. The initial effects of cooling are to stimulate *shivering, increased pulse rate, constriction of the blood vessels in the skin* and a *rise in blood pressure.* When the body temperature falls below **32°C** these compensatory mechanisms begin to fail, the nervous system becomes less efficient and consciousness is impaired. Death normally occurs at body temperatures of **26°C**. *Babies* and the *elderly* are particularly susceptible to cold, and deaths from hypothermia are not uncommon where old people live alone with inadequate heating. It is also the main cause of death in cases of **exposure** in mountainous regions where, in addition to cold, *high winds* and *wet clothes* contribute to a very rapid loss of heat.

Arthritis

This is a name given to several diseases of the **joints**. There are those due to *degeneration* and *inflammation* (the latter of which may be due to infection); *reaction to an organism* (**rheumatic fever**); *non-infective inflammation* (**rheumatoid arthritis** and similar diseases); and the presence of *crystals of uric acid* in the joints (**gout**). In some of these diseases symptoms may also occur elsewhere in the body. Arthritis is one of the most painful and crippling diseases in the Western world severely affecting older people and making a normal active life impossible for them.

There is no overall cure available. Arthritis caused by *bacteria* is treated with *antibiotics.* **Physiotherapy** keeps affected joints as flexible as possible, while a thin film of *hot wax* applied to arthritic hands has soothing properties but is not a cure. Pain relief can be obtained with *aspirin* and inflammation can be suppressed with *chloroquine* compounds, *gold* salts and *cortisone* derivatives.

Rheumatism

A frequently mis-used name for a variety of disorders which involve pains in the body. It is strictly a disease or set of symptoms related to the joints. It is more or less synonymous with arthritis.

Heart disease

1 Congenital. 1% of the population suffers from some sort of heart *structural* abnormality. The majority of these abnormalities involve defects of heart *valves* or *abnormal links* between the two normally separate circulations (see Section 3.5.4), leading to the mixing of *oxygenated* and *deoxygenated* blood. The defect may be a symptom of chromosome abnormality, e.g. in **Down's syndrome** a hole between the ventricles occurs (see Section 2.2.17). Heart defects are also common in children born to mothers who contract **rubella** (German measles) in the first 3 months of pregnancy. All of these defects can usually be cured by surgery.

2 Acquired.

(a) **Coronary ischaemia.** More common in *males* than in females and most often caused by **atheroma** (fatty deposits in blood vessels). Factors which contribute to this disease are *smoking, obesity, hypertension* (high blood pressure) and *lack of exercise.* The person is limited in exertion by *breathlessness* and *pain in the chest* (**angina pectoris**). The heart may *stop beating gradually* or there may be a *sudden blockage of an artery* supplying the heart, in which case part of the heart muscle dies (**myocardial infarction**). Angina can be controlled with drugs which dilate arteries or those which diminish the work rate of the heart. Surgery to clear diseased arteries may be possible.

(b) **Rheumatic fever.** Affects *joints*, the *heart*, and possibly the *skin*. It is due to **toxins** produced by a group of *streptococcal bacteria*. The *valves* of the heart may be permanently damaged, leading to **heart failure** in middle age. This is particularly liable to happen if the patient suffers recurrent attacks of rheumatic fever. The initial infection can be treated effectively with *antibiotics*.

2.2.20 DEFICIENCY DISEASES

Diabetes mellitus—deficiency of insulin

A condition which gives rise to a **high blood sugar level** and **loss of blood sugar** in urine. It is a common disorder, with more than 200 million sufferers in the world. In the Western Hemisphere, about 1−2% of the population are affected.
Types of diabetes:
1 Juvenile. Either insulin is not produced or the body does not react to insulin in the normal way.
2 Maturity onset. Confined mainly to overweight, middle-aged women and occurs when there is too little insulin to meet the demands of the body.
3 Stress. May occur during pregnancy or under physical stress. The body fails to respond to insulin at its normal levels in the blood.

Several diseases of the **endocrine glands** can cause diabetes, and it can also be caused as a side-effect when patients are on *steroid hormones* or *diuretic drugs* (those which increase urine production). In order to understand diabetes, it is necessary to know how the normal person uses carbohydrates.

Carbohydrates are digested to form **glucose**, which is absorbed into the bloodstream. The increased concentration of blood sugar is detected by special **beta cells** of the **islets of Langerhans** of the *pancreas*. These cells secrete the hormone **insulin**; the higher the glucose concentration, the greater the secretion. Insulin causes the glucose to be used for **energy release** or stored as **glycogen** or **fat** in the *liver*. The stored material can be reconverted to glucose when the body requires it. This is under the control of hormones produced by the **adrenal glands**. In this way, a **balance** is set up between *regulators* which remove glucose from the circulation, and those which put it back. A relatively *constant* blood sugar concentration of *0.1%* is controlled in this way and can be regarded as a form of **homeostasis** (see Section 3.6.6).

In a *diabetic*, this fine regulation is lost. The blood sugar concentration *rises* to a very high level and the **kidneys**, which normally reabsorb glucose back into the bloodstream, fail to cope. Glucose is lost in **urine** and this is a symptom of the disease. If glucose continues to be lost in this way, then the patient often suffers *unconsciousness*. Long-term treatment to control the problem consists of regular *injection* of carefully controlled doses of *insulin* and dietary regulation to *reduce carbohydrate intake*. **Emergency treatment** for a patient who has accidentally injected too much insulin is the administration of an immediate glucose supply to make up for the shortage of it in the body.

Scurvy—deficiency of vitamin C

A disease produced by an inadequate dietary intake of vitamin C (ascorbic acid), which is involved in the manufacture of **connective tissue** that acts like a sort of *cement* between cells of the body. Symptoms include *swollen, bleeding gums, loss of teeth, weakness in the legs and knees*, disorders of the skin such as prominence of hair follicles over the back and thighs, *coiling of hair* and *bleeding under the skin*. Old scars become tender and new ones heal slowly. There may be bleeding into the walls of the *heart, lungs* and *intestine*. Scurvy is rare in developed countries but still not totally eliminated. It is seen in elderly people who eat meals lacking in **fresh fruit** and **vegetables** and also in young children who are not given plenty of fruit juice or vitamin supplements. It is almost unknown in *breast-fed babies*. Treatment consists of daily administration of adequate amounts of ascorbic acid, either in the form of tablets or citrus fruits and blackcurrants.

2.2.21 CANCER

A disease of *multicellular* organisms, characterized by **uncontrolled multiplication** and spread within the body of **abnormal** forms of the organisms' cells.
There are three principal characteristics of the disease:
1 Increase in size resulting from the rapid multiplication of cells.
2 Invasion and destruction of surrounding normal structures by cancer cells.
3 Seemingly spontaneous development and independent nature of abnormal cells.

How a cancer cell may arise

A normal cell has the following features:
1 Immobilized because of contact with neighbouring cells.
2 Only divides if triggered by various regulator chemicals.

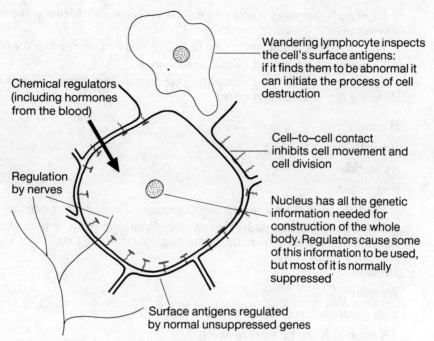

Fig. 2.17 How a normal cell is prevented from becoming a cancer cell

3 Has only normal surface antigens (chemicals that trigger an immune response).

Under certain circumstances there occurs either a **breakdown in cell regulation**:
(a) by expression of information that is normally suppressed,
(b) by failure in cell contact, hormone or nervous control,
(c) by failure of lymphocyte action after abnormal antigens have developed,
and/or an **abnormality in genetic information**:
(a) because of the presence of a virus,
(b) because of mutation altering the cell's genes,
(c) by loss of genetic information and therefore of normal surface antigens.
The result may be a cancer cell which *moves freely* around the body and has *few or no contact with other cells; divides in an uncontrolled way;* and has *abnormal surface antigens* or has lost some of its normal ones.

Common forms of cancer

Table 2.8 lists the most commonly occurring types of cancer found in men and women in the U.K.

Table 2.8 Common sites of cancer in males and females

Males	Females
Lung	Breast
Colon and rectum	Cervix
Prostate gland	Colon and rectum
Blood (leukaemia)	Lung

2.3 Personal Health and Hygiene

2.3.1 CARE OF THE SKIN, HAIR AND TEETH

Skin

Reasons

1 Prevention of infection by micro-organisms via sweat pores.
2 Prevention of accumulation of oil, sweat and micro-organisms which will encourage insect parasites.

Treatment

1 Frequently bathe or take a shower in hot water using soap, which will remove the oil and bacteria contained in it.

2 Wash one's feet every night and dry them thoroughly between the toes to prevent skin diseases developing.

3 Wash hands before meals, before handling food and after using the toilet.

4 Keep nails short, smooth edged, and clean.

5 Treat any open cuts with an antiseptic cream. They should be covered with a light bandage to prevent entry of micro-organisms.

Hair

Reasons

As for **skin**.

Treatment

1 Wash the hair at least once a week to remove dirt and micro-organisms.

2 Brush and comb hair daily. This removes dirt, micro-organisms and loose skin. It also increases the circulation of blood in the scalp, improving the growth of hair.

Mouth

Reasons

1 Prevention of tooth decay (see Section 3.4.2).

Treatment: Rules for healthy teeth

1 A pregnant woman must have a well-balanced diet so that her baby's first set of teeth will develop properly.

2 Visit the dentist every 6 months for a check-up from an early age.

3 Always brush teeth after meals and last thing at night.

4 Eat tooth-cleaning foods such as celery.

5 Renew old, worn out toothbrushes with new soft bristled ones.

6 Use toothpaste containing fluoride.

7 Brush teeth with a circular motion around the necks and between them.

8 Brush the backs of the front teeth and the biting surfaces of the back teeth.

9 Avoid chewing gum, sweets and other sugar-rich foods. Do not use teeth to crack nuts or to remove bottle-tops.

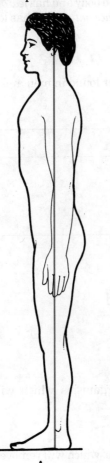

Fig. 2.18 Posture

A   B   C

2.3.2 CHARACTERISTICS OF GOOD POSTURE

1 Good posture. The vertical *axis of the body* and the *axial skeleton nearly coincide.* Note that the ear, hand and foot are on the same axis.

2 Round shoulders. The *head is pushed forward*, resulting in a *tilted pelvis* to maintain balance. Shoulders become very rounded, back muscles are strained and correct breathing is impossible.

3 Hollow back. The *shoulders are held back* and the person may think that he is standing well. However, his *abdomen is pushed forward* and his abdominal muscles have become slack. This may result in *digestive* and *respiratory* problems.

2.3.3 NEED FOR EXERCISE

During exercise, the **heart** beats *faster* and there is an *increase* in its stroke volume (the volume of blood pumped per beat). The *rate* and *depth* of **respiration** also increase so that the lungs completely fill and almost completely empty of air. **Lymph** flows out *faster* as body muscles contract and relax. Further effects of exercise and training programmes include increased *power* and *endurance* of muscles and *enhanced motor skills* by repeated practice of complex movement patterns. In general, all organs of the body function optimally.

2.3.4 NEED FOR SLEEP

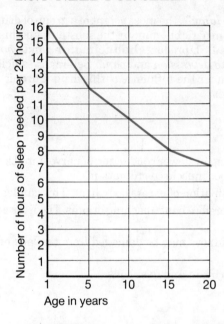

Sleep is required for the following:

1 To allow the brain and body to rest.

2 To provide a period of inactivity so that waste material, accumulated during activity, can be removed from cells.

3 To allow replacement and repair of damaged cells.

4 To allow long bones to regain their correct length after being compressed during exercise. This is particularly important in young children.

The **amount of sleep** needed varies with *age* and with *the individual.* A graph of the average number of hours of sleep needed by an individual per 24 hours against age shows a decline from birth to adolescence (see Fig. 2.19).

Fig. 2.19 Graph of the number of hours' sleep needed per 24 hours against age

2.3.5 DRUGS AND THE NERVOUS SYSTEM

Sedatives

Drugs which promote *relaxation* and *relief of anxiety.* **Barbiturates** and **morphine** are the most commonly used sedatives. There are two main disadvantages with this group of drugs:

1 There is a danger of people becoming **addicted.**

2 The drugs cause **drowsiness** even in moderate doses.

The first disadvantage is true of most drugs, but the second is partially overcome by **tranquillisers** such as chlordiazepoxide, diazepam, medazepam and meprobromate. These have considerable *calming* qualities with relatively little tendency to cause drowsiness.

Stimulants

Drugs which *quicken responses.* The main disadvantage with this group of drugs is that they can be *addictive.* **Caffeine** is the most readily available being present in drinks such as coffee, tea and cola. Drinamyl in tablet form was the basis of *'pep pills'*, which due to their addictive properties are now not available.

Narcotics

These have a very powerful effect on the nervous system and are only prescribed under very *strict supervision* and in *small doses.* **Overdoses** cause states of unconsciousness, or *comas*, and can be *fatal.* **Drug addiction** caused by narcotics is one of the most serious social problems of the world, leading to complete loss of *psychological* and *physiological* independence of the drug. Consequently, addicts will resort to all methods—particularly crime—to obtain narcotics. The most well-known narcotics are *cannabis, cocaine, opiates, heroin* and *LSD.* The preparation and sale of these is *illegal.*

Cannabis is a drug which produces *hallucinations*. It is a resin obtained from the leaves and flowering tops of the tropical **hemp plant.** In Europe and the Middle East, the resin is also known as *hashish*, and in India as *charas, bhang* and *dagga*. A crude preparation of the whole flowering top and upper leaves is known as **marijuana**. The resin contains a complex mixture of chemicals. Due to the lipid (fat-like) nature of one of these, the active ingredient in cannabis is rapidly passed from the blood to the brain. *Lung cancer* and a condition leading to the birth of *deformed children* are possible consequences of chronic cannabis addiction.

Cocaine was the first drug to be used as a *local anaesthetic*. It comes from the coca plant, which is native to Peru, Bolivia and Chile and is cultivated in other tropical countries. Cocaine is **toxic:** in *high dosage* it gives rise to excitement, then depression, loss of co-ordination, convulsions, respiratory paralysis and death. In 1905 it was superseded by a synthetic substitute, *Novocaine*, which is still in general use.

Opiates are derivatives of the dried latex seed capsule of the *opium poppy*, which is cultivated mainly in Turkey, Iran and India. The *narcotic* action of opiates is mainly due to their **morphine** content. Addiction to opium is very common in the Far East, where opium smoking is prevalent.

Heroin is a semi-synthetic drug obtained from *morphine*. It is more readily addictive than morphine and produces *side-effects* of nausea, vomiting and constipation. Addiction leads to *mental* and *moral* deterioration. Heroin is a drug of increasing abuse and its addiction is much harder to cure than addiction to morphine.

LSD is the abbreviation of *lysergic acid diethylamide*, the most potent of a group of drugs which affect a person's powers of *perception*. LSD itself is synthetic but many of the substances of this group of drugs are present in extracts of *fungi* and *wild plants*. LSD produces **hallucinations** and *emotional reactions* which may include anything from *euphoria* to *depression* and *panic*. Self-injury, suicide and murder have been known to have been committed under the influence of this drug. Chronic use may cause organic brain damage and foetal malformities.

2.3.6 ALCOHOL

Harmful effects:

1 Impairment of the nervous system, resulting in slower conduction of nerve impulses, slow reaction to stimuli, loss of accurate judgement and poor muscle co-ordination.

2 Dilation of skin blood vessels causing dissipation of excess body heat. This can lead to chilling.

3 A reduction in the volume of blood (and therefore heat) reaching organs. The liver and the kidneys, in particular, are seriously affected.

4 More water is passed out in sweat. The kidneys may be damaged from the lack of water passing through them.

5 Addiction produces permanent damage to brain and liver cells.

For **smoking** see Sections 3.2.6 and 4.1.5.

2.4 Public Health

2.4.1 WATER SUPPLY

Origin of surface water

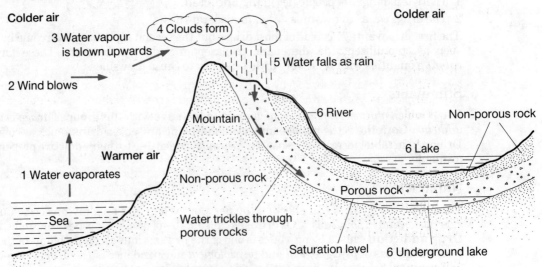

Fig. 2.20 Diagram to show the cycle of events that leads to the formation of rain, rivers and lakes

Stages in the supply of water for domestic purposes

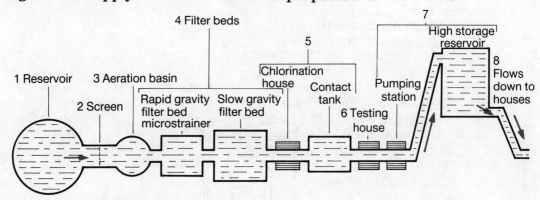

Fig. 2.21 Simple plan to show the order in which water is treated during purification

1 Storage in reservoirs.

2 Screening. Water passes through channels, partly blocked by metal screens: floating matter is trapped and raked away.

3 Aeration. Water is sprayed as fountains to facilitate oxygen in the air to dissolve in the water. The oxygen destroys many harmful anaerobic (thrive in the absence of oxygen) micro-organisms present in the water.

4 Filtration. Water passes through gravity filter beds.

Water trickles slowly through the sand and then more rapidly through the gravel and stones until it collects in pipes. All its *floating* matter, some of its *suspended* matter, and *micro-organisms* are left behind in the spaces between sand and gravel.

In all gravity filter beds, sand and the smallest stones are at the top and the largest stones are at the bottom so that particles are not carried along to the pipes but become trapped by the layers of progressively larger particles. Beds which use coarse sand as the top layer permit rapid filtration. These **primary filters** must be washed daily to remove the impurities from the sand and gravel. Clean water and air are blown upwards through the bed and the water now is allowed to flow away from the top carrying the dislodged impurities.

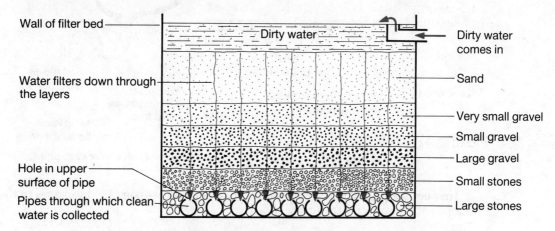

Fig. 2.22 Diagram to show the structure of a gravity filter bed

Those beds which have a top layer of very fine sand permit only *slow* filtration. They are **secondary filters**. In these, the impurities form a jelly-like film, the **zoogloea layer**, on the surface. This prevents rapid filtration but, more important, the micro-organisms in the film help to reduce the numbers of harmful bacteria in untreated water by eating them. Secondary filters are cleaned only once every few weeks and then by scraping off the top layer of dirty sand, washing it and adding clean sand.

Modern waterworks often filter water using *micro-strainers*. These are cylinders bearing a fine mesh. Dirty water is channelled through the cylinders and is forced through the mesh, which traps all the impurities. The mesh is washed continuously. Rapid and slow filter beds are also being replaced by *pressure filters*. These make use of a layer of sand for filtering but water is forced through them instead, rather than relying on gravity to produce a flow of water.

5 Chlorination. The filtered water is passed through a tank where *chlorine* is added (in carefully monitored minute quantities), approximately 1 part chlorine to 2 million parts water, to kill any remaining harmful micro-organisms. *Fluoride* may be added at this point.

6 The water is tested regularly throughout the day for *impurities* and *taste*.

7 The water is pumped to high level *storage reservoirs* for distribution to houses, offices and factories, etc.

2.4.2 SEWAGE DISPOSAL

Collection—domestic

1 Pipes

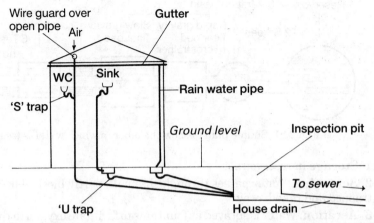

Fig. 2.23 Diagram to show the arrangement of the drainage pipes around a house

2 Traps. These are U- or S-shaped bends in pipes in which water collects. They prevent unpleasant smells getting back from the sewers into the house. The water in the traps acts as a seal. U-bends tend to be in pipes leading away from rainwater and kitchen drains and S-bends tend to be under baths, washbasins and toilets.

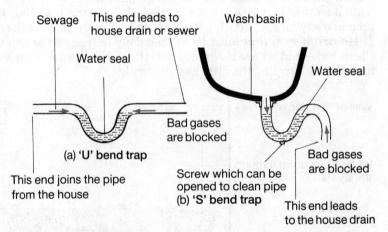

Fig. 2.24 Diagram to show the structure of traps in sewage pipes

3 Inspection pits. These are necessary to provide access points to blockages in the pipes and are sealed with gas-proof, heavy metal lids.

Treatment

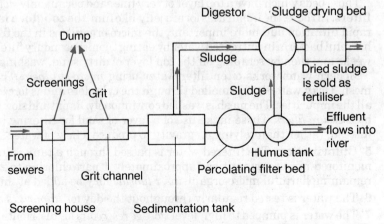

Fig. 2.25 Plan to show the order in which sewage is treated during its purification

1 Screening. In underground channels, sewage passes through *iron screens* that trap solid coarse material. The material is regularly scraped away, dumped on waste ground and covered with a layer of soil.

2 Settlement. Sewage is made to flow slowly through narrow *grit channels* so that any heavy solid particles settle to the bottom. The deposits are removed and dumped with the screenings. The sewage then passes into *sedimentation tanks*, where fine sand and organic matter settle in the form of sludge. The floor of each sedimentation tank is shaped like a funnel, sloping to a central exit pipe. This pipe is kept closed until the tank is ready to be emptied. Liquid emerging from the tanks is known as *effluent*. The sludge remaining on the floor of the tanks is periodically removed and pumped into a *digestor* building, where it is dried. Having a rich nutrient content, the dried sludge can be used as a fertilizer.

3 Aeration. Air is made to come in contact with as much of the effluent as possible. There are three methods of achieving this:

(a) *Percolating filtration.* This takes place in a round shallow filter bed filled with coke, clinker and small stones. The effluent is forced up through a vertical pipe in the centre of the bed and out through two or more horizontal side tubes which are perforated with many holes. The side tubes radiate from the vertical pipe like spokes on a wheel and constantly rotate about it, spraying jets of effluent onto the stones. Anaerobic micro-organisms in the effluent are killed by aeration or by being eaten by useful micro-organisms that grow on the surface of the filter bed stones. The clean effluent passes out of pipes at the base of the beds.

(b) *Activated sludge.* Streams of air are passed through aeration tanks containing the effluent. Harmful anaerobic micro-organisms are again killed by the oxygen or by the action of beneficial micro-organisms. The cleaner effluent is drawn off and some of the settled sludge is removed and dumped with the screenings. A thin layer of activated sludge is allowed to remain in the tanks to be mixed with the next flow of effluent and to act as a source of new colonies of useful micro-organisms.

(c) *Land filtration.* (Not often used in Britain.) On the basis that soil acts as a natural filter, the effluent is poured over any large area of flat land. Solid material eventually becomes dry, killing the micro-organisms, and is removed, the liquid part filters through the lands and becomes trapped within a depression in impervious rock.

4 Settlement of humus. Effluent is sent to humus tanks where any suspended material settles to form more activated sludge and this in turn increases the destruction of any remaining harmful micro-organisms. The sludge is sent to the digestor.

5 Discharge of the effluent—now harmless—into the sea or a convenient river.

2.4.3 REFUSE DISPOSAL

1 Incineration. This is the best way to dispose of dry refuse contaminated with harmful micro-organisms, e.g. a hospital's used wound dressings. Most modern methods reduce to a minimum contact between the refuse collectors' hands and the refuse. The resultant ash or clinker is dumped on local tips. The smoke and other potential air pollutants are filtered before being passed out through tall chimneys. The main problem of this method of disposal is expense.

2 Tipping. Special selected sites are used according to rules suggested by the Department of the Environment. These rules are:

(a) Refuse must not be allowed to reach rivers, ponds or reservoirs.

(b) Waste metal should be at the bottom of the tip as it takes a long time to deteriorate.

(c) Refuse should be spread not more than 2 m in depth if deterioration and decay are to proceed sufficiently quickly.

(d) Each layer of refuse should be covered by 50 cm of soil: micro-organisms in the soil will help in the breakdown of refuse materials.

(e) Screens should be used to stop waste paper from blowing about.

(f) Insecticides should be regularly sprayed on the tips.

(g) Each layer of refuse should be given sufficient time to settle before the next layer is added.

2.4.4 POLLUTION OF THE ENVIRONMENT

Pollution can be described as anything which when added to the environment destroys its purity.

Air

Table 2.9 Pollutants of air

Pollutant	Source	Effect	Control
Sulphur dioxide	Industrial combustion	Respiratory diseases	Use of smokeless fuels and sulphur dioxide extractors
Soot	Industrial combustion	Respiratory diseases. Reduction of plant photosynthesis	Smokeless fuels and chimney filters

Pollutant	Source	Effect	Control
Carbon monoxide	Internal combustion engines	Prevents oxygen combining with haemoglobin in red blood cells	Car exhaust afterburners converting carbon monoxide into carbon dioxide
Lead	Internal combustion engines	Poisons the nervous system	Reduction of lead in petrol and modification of car engines
Chloro-fluoromethanes	Aerosols	Breaks down ozone in the stratosphere and allows more ultraviolet light to reach the Earth, which may increase skin cancer	None, except reduction of use of aerosols

Land

Table 2.10 Pollutants of soil

Pollutant	Source	Effect	Control
Insecticides, herbicides, fungicides	Agricultural and medical destruction of pests	Build-up in food chains to toxic levels	Use of nontoxic, species specific types. Use of biological control
Radioactive wastes	Nuclear reactors	Mutation rates are increased. Increase in leukaemia	No satisfactory solution

Water

Table 2.11 Pollutants of water

Pollutant	Source	Effect	Control
Sewage	Humans	Spread of disease-causing micro-organisms. Reduction of oxygen in water by increased bacterial activity	Sewage treatment
Artificial fertilizers	Agriculture	Direct poisoning of organisms in water. Reduction of oxygen in water by increased activity of bacteria and other micro-organisms	Use of natural fertilizers
Oil	Oil tankers, oil rigs	Destruction of marine life	Effective laws banning dumping of oil
Heavy metals, e.g. mercury, lead, zinc, cadmium	Industrial effluent	Build-up in food chains to toxic levels	Purification of effluent

2.4.5 CONSERVATION

Man has helped to create an imbalance in nature by destroying forests and wildlife, damaging and depleting soil and wasting and polluting water. An active concentrated programme of conservation of resources will help restore the balance of nature, which is vital to the successful living of man.

Resources

1 **Nonrenewable.** Minerals and fossil fuels such as coal, oil and gas.
2 **Renewable.** Foods such as marine fish, wildlife such as tigers and whales, and vegetation, primarily trees.

Possible solutions to depletion of these resources

Minerals. Recycling of metals and reversing the policy of producing disposable (throw-away) items such as tin cans.

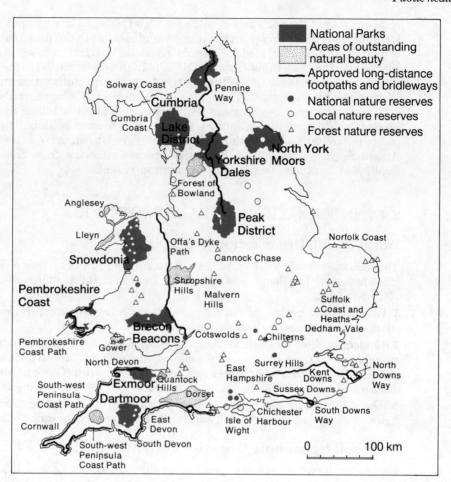

Fig. 2.26 Map to show the pattern of parks, paths, beauty spots and protected areas of biological interest in England and Wales

Fossil fuels. Use of other methods of energy conversion, e.g. tidal energy (Severn Estuary Project) and solar power. The public must be made to reduce fossil fuel consumption.

Foods. Expansion of fish farming projects. New sources of food in the form of micro-organisms. More use of primary producers as a source of protein, e.g. soya bean.

Wildlife. Stricter laws against destruction of endangered species. Education of the public to show the futility of hunting for sport, ivory, skins, aphrodisiacs. Use substitutes for whale oil and animal hides.

Trees. Continuous re-afforestation.

The conservation of wildlife and natural vegetation may, in the long term, be of more importance to man than its destruction for more immediate use. The public should be made aware of access to national parks and areas of outstanding beauty for recreation and enjoyment of nature.

2.4.6 THE PUBLIC HEALTH SERVICE

In Britain, the Department of Health and Social Security (DHSS) is responsible for the health and welfare of the population. It organizes the Environmental Health Services, Social Services and Social Security. Some of its services that aid the public include:

1 Clinics: *Ante-natal; Child welfare; Family planning;* and *Anti-smoking.*

2 Home Helps: *Home nursing;* care of the *elderly;* care of the *mentally handicapped;* care of the *physically handicapped;* and care of *children in need.*

3 Health Inspectors: *Food* inspectors; *safe-water* inspectors; *sewage and refuse disposal* and *town and country planners.*

4 Housing: *Pest* control; *noise* control; *air pollution* control; and *safety.*

The National Health Service (NHS)

Established in the UK in 1948. Its aim was to provide the best medical care for everyone at little or no cost. Through its actions the death rate since 1948 has dropped by 50% and there have been massive reductions in the cases of *tuberculosis, poliomyelitis* and *diphtheria.* The service was reorganized in 1973. The Department of Health and Social Security is responsible for its administration and it is the responsibility of the Secretary of State for Social Services in England. There are fourteen Regional Health Authorities throughout the country and each is divided into Area Health Authorities that are responsible for running medical schools, research, blood transfusion services and ambulances for a community that may number several million individuals. The NHS has recently undergone radical reorganization, leading to abolition of the Area Health Authorities and introduction of about 200 District Health Authorities. These are now the major units for the daily running of health services.

The cost of running the National Health Service is about £6 billion a year. About 88% of the money needed comes from the national budget and 12% from National Insurance Contributions and prescription charges. Exemption from charges is given to children under 16, adults of pensionable age, Armed Service Disablement Pensioners, people suffering from certain medical symptoms and families with incomes below a certain minimum level.

2.4.7 INTERNATIONAL HEALTH CONTROL

World Health Organization (WHO)

This was established in 1948. Its headquarters are in Geneva, Switzerland, and there is a regional office in Egypt, The Republic of the Congo, Denmark, India, Philippines and the USA. The WHO is responsible for:

1 Co-ordinating health information and research services on such topics as **nutrition, vaccines, drug addiction** and **radiation hazards.**

2 Control of diseases such as *malaria, tuberculosis, venereal* (sexually transmitted) *disease* and *smallpox.* It sponsors the control of epidemic and endemic diseases via **vaccination programmes, purification of drinking water** and **health education**. *Cholera, yaws* and *yellow fever* are some diseases which are being fought on an international level. It also organizes *quarantine* measures.

3 The administration of health policies by giving technical advice and conducting field surveys. It helps to set up *health centres* and aids the *training of medical staff.*

Food and Agriculture Organization (FAO)

Has its headquarters in Rome. It is responsible for increasing the efficiency of agriculture, fisheries and forestries. It provides the expert help necessary in these fields in the developing countries of the Third World.

United Nations International Children's Emergency Fund (UNICEF)

Has its headquarters in London and provides aid for the needs of children suffering from the effects of wars or of major disasters.

THEME 3
HUMAN STRUCTURE AND FUNCTION

3.1 The Skeleton and Movement

3.1.1 FUNCTIONS OF THE SKELETON

1 To act as a **framework** and to support the soft tissues of the body.

2 To enable **free movement** by the action of **muscles.**

3 To **protect** the delicate internal organs.

4 To **produce blood cells.** This is the function of *bone marrow.* In infants the red marrow of *all* bones is involved but in adults blood cells are produced in the red bone marrow of only the sternum, ribs, vertebrae, cranium and the 'heads' of the femur and humerus.

5 To store calcium. The calcium of *blood* is in equilibrium with that of bone.

3.1.2 THE SKELETAL SYSTEM

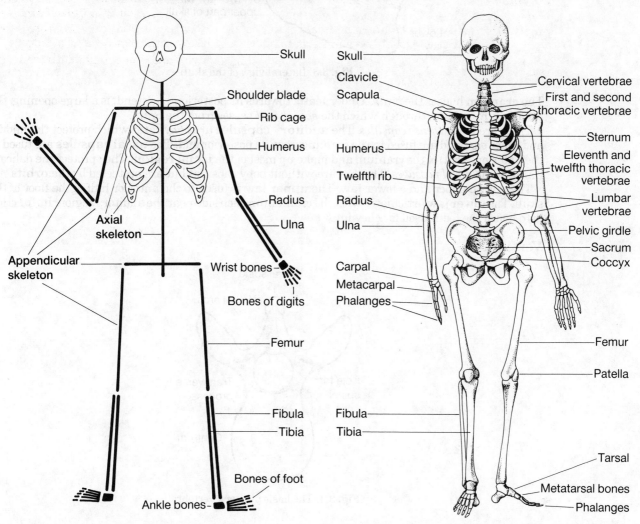

Fig. 3.1 The basic structure of the skeleton

Fig. 3.2 The human skeleton

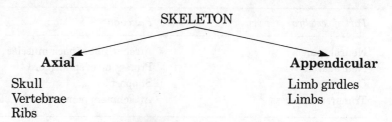

SKELETON

Axial	Appendicular
Skull	Limb girdles
Vertebrae	Limbs
Ribs	

3.1.3 AXIAL SKELETON

The skull

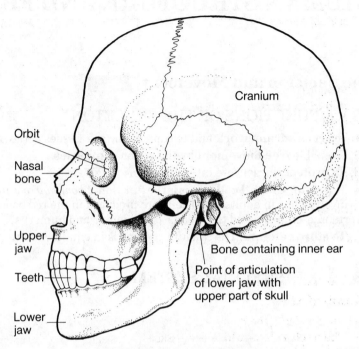

Fig. 3.3 Lateral view of the skull

The **cranium** houses the *brain*. Underneath, towards its posterior (back) end, is a large opening, the **foramen magnum**, through which the *spinal cord* passes from the brain.

There are paired *sense capsules*. The **auditory capsules** are bony cases which protect the middle and inner ears and are fused to the cranium near its posterior end. The **nasal capsules** are fused to the anterior (front) of the cranium and make up most of the **facial region**. They protect the delicate lining of the *nasal passages*. The *eyes* are without bony capsules but are protected by the **orbits**.

There is an upper and a lower **jaw**. The **upper jaw** is fused to the anterior half of the floor of the skull. The **lower jaw** articulates with the cranium on each side near the auditory region. Its function is to house the teeth used for chewing.

Vertebrae

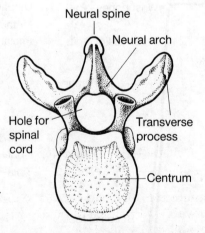

Fig. 3.4 The basic plan of a vertebra

Table 3.1 Structure and function of vertebrae

Part of vertebra	Function
Neural spine	Attachment of back muscles
Neural arch	Protection of spinal cord
Centrum	Support
Transverse process	Attachment of muscles

Table 3.2 Different types of vertebrae

Name of vertebra	Number	Function
Cervical/Neck	7	The first, the **atlas**, articulates with the skull and enables the head to move up and down. The second, the **axis**, articulates with the atlas and enables side to side movements of the head. The remaining five are for the *attachment of neck muscles* for movement of the head
Thoracic/Chest	12	To support the *ribs*
Lumbar/Abdominal	5	To support the whole weight of the body
Sacral	5 (fused)	To support the *pelvic girdle*
Coccygeal/Tail	4 (fused)	No function. A vestigal structure, the **coccyx**

Ribs

There are *12 pairs* (see Fig. 3.2). The last two pairs are *floating ribs* because their anterior ends are not attached to the sternum. The flexibility of the cartilages of the *sternum* and of the ribs, together with the joints with the vertebrae, enables the ribs to move when the *intercostal muscles* contract, thus allowing the volume of the thorax to be increased during inspiraiton.

3.1.4 APPENDICULAR SKELETON

Limb girdles

These consist of the bones with which the limbs articulate (Fig. 3.2). They are:

1 The **pectoral/shoulder girdle**, which consists of the two *clavicles* (collar bones) and two *scapulae* (shoulder blades).

2 The **pelvic/hip girdle**, which consists of two halves, the *innominate bones*, fused together. Each innominate bone is composed of three fused bones. These are the *ilium, ischium* and *pubis.*

Limbs

The limbs of all mammals are made from a basic plan, the **pentadactyl limb.**

Fig. 3.5 The pentadactyl limb (bones of the fore limb in normal type; those of the hind limb are in italics)

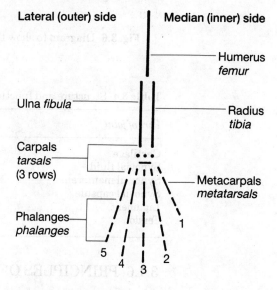

3.1.5 JOINTS

1 Fixed or **immovable** (fibrous) joints, e.g. sutures between skull bones.
2 Slightly movable (cartilaginous) joints, e.g. the *pubis, sternum/ribs* and between the *vertebrae.*
3 Freely movable (synovial) joints.

Table 3.3 Types of synovial joint

Joint	Position in body
(a) Gliding	Articular processes of vertebrae
(b) Hinge	Elbow, knee (see Figs 3.6, 3.16)
(c) Ball-and-socket	Hip, shoulder
(d) Condyloid	Radius/carpal in wrist
(e) Pivot	Atlas/axis in neck
(f) Saddle	Metacarpal of the thumb and the carpal of the hand

The structure of a synovial joint

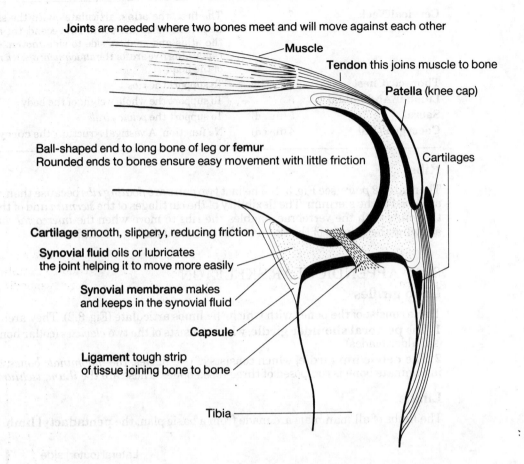

Joints are needed where two bones meet and will move against each other

Muscle

Tendon this joins muscle to bone

Patella (knee cap)

Ball-shaped end to long bone of leg or **femur**
Rounded ends to bones ensure easy movement with little friction

Cartilages

Cartilage smooth, slippery, reducing friction

Synovial fluid oils or lubricates
the joint helping it to move more easily

Synovial membrane makes
and keeps in the synovial fluid

Capsule

Ligament tough strip
of tissue joining bone to bone

Tibia

Fig. 3.6 Diagram to show the structure of the knee joint. This is looked at as if we had cut it in half

Table 3.4 Structure and function of parts of a synovial joint

Part of joint	Function
Cartilage	Helps to absorb shock
Synovial fluid	Helps to reduce friction
Synovial membrane	Secretes synovial fluid
Synovial capsule	Keeps synovial fluid in place
Ligament	Joins the bones together
Tendon	Joins muscle to bone allowing movement

3.1.6 PRINCIPLES OF LEVERS APPLIED TO THE SKELETON

Forces acting on a lever produce movements centred at a point, the **fulcrum**. Two forces are generally involved: the **load** and the **effort**. The effort is the force applied to hold the load in **equilibrium**. For example, it is the muscular effort needed to hold the head still in an inclined position or to lift a weight.

The **effect of a force** in a lever system is called its **moment** and equals the *product* of the *force* and the *distance* between the force and the fulcrum. At equilibrium, effort×distance of effort from fulcrum=load×distance of load from fulcrum.

Some levers are more efficient than others. Levers can be grouped into first, second and third orders.

First order levers

The *effort* and the *load* are on *opposite* sides of the *fulcrum* and a movement of the effort results in movement of the load in the *opposite* direction. When the fulcrum is central, at equilibrium the effort must *equal* the load. This type of lever produces movements of the trunk and head with very little contraction of the muscles involved.

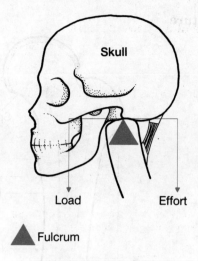

Fig. 3.7 First order lever

Second order levers

The *load* lies *between* the *fulcrum* and the *effort* and a movement of the effort results in movement of the load in the *same* direction. The *effort* is *less* than the *load*, and to maintain equilibrium any distance the effort moves from the fulcrum must be *greater* than the corresponding distance moved by the load. This type of lever action is seen when the body is raised on tiptoe.

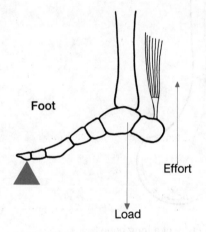

Fig. 3.8 Second order lever

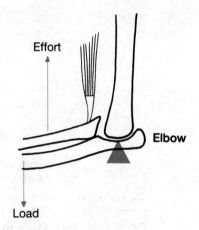

Fig. 3.9 Third order lever

Third order levers

The *effort* is *exerted between* the *fulcrum* and the *load* and movement of the effort results in movement of the load in the *same* direction. The *effort* is *greater* than the *load*, and to maintain equilibrium any distance the effort moves from the fulcrum must be *less* than the corresponding distance moved by the load. This is seen in the arm and is the commonest type of lever in the body. A variety of large movements can be made with very little shortening of the muscles involved.

3.1.7 BONE

Functions

1 To act as a strong framework to **support** the weight of the body.
2 To provide a secure **attachment** for the internal organs.
3 To provide a **store** of calcium, phosphorus and other essential minerals.
4 To **produce blood cells** (bone marrow).

Composition

50% water, 50% solid matter.
The solid matter consists of 67% calcium carbonate and calcium phosphate
33% organic matter (gelatine and collagen)

General structure

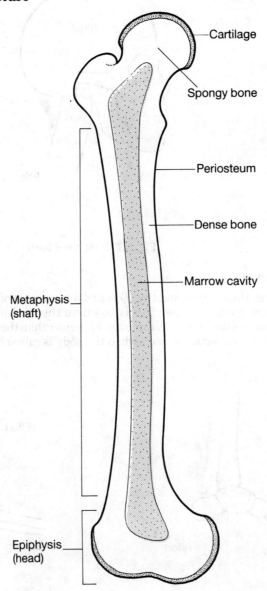

— Cartilage

— Spongy bone

— Periosteum

— Dense bone

— Marrow cavity

Metaphysis
(shaft)

Epiphysis
(head)

Fig. 3.10 The general structure of a long bone

Microscopic structure

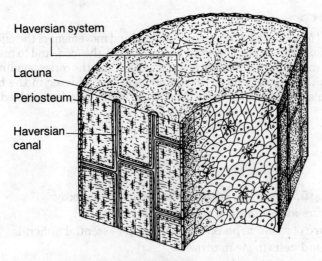

Haversian system

Lacuna

Periosteum

Haversian
canal

Fig. 3.11 A microscopic view of bone

The **Haversian system** contains the *Haversian canals* which run in a longitudinal direction parallel with the surface of the bone. The bone substance surrounding the Haversian canals contains concentrically arranged spaces, the **lacunae**, which contain the bone cells. Minute canals (canaliculi) join up the lacunae, and also communicate with the Haversian canals. *Blood vessels* and *lymphatics* run throughout the Haversian canals and nourish the bone cells.

Development of bone

1 In the developing foetus special connective tissue gives rise to a skeleton made entirely of cartilage. As the foetus grows the cartilage is gradually replaced by bone and becomes harder as *calcium salts* are deposited within its substance. Later, special bone cells, **osteoblasts,** enter the calcified cartilage together with other cells which remove the cartilage. The osteoblasts proceed to lay down bone in place of the cartilage which is absorbed.

2 Membranous bones, principally the flat bones of the skull, develop from special groups of connective tissue.

3.1.8 CARTILAGE

Microscopic structure

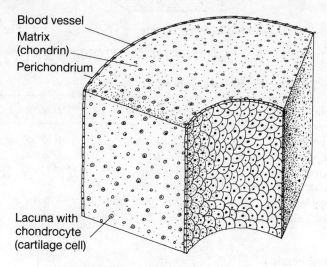

Fig. 3.12 A microscopic view of cartilage

This is firm bluish-white tissue, sometimes called **gristle**, that is made up mainly of fibres of **collagen** and **elastin** with a very small amount of *mineral matter.* The surface is covered by a membrane, the **perichondrium**, which is supplied with *blood vessels.* As the membrane and the ground substance of the cartilage are permeable, no blood vessels need enter cartilage tissue: materials in blood can diffuse through to the cartilage cells, which lie in special spaces, the **lacunae. Hyaline cartilage** is found lining *joints*, **fibro-cartilage** is found between the *vertebrae*, and **elastic cartilage** is found where a certain amount of elasticity is required, for example in the *epiglottis* and *pinna* of the ear.

3.1.9 MUSCLES

Table 3.5 Different types of muscles

Type	Position in the body
Smooth/Plain/Involuntary/Unstriated	Where sustained automatic contraction is needed, e.g. in walls of the **intestine** and **bladder.** Also in blood vessels. Arranged in *sheets*
Cardiac/Heart	**Heart**
Striated/Striped/Voluntary/Skeletal	Attached to the **skeleton** and under the control of *conscious effort.* Arranged in *bundles*

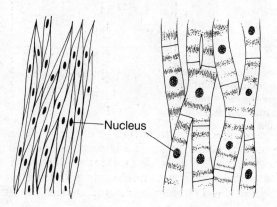

Fig. 3.13 Smooth muscle

Nucleus

Fig. 3.14 Heart muscle

The structure of striated muscle

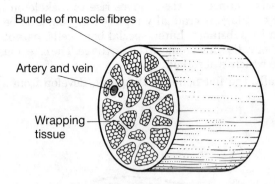

Fig. 3.15(a) Skeletal muscle

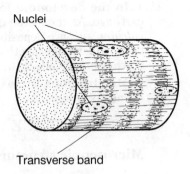

Fig. 3.15(b) Part of a muscle fibre

3.1.10 THE ANTAGONISTIC ACTION OF PAIRS OF MUSCLES

Table 3.6 Muscles of the arm and leg

Muscle	Origin	Insertion	Action
Biceps	Scapula	Radius	Flexes arm
Triceps	Scapula	Ulna	Extends arm
Quadriceps femoris (includes 4 muscles)	Pelvis and femur	Tibia	(a) Flexes hip joint (b) Extends leg at knee
Biceps femoris	Pelvis and femur	Fibula	Flexes leg at knee
Gluteus maximus	Pelvis	Femur	(a) Retracts leg (b) Straightens body by rotating it about the head of the femur
Gastrocnemius	Femur	Heel	Extends leg at ankle
Anterior tibial	Tibia	Metatarsal	Flexes leg at ankle

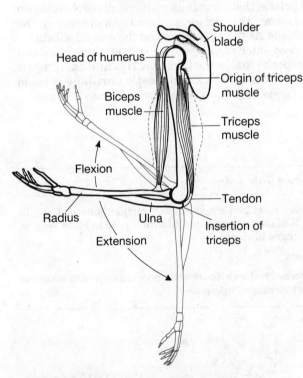

Fig. 3.16 The elbow joint, an example of a hinged joint. It is capable of flexion and extension but not rotation. The dotted lines show the movement of the lower arm during flexion and extension and the change in shape of the muscles concerned.

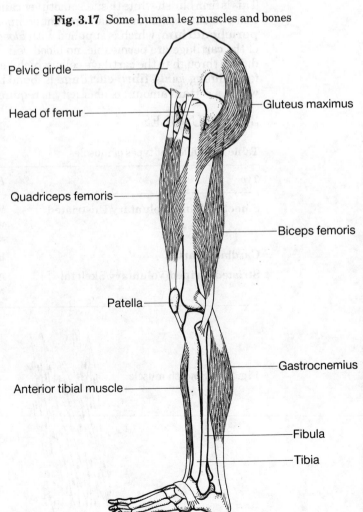

Fig. 3.17 Some human leg muscles and bones

The **antagonistic action** of muscles takes place when there is *opposing action* of two muscles such that the *contraction* of one is accompanied by the *relaxation* of the other.

The **point of origin** is that point of attachment of a muscle that does not move when the muscle contracts.

The **point of insertion** is that point of attachment of a muscle that moves when the muscle contracts.

3.1.11 THE PHYSIOLOGY OF MUSCLE ACTION

The *energy* used for the *contraction* of muscle cells comes from **adenosine triphosphate (ATP)**, which is a temporary store of chemical energy produced as a result of **respiration** (see Section 3.2.2).

Respiration takes place in muscle cells by **oxidation of glycogen** (a store of *glucose*). Glycogen makes up only 1% by weight of muscle and it is soon used during exercise, after which the muscle relies on fresh supplies of glucose from the *bloodstream*. To produce the maximum of ATP, **oxygen** is needed for the complete oxidation of glucose, and sometimes the oxygen supply to muscle cells lags behind their requirements. Under these circumstances, the muscle cells carry out respiration in the *absence of oxygen* (**anaerobic respiration**). This process results in *incomplete oxidation* of glucose with the production of *lactic acid* as a waste product. If exercise is vigorous or a muscle remains in a state of contraction for a long period, lactic acid accumulates. It may prevent the muscle from contracting further, causing **fatigue** and even *pain*.

When the exercise stops, the muscle *recovers* and will continue to use oxygen at a fast rate until the lactic acid is removed from the muscle via the bloodstream.

3.2 The Respiratory System

3.2.1 THE RESPIRATORY SYSTEM AND THE EXCHANGE OF GASES

Oxygen must be absorbed into the bodies of animals and plants for *respiration* to occur. In microscopically small organisms, the surface area in relation to volume is sufficiently large to permit adequate gaseous exchange and no special respiratory surfaces are required. The **rate of diffusion** is **inversely** proportional to the *distance travelled*, and so large animals such as man require a large surface area in contact with air. The characteristics of an efficient **respiratory surface** in active animals are as follows:

1 It must be **large in proportion to the animal's bulk.**

2 It must be **thin enough to allow gases to pass through easily.**

3 It has to be **moist so that carbon dioxide and oxygen can pass through** in solution.

4 It has to be **richly supplied with blood** to transport gases to and from the surface. The more active the animal, the greater will be the oxygen requirement, so in all vertebrates a means of **ventilating** or renewing the air at the surface is essential.

3.2.2 RESPIRATION AND THE PROVISION OF ENERGY

Respiration is the **release of energy from glucose** and occurs in *all* living cells.

$$C_6H_{12}O_6 \ + \ 6O_2 \ \xrightarrow{\text{Enzymes}} \ 6CO_2 \ + \ 6H_2O \ + \ \textbf{Energy}$$

$$\text{Glucose} \quad\quad \text{Oxygen} \quad\quad\quad \text{Carbon dioxide} \quad \text{Water} \quad\quad \textbf{ATP}$$

The equation is a *gross over-simplification* of the process because

1 It shows only the **reactants** and the **products** and gives no indication of the many *intermediate, enzyme-controlled reactions* which occur.

2 It implies that all the **energy** is liberated in one stage whereas it is really liberated in a succession of stages, a small amount at a time.

3 It implies that **oxidation** takes place *totally* by the addition of oxygen, whereas in fact most of the oxidation takes place by *removal of hydrogen* from glucose using a series of chemicals called **hydrogen carriers**. Oxygen is added during the *final* stages of oxidation only.

4 It gives us no idea of the form in which the energy is made available to the cell. The energy is in **adenosine triphosphate (ATP)**, which acts as the *energy currency* of the living organism, and is released and made available to the cell when this chemical *loses* one of its *phosphate groups* to become **adenosine diphosphate (ADP)**.

3.2.3 THE RESPIRATORY ORGANS

Table 3.7 The respiratory organs

Structure	Function
Larynx	The **voice box** for *sound production*
Trachea	The **windpipe** to *carry air* to the lungs via the bronchi
Intercostal muscles	Used during **breathing** movements
Lungs	The organs where **exchange of gases** occurs between the blood system and the atmosphere
Diaphragm	A *sheet of muscle* separating the thorax from the abdomen and used during **breathing** movements

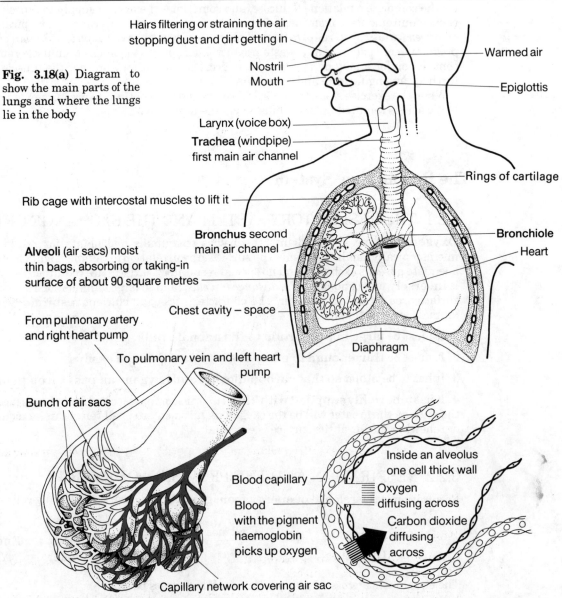

Fig. 3.18(a) Diagram to show the main parts of the lungs and where the lungs lie in the body

Hairs filtering or straining the air stopping dust and dirt getting in

Nostril
Mouth
Warmed air
Epiglottis

Larynx (voice box)
Trachea (windpipe) first main air channel
Rings of cartilage

Rib cage with intercostal muscles to lift it

Bronchus second main air channel
Bronchiole
Heart

Alveoli (air sacs) moist thin bags, absorbing or taking-in surface of about 90 square metres

Chest cavity – space

Diaphragm

From pulmonary artery and right heart pump

To pulmonary vein and left heart pump

Bunch of air sacs

Blood capillary

Inside an alveolus one cell thick wall

Blood with the pigment haemoglobin picks up oxygen

Oxygen diffusing across

Carbon dioxide diffusing across

Capillary network covering air sac

Fig. 3.18(b) The blood supply to air sacs

Fig. 3.18(c) Detailed section of one air sac

1 The **trachea** and **bronchi** are partially surrounded by horseshoe-shaped **bands of cartilage** which protect them from *pressure changes* during the passage of air in and out of the lungs and so keep them constantly open.

2 The **larynx** is closed by a flap of muscle, the **epiglottis**, which prevents food entering the trachea.

3 The **tubular parts** of the respiratory system are lined with cells which have minute hair-like **cilia**. The cells secrete **mucus**, which traps dust particles, etc., and the cilia move the particles in the mucus away from the lungs to the throat. Thus the system is kept free of unwanted pollutants.

4 The **bronchi** divide to form narrower **bronchioles** which terminate in air sacs or **alveoli**. Here *gaseous exchange* takes place.

3.2.4 THE MECHANISM OF BREATHING

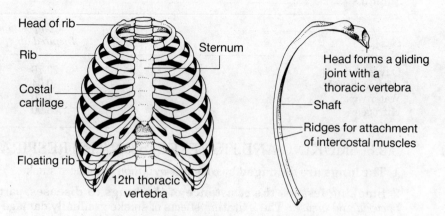

Fig. 3.19(a) The thoracic cage and a left rib

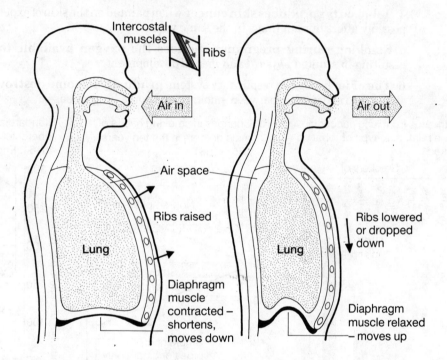

Fig. 3.19(b) Inspiration—taking air in   **Fig. 3.19(c)** Expiration—pushing air out

Stages of inspiration

1 Muscles of the diaphragm contract causing it to *flatten*. This *increases the volume* of the thorax but *decreases the pressure* inside it.

2 Inspiratory intercostal muscles contract pulling the lower ribs (which pivot at the vertebrae) *upward* and *outard*.

3 A partial vacuum is thus created so that air is *sucked in*.

Stages of expiration

1 Muscles of the diaphragm relax while those of the **abdominal wall** contract. This action pushes the stomach and liver *upwards* so that the diaphragm becomes dome shaped.

2 Inspiratory intercostal muscles relax, allowing the ribs and sternum to fall under gravity. This *increases the pressure* within the thorax but *decreases the volume*, forcing air out.

3 The natural **elastic nature of the lung tissue** causes the lungs to *expel air* when there is no pressure on them.

3.2.5 THE DIFFERENCES BETWEEN INSPIRED AND EXPIRED AIR

Table 3.8

Gas	Composition, as percentage of volume	
	Inspired air	*Expired air*
Oxygen	20.70	14.6
Carbon dioxide	0.04	3.8
Water vapour	1.26	6.2
Nitrogen	78.00	75.4

3.2.6 SMOKING AND ITS EFFECTS ON THE RESPIRATORY SYSTEM

1 The lungs are damaged by constant *irritation* of tobacco smoke.

2 Smoking lessens the resistance of the lungs to diseases, particularly to those caused by *bacteria* and *viruses*. The irritating effects of smoke gradually damage the cells which then can be attacked by *pathogens*. **Chronic bronchitis** may be linked with smoking.

3 Heavy smoking impairs athletic performance as it makes *gaseous exchange inefficient.*

4 Tobacco tar produces skin cancer when painted on the skin of experimental animals and could possibly affect human lungs in the same way.

5 Smoking during pregnancy reduces the oxygen available to the developing foetus, resulting in stunted *physical* and *mental* development.

6 The cilia, lining the respiratory system, **gradually become destroyed by smoke.** Figure 3.20 shows the relationship between smoking and some lung diseases:

(a) Death rates from lung cancer in men in relation to type of tobacco smoked

(b) Changes in smoking habits of male doctors in the ten years, 1951–1961

(c) Standardized death rates from cancer, tuberculosis, bronchitis – men aged 45–64. England & Wales 1916–59

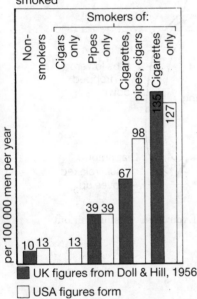
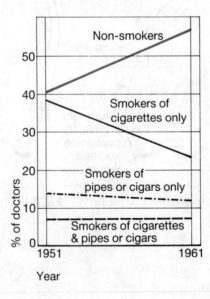
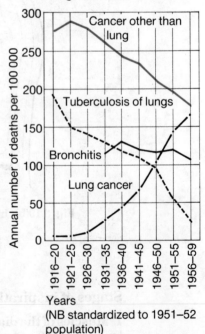

Fig. 3.20(a)–(c) Graphs: (a) Death rates from lung cancer in men in relation to type of tobacco smoked; (b) Changes in smoking habits of male doctors in the ten years 1951–61; (c) Standardized death rates from cancer, tuberculosis, bronchitis—men aged 45-64. England and Wales 1916–59.

3.3 Food and Nutrition

3.3.1 CLASSES OF FOOD

Food is required **as a source of energy** and for the **manufacture of new protoplasm** during growth. There are **six basic classes** of food required by man. These are:

1 Carbohydrates   3 Fats   5 Vitamins

2 Proteins   4 Mineral salts   6 Water

Carbohydrates

The chemical elements present are **carbon, hydrogen** and **oxygen**. They have the general formula $C_x(H_2O)_y$ and the important point to remember is that their molecules always have *twice* as many *hydrogen atoms* as *oxygen atoms*. They are generally divided into **sugars** (such as *glucose, fructose, lactose, maltose* and *sucrose*) and **polysaccharides** (such as *starch* and *glycogen*). Carbohydrates are used mainly as a source of *energy* (see Section 3.2.2).

Proteins

The chemical elements present are **carbon, hydrogen, oxygen, nitrogen** and sometimes **phosphorus** and **sulphur**. They are made of basic units, the **amino acids**, which are held together by chemical bonds called **peptide links**. Proteins are generally used for *building new cells*.

Fats

The chemical elements present are **carbon, hydrogen** and **oxygen**. Fats are made of two basic units, **glycerol** and **fatty acids**, and are generally used as a *store of energy* and for *insulation*.

Mineral salts

Besides the elements present in the above classes of foods, we need a considerable number of others. Mineral salts cannot be made by living creatures. Plants obtain them from the soil and animals acquire them, directly or indirectly, from plants. Mineral salts are required in small quantities for a variety of purposes (see Table 3.9).

Vitamins

Like mineral salts, vitamins have *no energy value* but are essential for the *chemical reactions* which take place in the body. They are needed in only very small quantities but without them we suffer from *deficiency disease* (see Table 3.10).

Water

The **protoplasm** of cells is made up of about 75% water. It plays a part in *transport* of materials around the body, *removal of waste products*, maintaining a *constant body temperature* and for all *chemical reactions* taking place in the body.

3.3.2 BASIC FOOD REQUIREMENTS

Table 3.9 Food requirements

Food substance	Chemical formula or symbol	Use	Source
Carbohydrates			
Glucose	$C_6H_{12}O_6$	Provides energy	Grapes, carrots
Fructose	$C_6H_{12}O_6$	Provides energy	Honey, fruits
Lactose	$C_{12}H_{22}O_{11}$	Provides energy	Milk, cheese
Maltose	$C_{12}H_{22}O_{11}$	Provides energy	Malt
Sucrose	$C_{12}H_{22}O_{11}$	Provides energy	Sugar cane, sugar beet
Starch	$(C_6H_{10}O_5)_n$	Provides energy	Potatoes, wheat, rice
Glycogen	$(C_6H_{10}O_5)_n$	Provides energy	Liver, lean meat
Fats		Provide energy; insulation. Can be stored under the skin	Butter, lard, cheese, suet, fish oil
Proteins		Building new cells	Lean meat, fish, milk, eggs, cheese, peas, wheat
Minerals			
Calcium	Ca	Bone formation, teeth, blood clotting	Cheese, milk, bread
Phosphorus	P	Bone formation, cell division	Most foods containing protein
Potassium	K	Formation of new protoplasm	Meat and most vegetables
Sulphur	S	Protein formation	Most foods with proteins
Chlorine	Cl	Constituent of body fluids and hydrochloric acid	Common salt
Sodium	Na	Constituent of body fluids; in transport of carbon dioxide	Common salt
Magnesium	Mg	Formation of bones and teeth	Most foods

Food substance	Chemical formula or symbol	Use	Source
Iron	Fe	Formation of haemoglobin	Liver, kidney, eggs
Fluorine	Fl	Formation of tooth enamel	A trace element in some water
Iodine	I	Formation of hormone thyroxine	Sea foods
Zinc	Zn	Formation of hormone insulin	A trace element in plants
Copper	Cu	Formation of haemoglobin	A trace element in plants
Cobalt	Co	Formation of haemoglobin	A trace element in plants
Water	H_2O	Dissolving foods; a general solvent for all chemical reactions in the body	Most foods, all liquids

3.3.3 VITAMINS

Table 3.10 Vitamins

Vitamin	Deficiency effects	Source
A (fat soluble)	Poor skin and mucous membranes. Night blindness	Green vegetables, milk, butter, fish liver oils
B₁—thiamin (water soluble)	Beri-beri. Disorders of the nervous system, muscular atrophy	Yeast, wholemeal bread, peas and beans
B₂—riboflavin (water soluble)	Disorders of the skin and digestive system	Yeast, meat, milk, liver, eggs
B₁₂—cobalamin	Pernicious anaemia	Liver, fish, eggs
C—ascorbic acid (water soluble)	Scurvy—internal bleeding, swelling of gums	Citrus fruits and vegetables
D (fat soluble)	Rickets—bones soften and become pliable	Fish liver oils, eggs, butter. Formed by the action of sunlight on skin
E (fat soluble)	Embryo fails to develop. Loss of fertility (in rats)	Wheatgerm oil, eggs, liver, green vegetables

Additional notes on the deficiency effects of vitamins

Vitamins play an essential role as **enzyme co-factors**. These are substances which help enzymes work properly, and without them the biochemical pathways that take place in the body would come to a halt. (However, not all co-factors are vitamins—*metallic ions* and other chemicals also act as co-factors for certain enzymes.) Here are some examples of the biochemical cause and the symptoms of vitamin deficiency.

1 Vitamin A acts as a co-factor in the pathway leading to the formation of **visual purple**, a substance essential for *vision* found in the cells of the **retina**, hence the link with *night-blindness*.

2 Vitamin B₁ plays an essential role in the cellular processes involved in **respiration**, that is the utilization of oxygen and the production of carbon dioxide during the liberation of energy from glucose. A shortage of this co-factor will interfere with one of life's most essential functions. Indeed, most of the vitamin B group are respiratory co-enzymes.

3 Vitamin C has two specific functions:

(a) A **respiratory** function, in which the vitamin aids in the important *energy release* mechanisms of the cell.

(b) A **regulation** function, this concerning the formation of *intercellular material* that binds cells into tissues. Symptoms observed in vitamin C-deficient patients result from a breakdown of this material. *Capillaries rupture* because of inadequate 'cementing' between the cells.

4 Vitamin D is essential for the metabolism of *calcium* and *phosphorus*. As these two elements are the major constituents of **bone**, vitamin D deficiency results in abnormalities of bone.

5 Vitamin E appears to have a role in the biochemistry of the *human reproductive system*, but this is still a matter of conjecture.

3.3.4 THE IMPORTANCE OF A BALANCED DIET

A balanced diet must satisfy the following requirements:

1 It must contain sufficient **energy** to be released for the *metabolism* of the individual. (On average between 10 500 and 14 000 kilojoules a day.)

2 It must contain roughly **20% protein, 20% fat** and **60% carbohydrate**.

3 It must contain some *fresh foods, green vegetables*, etc., to provide the necessary **vitamins** and **roughage** (in the form of *cellulose*) to stimulate the peristaltic action of the alimentary canal.

4 It must contain a range of **mineral elements**, especially *calcium, potassium, sodium* and *iron.*

5 It must contain an adequate amount of **water.**

6 It must be **palatable** and **easily digested**.

If a person does not receive a balanced diet, then he/she is likely to suffer from malnutrition. This may mean either *under-* or *over-nutrition.* Protein and energy (joule) deficiency is common in under-developed countries while over-nutrition, causing **obesity**, is common in developed countries.

3.3.5 DAILY ENERGY REQUIREMENTS

Table 3.11 Daily energy requirements

Person	Occupation/Activity	Requirements in kilojoules (kJ)
Newborn baby	Sleeping, moving	1900
Adult in bed	Resting	7600
Girl age 8 years	Very active in playing	8000
Boy age 8 years	Very active in playing	8400
Woman	Light work, e.g. office	8800
Man	Light work, e.g. office	10 500
Pregnant woman	Feeding the embryo	10 500
Girl age 15 years	Active in games, e.g. tennis	11 800
Woman breast feeding	Feeding a baby	12 600
Man	Moderate work, e.g. carpentry	14 300
Boy age 15 years	Active in games, e.g. football	14 700
Man	Heavy work, e.g. labouring	18 900

Note that the **joule (J)** is the *unit of energy* that is now used internationally. It has replaced the calorie as a unit of energy.

A **calorie** is the amount of heat energy required to raise the temperature of **1 g** of water through **1 °C.** A **kilocalorie** = 1000 calories.

A **joule** is the work done when the point of application of a force of **1 newton** is displaced through a distance of **1 metre** in the direction of the force.

A **kilojoule (kJ)** = 1000 joules. 1 kilocalorie = 4.2 kilojoules.

A simple experiment to measure the heat energy in a peanut

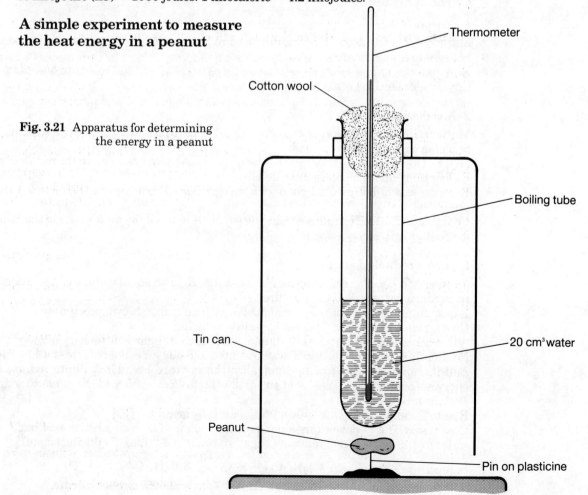

Fig. 3.21 Apparatus for determining the energy in a peanut

Thermometer

Cotton wool

Boiling tube

Tin can

20 cm³ water

Peanut

Pin on plasticine

Procedure

1 Weigh a large peanut and mount it on a pin as shown in the diagram.
2 Place 20 cm^3 water in the boiling tube.
3 Note the temperature with the thermometer.
4 Set light to the peanut with a Bunsen burner and place the boiling tube over it to catch as much of the heat as possible.
5 Read the temperature as soon as the peanut has been completely burned.
6 Record the temperature increase.
7 Work out the number of joules of heat the water has received as follows:

$$4.2 \text{ J raise 1 g water } 1°C$$
$$\text{Temperature increase} = Y°C$$
$$\text{Mass of peanut} = X \text{ g} \quad \text{Mass of water} = 20 \text{ g}$$
$$\text{Heat gained by water} = 20 \text{ g} \times Y \times 4.2 \text{ J}$$
$$\text{Heat produced by 1 g of sample} = \frac{20 \times Y \text{ g} \times 4.2}{1000 \times X} \text{ kJ/g}$$

Note that possible sources of error include:
(a) heat loss around sides of boiling tube,
(b) heat loss raising the temperature of the thermometer and the glass of the boiling tube,
(c) incomplete burning of the peanut.
An improvement would be to insulate the apparatus.

3.3.6 FOOD TESTS

Note: When writing reports of food tests or any other investigation, always keep your accounts of the **method, results** and **conclusion** separate. Your description of the method must be written clearly such that the reader could obtain the same results if he or she repeated your technique. Your results should be a clear statement of what you detected or experienced with either your eyes, nose, touch receptors or ears. NEVER TASTE laboratory chemicals—they may be toxic. DO NOT USE the terms *'positive'* or *'negative'* without qualifying the terms by saying exactly what such a result means for a particular investigation.

Carbohydrates

1 Starch

METHOD Add a few drops of *iodine* dissolved in *potassium iodide* to a solution/suspension of the food believed to contain starch.
EXPECTED RESULT The solution/suspension turns from its original colour to *blue-black*.
CONCLUSION The food contains starch.

2 A reducing sugar

METHOD Add *Benedict's solution* (or *Fehling's A & B*) to an equal volume of a solution believed to be a reducing sugar. *Boil* the mixture.
NOTE. **Do not say** *'heat'* or *'warm'* the mixture as these are relative terms. *'Boil'* means *'bring to boiling point'* and is a precise instruction.
EXPECTED RESULT The mixture changes from *light blue*, through *green*, then *yellow*, to an *orange-brown precipitate*.
CONCLUSION The food contains a reducing sugar. (It reduced the *copper salts* in the Benedict's solution [or Fehling's] to *copper oxide*.)

3 A non-reducing sugar

METHOD Add *Benedict's solution* (or *Fehling's A & B*) to an equal volume of a solution believed to be a non-reducing sugar. *Boil* the mixture.
EXPECTED RESULT The solution *remains blue* with no orange-brown precipitate.
CONCLUSION The solution does not contain a reducing sugar.
    In order to find out if it does contain a non-reducing sugar, continue as follows:
METHOD Take *1cm^3* of the solution to be tested and add an *equal volume* of dilute *hydrochloric acid*. *Boil* the mixture then *cool* it. Neutralize the mixture by adding dilute *sodium hydroxide* until effervescence (fizzing) ceases. Add an equal volume (2cm^3) of *Benedict's solution* (or *Fehling's A & B*). *Boil* the mixture.
EXPECTED RESULT An *orange-brown precipitate* is formed.
CONCLUSION The food contains a non-reducing sugar. (The hydrochloric acid has *hydrolysed* [added water to] the original non-reducing sugar and changed it into a reducing sugar.)

$$C_{12}H_{22}O_{11} + H_2O \xrightarrow{\text{HCl}} C_6H_{12}O_6 + C_6H_{12}O_6$$
$$\text{non-reducing sugar} \qquad \text{reducing sugar}$$

4 Soluble proteins—The Biuret test

METHOD Add 2cm³ of *20% sodium hydroxide* to 2cm³ of the solution containing the suspected protein. Add 3 drops of *1% copper sulphate* to the mixture.
EXPECTED RESULT A *violet* colour is seen in the mixture.
CONCLUSION The solution contains a protein.

5 Fat

METHOD Rub a sample of the suspected fat on to a piece of paper.
EXPECTED RESULT A *translucent patch* is seen on the paper which persists after drying.
CONCLUSION The food tested contains fat.

6 The DCPIP test for ascorbic acid (Vitamin C)

Ascorbic acid is a powerful **reducing agent** and a dye, **DCPIP**, can be used to detect it. The vitamin causes the normally *blue dye* to be *decolourized*.
METHOD Pour *1cm³ DCPIP* solution into a test tube. Take a *1cm³ syringe* full of sample material, e.g. lemon juice. Record the *volume* of sample material you need to add to the DCPIP to decolourize it.

Repeat the test with 1cm³ of fresh DCPIP using an ascorbic acid solution of known concentration. Record the volume of the second, standard solution needed to decolourize the DCPIP solution.

SAMPLE RESULTS

Volume of *lemon juice* used to decolourize 1cm³ of DCPIP solution = 0.5cm³
Volume of *ascorbic acid* of known concentration used to decolourize 1cm³ of DCPIP solution = 0.4cm³

CONCLUSION The lemon juice was $\frac{0.4}{0.5}$ times as concentrated as the standard ascorbic acid solution.

If the standard ascorbic acid solution contained *1mg ascorbic acid per cm³ water*, then the lemon juice must contain $1 \times \frac{0.4}{0.5} = 0.8mg$ *ascorbic acid per cm³ water*.

3.4 The Digestive System

3.4.1 PRINCIPLES OF DIGESTION

Food has to be **broken down** before it can be transported to the cells that need it. This is done both **mechanically** and **chemically**. Firstly, in the *mouth* food is broken into small pieces that have a relatively *large surface area* for the action of **digestive enzymes** in *saliva*. These enzymes are responsible for the first stage of chemical breakdown. After the process of **chewing**, the food is passed along the **alimentary canal** by muscular action, which also helps to mix the food with other enzymes secreted by various cells associated with the wall of the gut. There are digestive enzymes for each of three classes of food: *carbohydrates, fats* and *proteins*. These are *carbohydrases, lipases* and *proteases*, respectively. Within each category of enzymes there are several different types, each carrying out a specific function and often requiring a certain level of *acidity* or *alkalinity* that is provided by additional gut secretions. Eventually, *carbohydrates* are converted to **glucose**, *proteins* to **amino acids**, and *fats* to **glycerol** and **fatty acids**. All of these end-products are of a molecular size sufficiently small for them to pass through the gut wall. The wall of the gut may be modified to increase the surface area for absorption of the products of digestion. Once absorbed, the materials are transported to the cells by the blood system.

3.4.2 TEETH

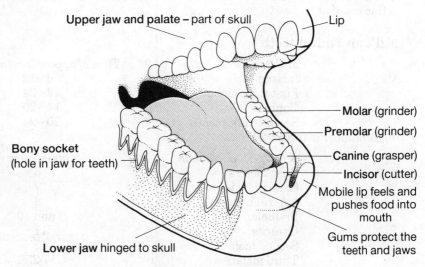

Fig. 3.22 Teeth and jaws

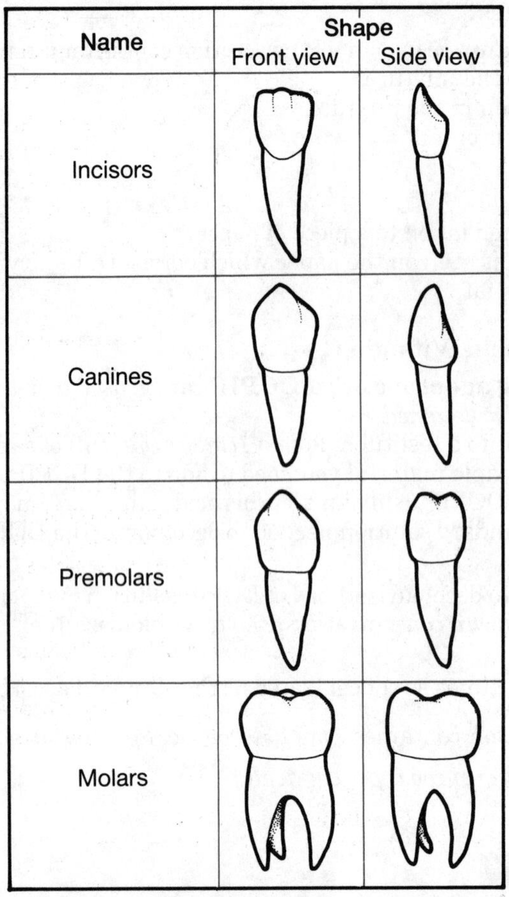

Name	Shape	
	Front view	Side view
Incisors		
Canines		
Premolars		
Molars		

Fig. 3.23 Types of teeth

Table 3.12 Types of teeth

Tooth	Function	Numbers (in each half of upper and lower jaw in an adult)
Incisor	Cutting	2
Canine	Grasping	1
Premolar	Grinding	2
Molar	Grinding	3

Structure

Dentine is very hard and resembles *bone* in composition.
Enamel is the hardest substance in the body.
The **pulp cavity** contains *soft connective tissue, blood vessels* and *nerves* which enter the **root** through a fine canal at its base.

Milk and adult teeth

Milk/temporary teeth	*Time of appearance (months)*
Incisors	6−12
First milk molars	12−24
Canines	14−20
Second milk molars	20−24

Total number of teeth=**20**

Adult/permanent teeth	*Time of appearance (years)*
First molars	6
Central incisors	7
Lateral incisors	8
Premolars	9 and 10
Canines	11
Second molars	12
Third molars	17-25

Total number of teeth=**32**

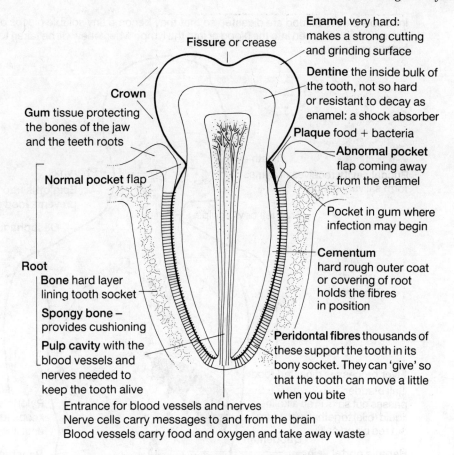

Fig. 3.24 Diagram of a tooth

Care of teeth (see also Section 2.3.1)

A surface film, **plaque**, normally covers teeth and is difficult to remove, even by brushing with a good toothbrush. Plaque contains **bacteria** that break down *carbohydrates* into *acids* which attack the *enamel* and eventually cause **tooth decay**. Decay is undoubtedly reduced when the concentration of **fluoride** in drinking water is about *1 part per million:* fluoride helps to make the enamel more acid-resistant.

3.4.3 THE ALIMENTARY CANAL

Table 3.13 The alimentary canal

Region of the alimentary canal	Function
Buccal cavity and pharynx	1 Ingestion of food 2 Mastication by teeth, food rolled into a ball and pushed into oesophagus by tongue and cheek muscles 3 Saliva added, containing: (a) water, (b) mucin (a constituent of mucus), and (c) salivary amylase (the enzyme ptyalin) 4 Food tasted by tongue
Oesophagus	Transports food to stomach by peristalsis
Stomach	1 Churns food 2 Adds water 3 Adds hydrochloric acid 4 Adds various digestive enzymes 5 Secretes gastrin (hormone) 6 Absorbs alcohol and glucose 7 Stores food
Duodenum	1 Receives bile 2 Receives pancreatic juice 3 Secretes secretin (hormone)
Ileum	1 Secretes succus entericus (a mixture of digestive enzymes) 2 Absorbs the end-products of digestion
Colon	Absorbs water
Rectum	Stores faeces prior to removal via anus (egestion)

Insoluble pieces of food are digested so that they become tiny soluble pieces of food that can be easily absorbed into the blood or into the lymph where they will be taken to the liver for further processing

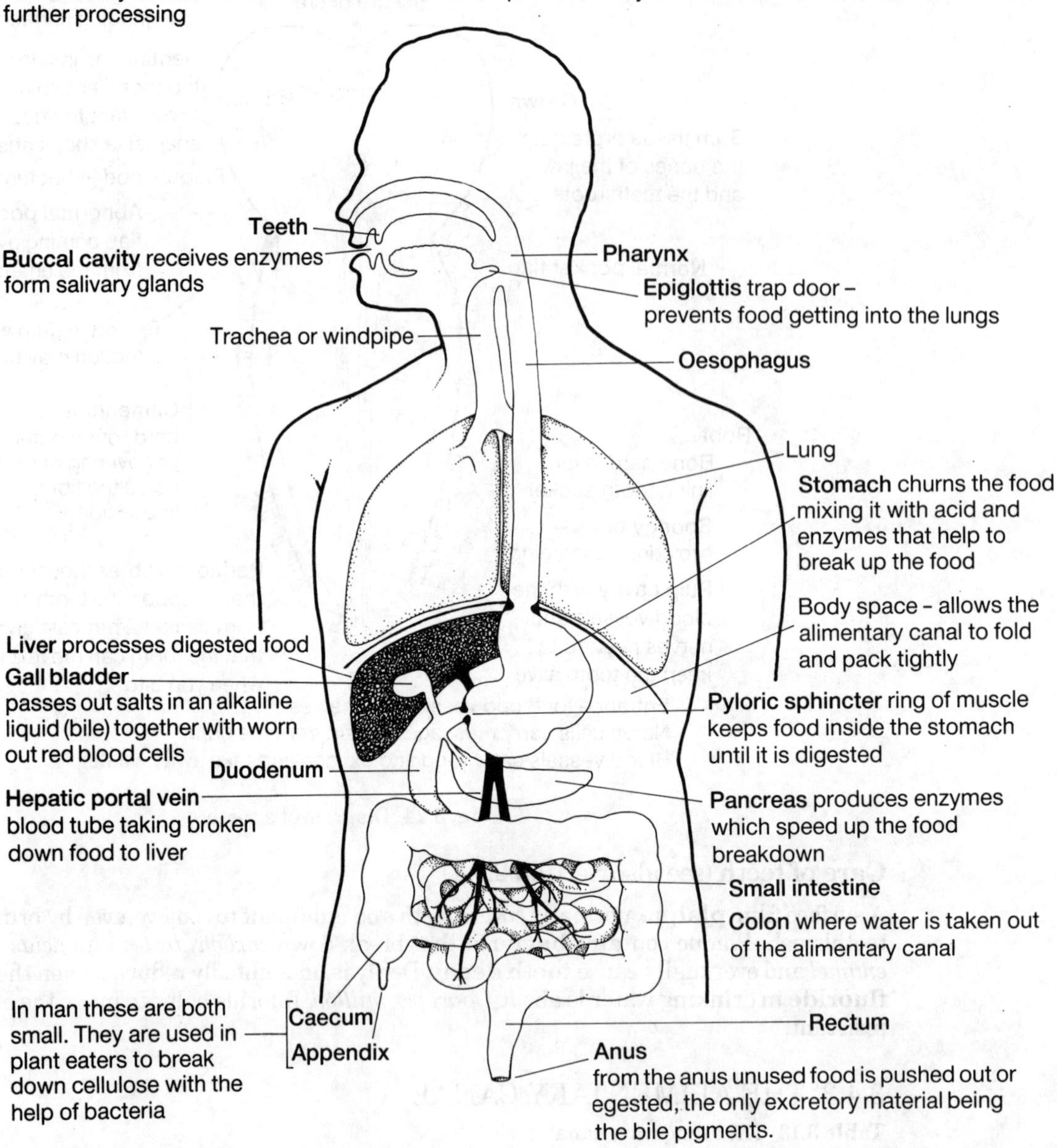

Teeth

Buccal cavity receives enzymes form salivary glands

Trachea or windpipe

Liver processes digested food

Gall bladder passes out salts in an alkaline liquid (bile) together with worn out red blood cells

Duodenum

Hepatic portal vein blood tube taking broken down food to liver

In man these are both small. They are used in plant eaters to break down cellulose with the help of bacteria

Caecum
Appendix

Pharynx

Epiglottis trap door – prevents food getting into the lungs

Oesophagus

Lung

Stomach churns the food mixing it with acid and enzymes that help to break up the food

Body space – allows the alimentary canal to fold and pack tightly

Pyloric sphincter ring of muscle keeps food inside the stomach until it is digested

Pancreas produces enzymes which speed up the food breakdown

Small intestine

Colon where water is taken out of the alimentary canal

Rectum

Anus from the anus unused food is pushed out or egested, the only excretory material being the bile pigments.

Fig. 3.25 The alimentary or food canal

Swallowing

The following diagrams illustrate the position of both the **false palate** and **epiglottis** during swallowing. Their action is *automatic* and prevents food entering the *respiratory passages* when food is passed into the **oesophagus**.

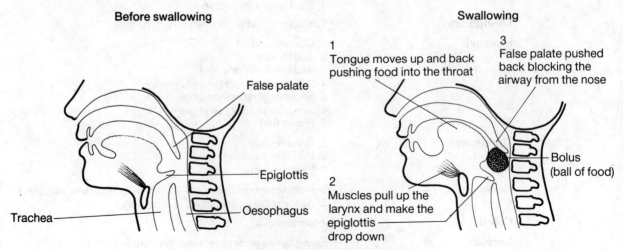

Before swallowing

Swallowing

1
Tongue moves up and back pushing food into the throat

3
False palate pushed back blocking the airway from the nose

False palate

Epiglottis

Oesophagus

Trachea

2
Muscles pull up the larynx and make the epiglottis drop down

Bolus (ball of food)

Fig. 3.26 How we swallow

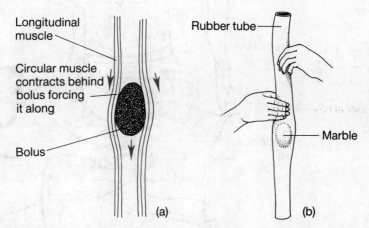

Fig. 3.27 Peristalsis. **(a)** The action of circular muscles of the gut in pushing the food along—peristalsis. **(b)** Demonstration of peristaltic movement; the marble is pushed along the rubber tube by hand

Peristalsis

This is the **automatic contraction and relaxation** of muscles along the *whole length* of the **alimentary canal** and is responsible for the movement of food. It can be simulated by pushing a marble along a rubber tube, as shown in Fig. 3.27.

3.4.4 THE LIVER

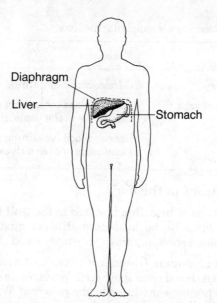

Fig. 3.28 Diagram to show the position of the liver in the body

Blood supply

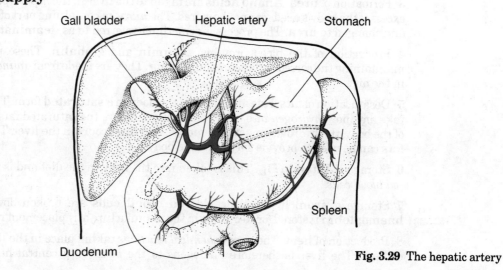

Fig. 3.29 The hepatic artery

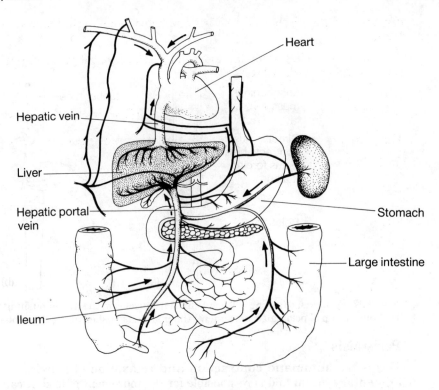

Fig. 3.30 The hepatic portal vein

Table 3.14 Blood vessels supplying the liver

Blood vessel	Function
Hepatic artery	Carries blood containing *oxygen* to the liver
Hepatic portal vein	Carries blood containing *digested food materials* to the liver. It begins as capillaries in the *ileum* and ends as capillaries in the liver
Hepatic vein	Carries blood containing *waste products* and materials produced by the *metabolism of liver cells* away from the liver

Main functions of the liver

1 The formation of **bile**. Bile is stored in the **gall bladder** and is used to *emulsify fats* before their digestion by *lipase* in the duodenum. Bile is a mixture of *alkaline mucus, bile pigments* (breakdown products of haemoglobin), *emulsifying agents* and *cholesterol.*

2 Storage of **glycogen. Glucose** is taken to the liver in the *hepatic portal vein*. If the concentration of glucose in the blood rises above *0.1% by weight*, the excess is converted to glycogen under the control of **insulin**, a hormone produced by the *pancreas*. When the level of *blood sugar* (glucose) tends to fall below its normal level, the glycogen is reconverted into glucose under the control of **adrenaline** (produced by the adrenal glands) and other hormones.

3 Formation of **urea. Amino acids** are taken to the liver in the *hepatic portal vein*. Those that are in excess of the body's needs cannot be stored. The *nitrogen*-containing part of the amino acids is removed and changed to **urea**. The process is sometimes referred to as **deamination**.

4 Production of the blood proteins, **albumin** and **globulin**. These proteins are important in maintaining the correct balance of the **plasma**. They are made from *amino acids* derived from protein in the diet.

5 Desaturation of **fats**. Fats are stored in the body in a **saturated** form. This means that they cannot take any more *hydrogen* into their composition. Before the saturated fats can be used by the tissues of the body, the hydrogen must be removed, and this occurs in the liver. The resultant **unsaturated fats** can be used to provide *energy* for the body.

6 Storage of **Vitamin B$_{12}$**. This is taken into the body in the diet and is used in the manufacture of *red blood cells.*

7 Storage of **iron**. In the liver, old **red blood cells** are broken down and the *iron* from the **haemoglobin** is stored for re-cycling in the manufacture of replacement red cells in the *bone marrow*.

8 Production of **heat**. The many *chemical reactions* taking place in the liver result in the formation of **heat**. The liver is therefore analogous to the *boiler* in a central heating system. The heat is distributed through the *blood vessels* and helps to maintain the **body temperature** at a constant level.

9 Production of **blood clotting agents. Fibrinogen** and **prothrombin** help in the process of blood clotting and are made by the liver cells.

3.4.5 THE CHEMISTRY OF DIGESTION

Enzymes of the alimentary canal and their functions

Table 3.15 Digestive enzymes

Region	Enzyme	Food substance acted upon (substrate)	Product
Mouth (saliva)	Ptyalin	Starch	Maltose and dextrin
Stomach (gastric juice)	Pepsin	Proteins	Peptones and proteoses
	Rennin	Milk protein	Coagulated milk
Duodenum (enzymes secreted by the pancreas)	Lipase	Fats	Fatty acids and glycerol
	Amylase	Starch and dextrin	Maltose (see below)
	Trypsinogen (has to be made active by another enzyme, enterokinase (see below)		
Ileum (succus entericus)	Maltase	Maltose	Glucose
	Sucrase	Sucrose	Glucose and fructose
	Lactase	Lactose	Glucose and galactose
	Erepsin (a mixture of enzymes)	Proteoses and peptones	Amino acids
	Enterokinase	Activates trypsinogen to form trypsin	
	Trypsin	Proteins and peptones	Amino acids

Digestion is the breakdown of large molecules of food into smaller molecules so that they can be absorbed into the blood system.

3.4.6 INVESTIGATIONS WITH DIGESTIVE ENZYMES

Salivary amylase (ptyalin)—to investigate its action on starch

Method

Obtain a sample of **saliva** from your mouth and with distilled water make it up to 2cm^3 in a test tube. Divide the sample into two equal parts in separate test tubes. Label the test tubes **A** and **B**. Sample A will be used for the **test** investigation. Sample B must be *boiled* to denature the digestive enzyme in it. (Remember, all enzymes are proteins and all proteins are denatured when boiled.) B is the **control** for the investigation.

NOTE: A *control experiment* is an exact replica of the test experiment with the exception of the single material or condition under investigation. In this case, the control B has the *same materials* as the test A *except* for the active enzyme. (B is used to prove that it is the enzyme in saliva that is responsible for the breakdown of starch.)

Add 1cm^3 of 0.5% starch suspension to test tube A. Add 1cm^3 of 0.5% starch suspension to test tube B after cooling solution B. Place both tubes in a water bath at *37°C*. Using separate pipettes, **immediately** take *one drop* from each of test tubes A and B and add the drops to separate quantities of *iodine in potassium iodide* placed on a white tile. Note the results. Repeat the tests with the iodine at 1 minute intervals.

Expected results

Time in minutes	Colour of sample from A with iodine	Colour of sample from B with iodine
0	Dark blue	Dark blue
1	Dark blue	Dark blue
2	Light blue	Dark blue
3	Purple	Dark blue
4	Brown	Dark blue
5	Brown	Dark blue

Conclusion

The enzyme in saliva breaks down starch completely at 37°C after four minutes. In order to find out the *product* of the breakdown of starch by the enzyme, *boil* the contents of tube A with an equal volume of *Benedict's* (or *Fehling's A & B*) *solution*. An *orange-brown precipitate* will confirm that the starch has been digested to a reducing sugar.

To investigate the action of pepsin on egg white

Method

Take the *white* (albumen) of an egg. Draw the albumen into five pieces of capillary tubing, each 2 cm long. Put these capillary tubes into a beaker of *boiling water* and leave them there for 2 minutes. The capillary tubes will then contain *hard-boiled* egg white. Measure the *lengths* of the egg white in each tube. Place the capillary tubes in test tubes as shown in Fig. 3.31.

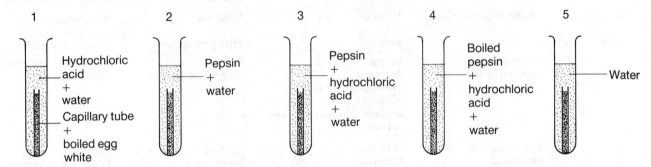

Fig. 3.31 The digestion of protein

Place these test tubes in a water bath at *37°C* for *30 minutes*. Then again measure the lengths of egg white in each tube.

Expected results

The egg white in tube 3 will have decreased in length. In each of the other tubes the egg white will have maintained its original length.

Conclusion

Unboiled pepsin, in the presence of hydrochloric acid at 37°C, digests egg albumen after 30 minutes.

3.4.7 THE FATE OF THE PRODUCTS OF DIGESTION

Table 3.16 The fate of the products of digestion

End-product of digestion	Destination in the body	Fate of the end-product
Glucose	Taken to the **liver** in the hepatic portal vein	1 Sent from the liver for use by cells in **respiration** 2 Converted to **glycogen** under the control of insulin and stored in the liver
Amino acids	Taken to the **liver** in the hepatic portal vein	1 Used to make **protoplasm** and other substances 2 **Repair** of worn out tissues 3 Excess cannot be stored and is **deaminated**, forming **urea** in the liver
Fats, fatty acids and glycerol	Absorbed by the **lacteals** and taken to the main lymph system which opens into the venous system	Fatty acids and glycerol are reformed into **fats** which are used as a store of energy and as heat insulation

Absorption

The folded internal surface of the *ileum* is covered with finger-shaped **villi**. These are lined with cells which themselves have projections, the **microvilli**. There is, consequently, an enormous surface area presented to the contents of the ileum for absorption of the products of digestion. The long length of the ileum and its rich *blood* and *lymph* supply are also adaptations for absorption.

Structure of the inner surface of the ileum

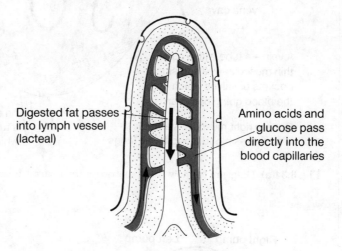

Folded wall with tiny pieces sticking up called villi

Circle of muscle cut across

Muscles running along
the food canal

Muscles going round
the food canal

Two sets of muscles —shortening threads
squeeze the food along –mechanical action

Fig. 3.32 Part of the small intestine cut across

Digested fat passes
into lymph vessel
(lacteal)

Amino acids and
glucose pass
directly into the
blood capillaries

Fig. 3.33 A single villus

3.5 The Circulatory System

3.5.1 THE NEED FOR A BLOOD SYSTEM

Blood is needed to *distribute* substances to the cells of the body. Very small organisms can rely on simple diffusion for this process, but in larger animals diffusion is inadequate. In man, **food, oxygen** and other essential substances are distributed to the cells, and their **waste products** collected, by the blood system. Blood can therefore be described as the **transport medium** of the human body. All mammals have a *continuous system* of vessels that conduct blood round the body. The blood is circulated by *muscular contractions* of the **heart**. It is first pumped to the *lungs* but returns to the heart to be pumped round the *circulatory system*.

3.5.2 PASSAGE OF BLOOD THROUGH THE HEART

Blood from the veins of the head, neck and fore limbs enters the **right atrium** via the **superior vena cava,** and from the rest of the body by the **inferior vena cava** (Fig. 3.34(a)). It then passes through the **right antrio-ventricular opening** into the **right ventricle**. The opening is guarded by the **tricuspid valve**. Blood leaves the right ventricle by the **pulmonary artery**. This divides and passes to the capillaries of the *lungs*. The blood is collected by the **pulmonary veins**, which pass to the **left atrium**. Four of these large pulmonary veins enter the left atrium. The **left atrio-ventricular opening** is guarded by the **mitral valve**. Blood leaves the left ventricle by the large, main artery, the **aorta**. Both the openings of the pulmonary artery and the aorta are guarded by **semi-lunar valves**.

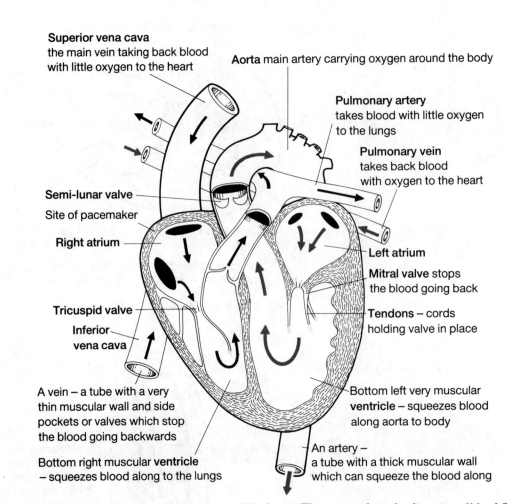

Superior vena cava
the main vein taking back blood
with little oxygen to the heart

Aorta main artery carrying oxygen around the body

Pulmonary artery
takes blood with little oxygen
to the lungs

Pulmonary vein
takes back blood
with oxygen to the heart

Semi-lunar valve

Site of pacemaker

Right atrium

Left atrium

Mitral valve stops
the blood going back

Tricuspid valve

Tendons – cords
holding valve in place

**Inferior
vena cava**

A vein – a tube with a very
thin muscular wall and side
pockets or valves which stop
the blood going backwards

Bottom left very muscular
ventricle – squeezes blood
along aorta to body

An artery –
a tube with a thick muscular wall
which can squeeze the blood along

Bottom right muscular **ventricle**
– squeezes blood along to the lungs

Fig. 3.34(a) Diagram to show the structure of the heart (The arrows show the direction of blood flow)

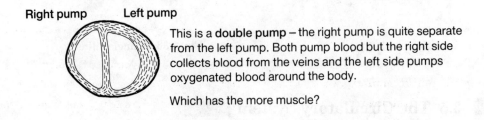

Right pump   **Left pump**

This is a **double pump** – the right pump is quite separate
from the left pump. Both pump blood but the right side
collects blood from the veins and the left side pumps
oxygenated blood around the body.

Which has the more muscle?

Fig. 3.34(b) Cross-section of the heart

3.5.3 THE PULSE

Each time the **left ventricle** contracts it forces blood into the **aorta**. The aorta, like all *arteries*, is **muscular** and **elastic** and *dilates* to accommodate the additional amount of blood. A wave of expansion is generated, and travels through the arterial system, diminishing as it reaches the *capillaries*. This wave of expansion is the **pulse**, which results from the elastic layer in the arteries *recoiling* as the heart pumps blood. The pulse can be felt and often seen in the superficial arteries, but it is customary to measure it in the **radial artery** at the wrist.

The normal rate of the pulse, and therefore the heart-beat rate, is about *72 beats per minute* in an adult at rest, but it increases with exercise, emotional disturbance and disease.

Normal pulse rates (beats per minute)

Adults, at rest	60−80
Infants	100−120
Children 6−10	80−100

3.5.4 STRUCTURE, FUNCTION AND ACTION OF THE HEART

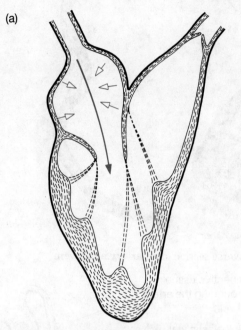 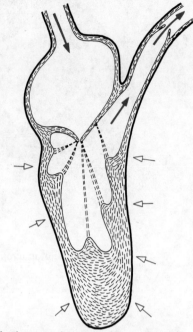

(a)

(b)

Auricular (atrial) systole small arrows show the contraction of auricle which forces blood into ventricle as shown by the large arrow.

Ventricular systole small arrows show the contraction of ventricle. Large arrows show the direction of blood flow. Semi-lunar valves open: valves between auricle and ventricle close.

3.35(a)–(b) Auricular (atrial) and ventricular systole

Table 3.17 Structure, function and action of the heart

Part of heart	Function
Aorta	The largest artery in the body. Carries *oxygenated* blood to all the organs except the lungs
Pulmonary artery	Carries *deoxygenated* blood to the lungs
Pulmonary vein	Carries *oxygenated* blood from the lungs to the left atrium of the heart
Left atrium	Receives *oxygenated* blood from the lungs via the pulmonary veins
Left ventricle	The most muscular part of the heart. It *pumps blood to all parts of the body*, except the lungs, via the aorta
Bicuspid (mitral) valve	Prevents *back-flow* of blood to the left atrium when the left ventricle contracts*
Tendons of the mitral valve (chordae tendinae)	Prevents the mitral valve from turning *'inside out'* when the left ventricle contracts*
Right ventricle	Pumps *deoxygenated* blood to the lungs via the pulmonary arteries
Tricuspid valve	Prevents *back-flow* of blood to the right atrium when the right ventricle contracts*
Semi-lunar valves	Prevents *back-flow* of blood from the pulmonary arteries when the right ventricle relaxes*
Right atrium	Receives *deoxygenated* blood from the organs of the body, except the lungs, via the venae cavae
Venae cavae	The main veins of the body which return *deoxygenated* blood to the right atrium

* When parts of the heart **contract** they are said to be in a state of **systole.**
When parts of the heart **relax** they are said to be in a state of **diastole.**

3.5.5 DIFFERENCES BETWEEN ARTERIES AND VEINS

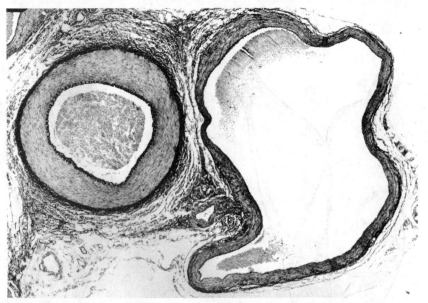

Fig. 3.36(a) Photomicrograph of a transverse section of an artery and a vein

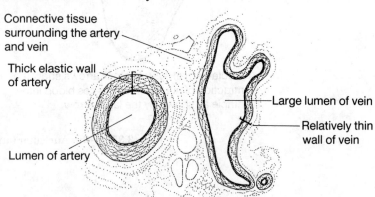

Connective tissue
surrounding the artery
and vein

Thick elastic wall
of artery

Large lumen of vein

Relatively thin
wall of vein

Lumen of artery

Fig. 3.36(b) Drawing of the photomicrograph

Functional differences

Table 3.18 Functional differences between arteries and veins

Arteries	Veins
1 All arteries carry blood **away** from the heart	All veins carry blood **towards** the heart
2 With the exception of the pulmonary arteries, all arteries carry **oxygenated** blood	With the exception of the pulmonary veins, all veins carry **deoxygenated** blood
3 They carry blood which is usually **rich in digested food materials**	Apart from the hepatic portal vein, they carry blood which usually has **little digested food materials**
4 They carry blood which has **little waste materials**	They carry blood which is usually **rich in waste materials**
5 They carry blood at a **high pressure**	They carry blood at a **low pressure**

Structural differences

Table 3.19 Structural differences between arteries and veins

Arteries	Veins
1 They have **thick, muscular** and **elastic** walls	They have **thin, inelastic** walls with **little muscular tissue**
2 They have relatively **small lumens** (internal diameter)	They have relatively **large lumens**
3 They **do not have valves**	**They have valves** to prevent flow of blood away from the heart

NOTE: Capillaries link veins and arteries via **venules** (small veins) and **arterioles** (small arteries). They have walls that are *one cell thick* and are the **smallest** blood vessels of the body. It is through the walls of the capillaries that **exchange** of materials between the *blood* and *tissue fluid* (lymph) takes place.

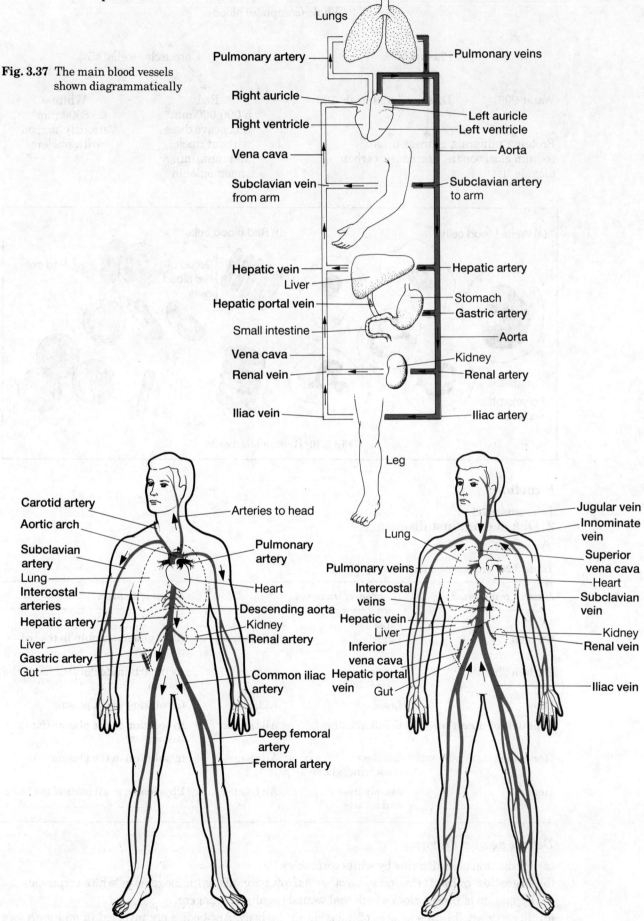

Fig. 3.37 The main blood vessels shown diagrammatically

Fig. 3.38 The main arteries of the body

Fig. 3.39 The main veins of the body

3.5.6 STRUCTURE AND FUNCTIONS OF BLOOD

Structure

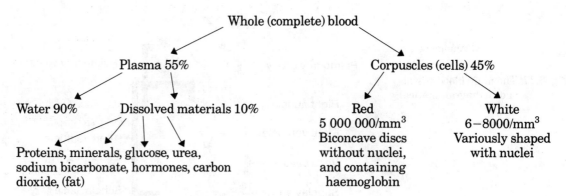

Whole (complete) blood

Plasma 55%

Corpuscles (cells) 45%

Water 90% Dissolved materials 10%

Red
5 000 000/mm³
Biconcave discs
without nuclei,
and containing
haemoglobin

White
6 – 8000/mm³
Variously shaped
with nuclei

Proteins, minerals, glucose, urea,
sodium bicarbonate, hormones, carbon
dioxide, (fat)

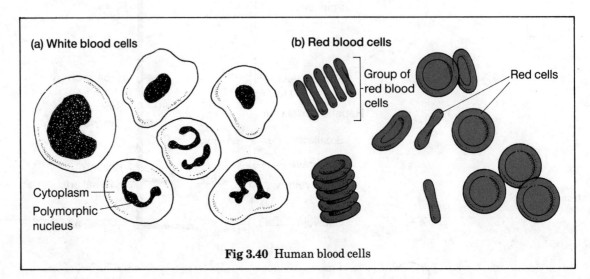

(a) White blood cells

(b) Red blood cells

Group of
red blood
cells

Red cells

Cytoplasm
Polymorphic
nucleus

Fig 3.40 Human blood cells

Functions

1 Transport
2 Defence against disease

Transport

Table 3.20 Transport of materials by blood

Material transported	Direction of transport		Means of transport
	FROM	TO	
Oxygen	Lungs	All tissues	As **oxyhaemoglobin** in the red corpuscles
Carbon dioxide	All tissues	Lungs	As **bicarbonates** in solution in the plasma
Urea	Liver	Kidneys	In **solution** in the plasma
Products of digestion	Small intestine	All tissues	In **solution** in the plasma (fat in suspension)
Hormones	Ductless (endocrine) glands	All tissues	In **solution** in the plasma
Heat	Mainly liver and muscle	All tissues	**Physically,** in all parts of the blood

Defence against disease

(a) Production of **antitoxins** by white corpuscles.

(b) **Ingestion of bacteria** and some other harmful organisms (pathogens) by white corpuscles.

(c) Formation of **blood clots** which seal wounds against pathogens.

(d) To carry **antibodies** to sites of infection in the body. Antibodies are involved in *immunity* (see Section 2.2.12).

A SIMPLIFIED SUMMARY OF CLOTTING

PLATELETS—formed from cells in bone marrow

Damage to blood vessel
or contact with a
foreign body

Release of

THROMBOKINASE—an enzyme that causes *prothrombin* to work in the
presence of calcium and vitamin K

Acts on

PROTHROMBIN—formed in the liver and present in blood plasma at all
times

Changed to

THROMBIN

Acts on

FIBRINOGEN—formed in the liver and present in blood plasma at all
times

Changed to

FIBRIN—a blood clot

3.5.7 BLOOD GROUPS

ABO blood groups

The ABO blood groups were discovered in 1900 by **Karl Landsteiner**. He found that the **antibodies** of the ABO system are naturally occurring in blood and appear consistently. The **four** main blood groups made known by his research are **A, B, AB** and **O**. Group A blood has in its red corpuscles a chemical substance (**antigen**) A; Group B has the antigen B; Group AB has both A and B antigens; while Group O has neither of them.

Blood Group	Antibody in plasma
A	anti-B only
B	anti-A only
AB	none
O	both anti-A and anti-B

NOTE: An **antigen** is any substance which can stimulate an **immune response** (the production of *antibodies*).

The Karl Landsteiner Rule states that when an *antigen* is *present* in the red cells, the corresponding *antibody* is *absent* from the serum (plasma without the clotting agents), and when the *antigen* is *absent* the corresponding *antibody* is *present*.

A, B and AB groups may be identified by their reaction with the two antibodies, anti-A and anti-B. The chief characteristic of these blood group antibodies is that they will cause the red corpuscles containing the appropriate antigen to come together in 'clumps'—**agglutination**—and if strong enough, may *destroy* the corpuscles completely. Thus anti-A will clump corpuscles containing *A antigen* (Groups A and AB), while anti-B will cause agglutination of corpuscles containing *B antigen* (Groups B and AB). Neither of them will react with Group O corpuscles. Therefore *Group O* can be identified by the *absence* of agglutination with both antibodies.

The application of Landsteiner's work is seen when **blood transfusions** are necessary. Below is a simplified summary of *dangerous* (because of agglutination) and *safe* blood transfusions, but it must be realized that it shows only the theoretical reactions of the ABO system.

Table 3.21 Blood transfusions—the ABO system

		Recipient's plasma			
		Group A (anti-B antibody)	Group B (anti-A antibody)	Group AB (No antibody)	Group O (anti-A and anti-B antibodies)
Donor's red cells	*Group A (A antigen)*	safe	clumps	safe	clumps
	Group B (B antigen)	clumps	safe	safe	clumps
	Group AB (A and B antigens)	clumps	clumps	safe	clumps
	Group O	safe	safe	safe	safe

From this table you can see that *Group A* can be **donated** to *Group AB* but *Group AB* **cannot be donated** to a recipient with *Group A*. This is because the plasma with anti-B is diluted by the recipient's AB blood. Also, *Group O* blood can be donated to a recipient with *any type* of ABO blood group; it is a **universal donor.**

3.5.8 THE RHESUS FACTOR

In 1940, Landsteiner and Weiner injected cells from a **Rhesus monkey** into *rabbits* and *guinea pigs*, which subsequently produced an antibody against the Rhesus monkey cells. This antibody was shown to *agglutinate* red blood cells of about 85% of humans. Landsteiner and Weiner suggested that this serum *antibody* was detecting a previously undescribed *antigen*, which may or may not be present on human red cells: they called this antigen 'Rhesus'. People with the antigen are called **Rhesus positive (Rh^+)** and those without it are called **Rhesus negative (Rh^-)**. The discovery in 1941 by Levine that *anti-Rh antibodies* could cause **transfusion reactions** established their medical importance. It became apparent later that the reagent (antibody) produced by rabbits does not react in exactly the same way as the human antibody, although it detects related antigens.

The Rhesus antigen is **inherited** as a **dominant factor** and, under certain circumstances, this may lead to *agglutination* in **foetal blood**. If **both** parents are **Rh positive**, their offspring will be **Rh positive**. If **one** of the parents is **Rh positive**, their offspring will probably be **Rh positive**. But if the **mother is Rh negative** and her **child is Rh positive**, in certain cases the mother then becomes *sensitive* to the positive factor in the child's blood and she develops the *anti-Rh antibodies*.

Father	×	Mother
Rh^+		Rh^-
	Child	
	Rh^+	

In future pregnancies any *anti-Rh antibodies* produced by the mother may affect the Rh^+ red cells of the foetus should they seep through the placenta and enter the foetal circulation.

3.5.9 THE LYMPHATIC SYSTEM

Lymph is a *colourless body fluid*, derived by *filtration* from the blood. It bathes all the tissues of the body and drains from tissue spaces into very fine vessels that join and form the main lymph vessel of the body, the **thoracic duct**. This empties into the *venous system* at the main veins coming from the arms, the **subclavian veins**.

Lymph has two main functions:

1 It acts as a **'middle-man'** between the *tissues of the body* and the *blood*. Materials needed by tissue cells pass out through the walls of the blood vessels and become *dissolved* in lymph, which is in contact with the cells' surface. Waste materials and cell products such as hormones pass from tissue cells to the lymph and then to the blood vessels. There are specialized lymph vessels in the villi of the *small intestine* that are responsible for transporting suspensions of *fat* to the blood system.

2 It is involved in **defence against disease**. Lymph contains **lymphocytes**, cells which act like some white blood corpuscles by producing **antibodies**. Lymphocytes are made in **lymph nodes** (glands), some of which are shown in Fig. 3.41. Lymphoid tissue found elsewhere in the body includes

(a) The **tonsils**

(b) A mass on the posterior wall of the *pharynx* (throat), the **adenoids**

(c) Scattered patches in the small intestine, **Peyer's patches**

(d) The **spleen**

(e) The **appendix**

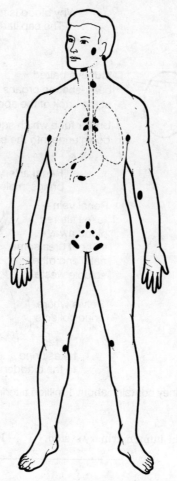

Fig. 3.41 The positions of the main lymph nodes

3.6 Regulation/Homeostasis

3.6.1. EXCRETION

Definition: The elimination of **waste products** of the body's metabolism.

Metabolism is the sum of the chemical building up process (*anabolism*) and the breaking down process (*catabolism*) taking place in living organisms.

Excretory organ	Excretory product
1 Lungs	Carbon dioxide and water
2 Kidneys	Urea, water, mineral salts, uric acid, urates
3 Skin	Water, mineral salts, urea

3.6.2 THE KIDNEYS

The kidneys have two main functions:

1 Removal of **harmful waste products**, e.g. urea, uric acid.
2 Regulation of **body fluids** by controlling the water and mineral salt content of the blood.

3.6.3 FORMATION OF URINE

In the kidneys two processes are involved in the formation of urine:

1 **Filtration**
2 **Absorption**

The average composition of urine in g per 100 cm^3 is:

Urea 2.0
Other nitrogenous substances 0.2
Sodium chloride 1.0
Other mineral salts 0.8

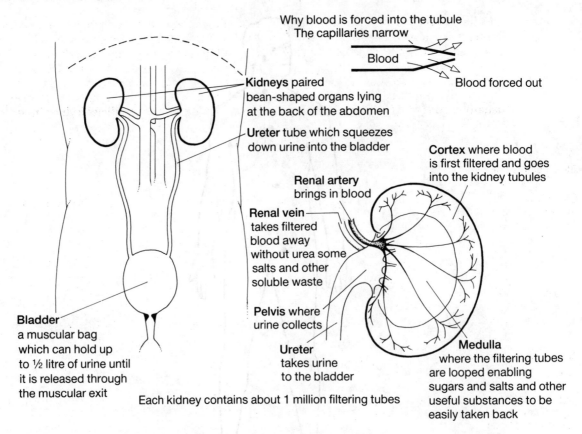

Why blood is forced into the tubule
The capillaries narrow

Blood

Blood forced out

Kidneys paired
bean-shaped organs lying
at the back of the abdomen

Ureter tube which squeezes
down urine into the bladder

Renal artery
brings in blood

Renal vein
takes filtered
blood away
without urea some
salts and other
soluble waste

Cortex where blood
is first filtered and goes
into the kidney tubules

Pelvis where
urine collects

Bladder
a muscular bag
which can hold up
to ½ litre of urine until
it is released through
the muscular exit

Ureter
takes urine
to the bladder

Medulla
where the filtering tubes
are looped enabling
sugars and salts and other
useful substances to be
easily taken back

Each kidney contains about 1 million filtering tubes

Fig. 3.42 A diagram of the human urinary system   **Fig. 3.43** Section through a kidney

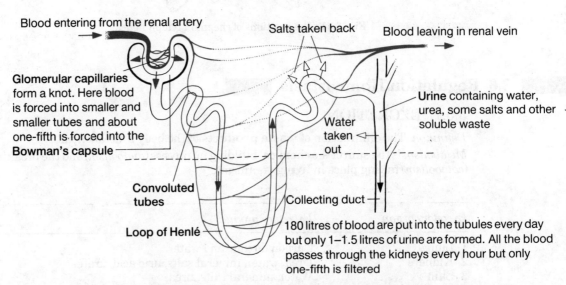

Blood entering from the renal artery

Salts taken back

Blood leaving in renal vein

Glomerular capillaries
form a knot. Here blood
is forced into smaller and
smaller tubes and about
one-fifth is forced into the
Bowman's capsule

Urine containing water,
urea, some salts and other
soluble waste

Water
taken
out

**Convoluted
tubes**

Collecting duct

Loop of Henlé

180 litres of blood are put into the tubules every day
but only 1–1.5 litres of urine are formed. All the blood
passes through the kidneys every hour but only
one-fifth is filtered

Fig 3.44 Diagram of a single kidney tubule (nephron)

Filtration This is a physical process which takes place through the **glomeruli** (about 1 million per kidney). *Water, salts, urea* and *glucose* are the main substances that are filtered from blood in the glomeruli and pass into the **convoluted tubules**.

Absorption All the *glucose* and some *mineral salts* and *water* are **actively pumped** by the cells of the convoluted tubules back into the associated blood capillaries. The amount of *water* absorbed in this way depends on the state of **dehydration** of the body. The amount of water in the blood influences the production of **anti-diuretic hormone (ADH)** by the **hypothalamus** which is situated on the ventral side of the mid-brain.

3.6.4 AN ARTIFICIAL KIDNEY

An artificial kidney functions on the physical principle of **dialysis**. This is the movement of small molecules through a **thin, semi-permeable barrier** whose pores are of such a size that they prevent the passage of larger molecules. Starting with a mixture of small and large molecules on one side of the barrier and water on the other, the small molecules go through the barrier into the water while the larger ones are left behind. In the artificial kidney the **patient's blood** is on one side of the barrier, and on the other is a prepared solution of **salts** of approximately the same concentration as blood. **Waste products** in the patient's blood cross the barrier into the salt solution, which is continually being replaced. In this way the blood is cleaned of all the substances that the kidneys would normally remove; essential substances remain in the blood. The membrane is therefore permeable to substances such as *urea, uric acid, creatinine, sodium, potassium* and *water*—the main chemical ingredients of **urine**—but not to *proteins* or other relatively large molecules. Such membranes are usually made of *Cellophane* or *Cuprophane*. The two main types of artificial kidney in use are shown in Figs 3.45(a) & (b).

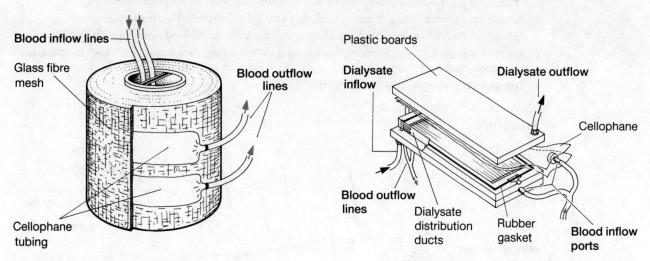

Fig. 3.45(a) A coil dialyser. Blood passes through the Cellophane tubing as the dialysing fluid permeates the glass fibre mesh

Fig. 3.45(b) A flat-bed or Kiil dialyser. Blood passes through two sheets of Cellophane which are held between plastic boards. The dialysing fluid passes in the opposite direction

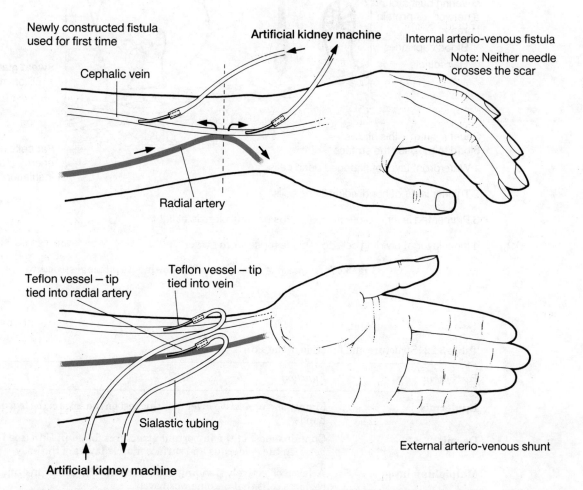

Fig 3.46 Linking an artificial kidney with a patient's bloodstream. The top diagram shows an *internal fistula*, in which the blood leaves and re-enters the body through a vein which has been joined to an artery. The bottom diagram shows an *arterio-venous shunt*, in which an artery and vein are connected to the kidney machine by tubes.

3.6.5 SKIN

General functions

1 Protection of tissues and organs from **mechanical damage** by providing a covering of cells replaceable from below.

2 Maintenance of **body shape**. The *elasticity* of skin restores the shape when joints are used during movement.

3 Protection against excessive **loss of water** from the body by *evaporation*.

4 Protection against entry of bacteria, fungi and other **harmful organisms**.

5 Acts as an **excretory organ** by removing excess *salts*, *water* and *urea* from the body.

6 Acts as a **sense organ** as it contains various tiny sensory structures that react to stimuli such as *temperature, pain* and *touch*.

7 **Temperature regulation** (See Section 3.6.7).

Structure

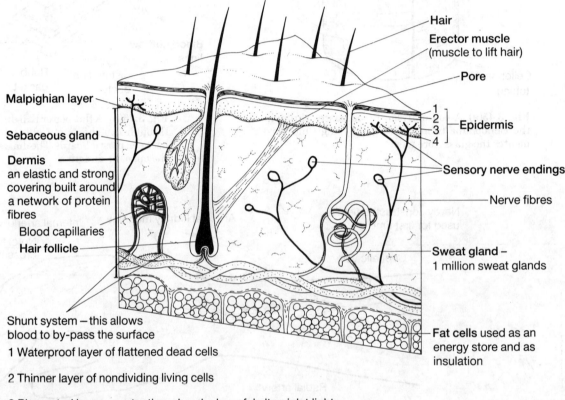

Shunt system — this allows blood to by-pass the surface

1 Waterproof layer of flattened dead cells

2 Thinner layer of nondividing living cells

3 Pigmented layer — protective, absorbs harmful ultraviolet light

4 Inner layer of dividing cells to replace those worn away

Fig. 3.47 Diagram of a wedge of skin showing its internal structure

Table 3.22 Structure and function of the skin

Part of skin	*Function*
Epidermis	Mainly as a protective layer; it is thickest on the soles of the feet and palms of the hands
Dermis	Contains most of the important structures found in skin (see below); the link between the epidermis and surface muscle layers of the body
Malpighian layer	A layer of actively dividing cells between the epidermis and dermis which replaces cells that become worn away
Sebaceous gland	Secretes oily sebum to lubricate the hair
Blood capillaries	Temperature regulation by controlling the flow of blood through the dermis (see Section 3.6.7)

Part of skin	Function
Sweat gland	Produces sweat for temperature regulation and excretion (see Section 3.6.7)
Sensory nerve endings	To detect extremes of temperature and pressure on the skin; particularly numerous in the finger tips and lips
Hair	Mainly for temperature regulation
Erector muscle	Controls the erection of the hair

3.6.6 ORGANS CONCERNED WITH HOMEOSTASIS

Homeostasis is the maintenance of a constant environment immediately around cells. In man this concerns the **tissue fluid** (lymph), the composition of which is kept constant by the action of a variety of organs, each of which regulates particular factors in the blood (the source of tissue fluid).

Table 3.23 Organs concerned with homeostasis

Organs	Blood factors regulated	Blood levels in a healthy man
Liver and pancreas	Glucose	1 g/litre
Skin and liver	Temperature	36.8°C
Kidneys	Water	90%
	Acidity/alkalinity	pH 7.4
	Urea	0.3 g/litre
Lungs	Carbon dioxide	550 cm^3/litre
	Oxygen	193 cm^3/litre

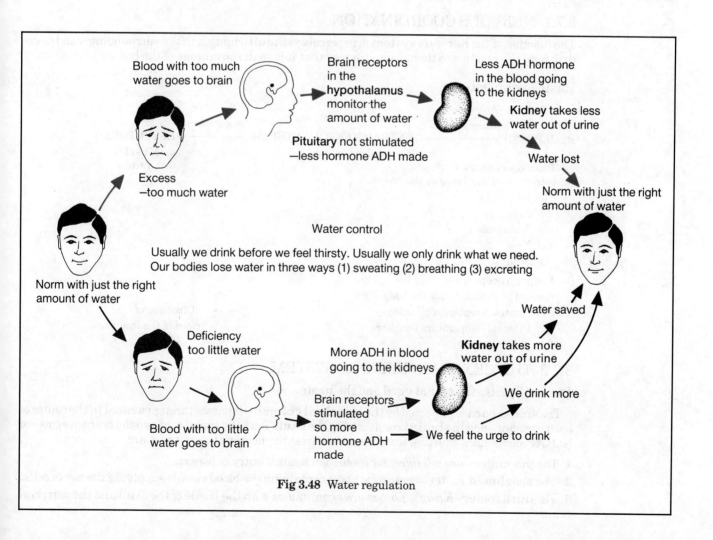

Fig 3.48 Water regulation

3.6.7 TEMPERATURE REGULATION

Diagram of the skin in cold conditions	**Diagram of the skin in hot conditions**
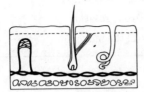	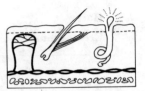
Surface blood vessels **contract** Blood takes a path in the skin **far** from the surface	Surface blood vessels **relax** Blood takes a path in the skin **near** to the surface
Sweat glands **stop** producing sweat	Sweat glands produce **more sweat**, which cools the skin down as it evaporates from the surface (We can produce 1 litre of sweat per hour)
Hairs **pulled up** by erector muscles so layer of air trapped against skin surface is thicker. This provides insulation rather like double glazing	Hairs **drop down** against skin surface as erector muscles contract—less air is trapped for insulation
Shivering occurs—rhythmic contracting of skin muscles makes heat as a by-product	No shivering

3.7 Coordination

3.7.1 NERVOUS COORDINATION

The function of the **nervous system** is to perceive **stimuli** (changes in the surroundings) and to **co-ordinate** the reaction to them in such a way that it is to the advantage of the body.

Basic organization

Afferent or sensory nerves   *Efferent or motor nerves*

RECEPTORS ⟶ CENTRAL NERVOUS SYSTEM ⟶ EFFECTORS
                          (Brain and spinal cord)   (a) **Muscles**
                                                           (b) **Glands**

(a) **Exteroreceptors**—
respond to stimuli *outside* the body
    (*i*) Eyes
    (*ii*) Ears
    (*iii*) Taste buds
    (*iv*) Nose
    (*v*) Skin

(b) **Proprioreceptors**—
respond to stimuli *inside* the body
    (*i*) Stretch receptors of muscles
    (*ii*) Internal temperature receptors

⟶ = Direction of travel of the impulse

3.7.2 THE CENTRAL NERVOUS SYSTEM

Two main parts: the **spinal cord** and the **brain.**

The **spinal cord** is protected by the **vertebral column**—it passes through a canal in the centre of each vertebra—and the **brain** is protected by the **skull**. Both the spinal cord and the brain are covered by *three membranes*. Starting from the one nearest the nervous tissue, these are:

1 The **pia mater**—*one cell thick;* for protection against entry of *bacteria.*
2 The **arachnoid mater**—*connective tissue* containing the blood vessels supplying the nerve cells.
3 The **dura mater**—a *tough, fibrous layer* continuous with the inside of the skull and the vertebral column.

The collective name for these membranes is the **meninges**. The space between the pia mater and the arachnoid mater is filled with a clear watery fluid, the **cerebrospinal fluid**, which circulates in the cavities (ventricles) of the brain and in the central canal of the spinal cord. The main function is to *cushion* the brain from contact with the skull when the head is moved vigorously.

The spinal cord

(a)

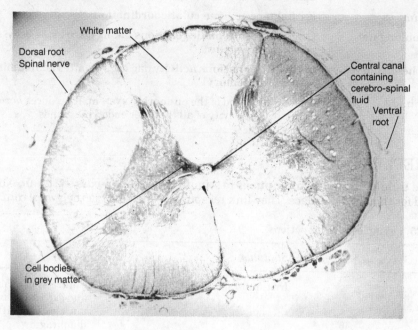

Fig. 3.49 The spinal cord

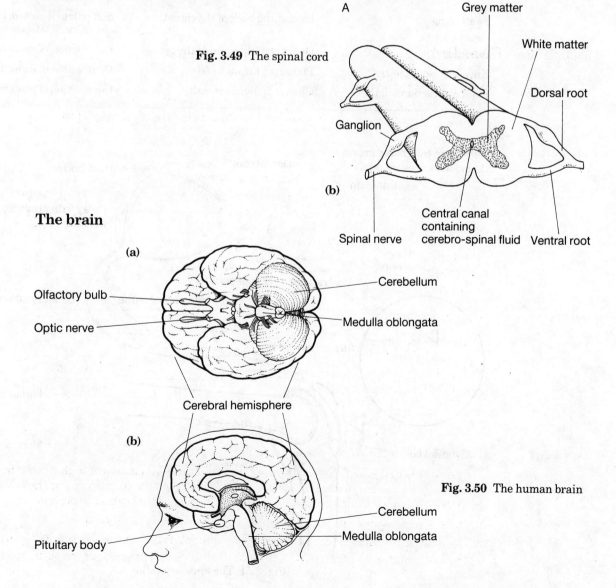

The brain

Fig. 3.50 The human brain

Table 3.24 Structure and function of the brain

Part of the brain	Function
Olfactory bulb	Concerned with the sense of **smell**
Optic nerve	Conveys impulses to the *optic lobes* of the brain for the sense of **sight**
Cerebellum	For **balance** and **muscular coordination**
Medulla oblongata	Controls the **automatic reactions** taking place in the body, e.g. *heart beat, peristalsis, breathing*
Cerebral hemispheres	Control all **conscious activity** and act as centres for retaining past sensations (**memory**)
Pituitary body	The master gland of the **endocrine system**. It produces *hormones* which regulate the activity of all the other endocrine glands

3.7.3 REFLEX ACTIONS

These are **quick, automatic responses** to stimuli which can *by-pass* the brain. No conscious effort is needed for them to take place. They link receptors to effectors via the *spinal cord*.

Table 3.25 Examples of reflex actions

Reflex	Stimulus	Response
Coughing	Irritant in the throat	Contraction of abdominal muscles and expiratory intercostal muscles; relaxation of the diaphragm
Swallowing	Food at the back of the throat	Soft palate is raised; epiglottis is closed; peristalsis takes place
Blinking	Object coming towards the eye	Contraction of eyelid muscles
Knee-jerk (see below)	Pressure/pain on knee	Contraction of flexor muscles
Pupil contraction/dilation	Change in light intensity	Contraction of muscles of the iris

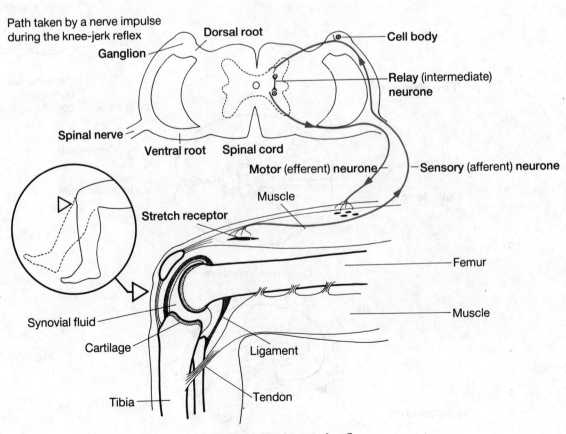

Fig. 3.51 The knee-jerk reflex

3.7.4 COMPARISON OF A TYPICAL SPINAL REFLEX ACTION AND A VOLUNTARY ACTION

Table 3.26 Comparison of a reflex and a voluntary action

Reflex action	Voluntary action
1 A very **rapid** response	The response **may be slow**
2 The nervous impulse takes the **shortest** path	The nervous impulse takes a **long** path
3 Often only the **spinal cord** is used	The **forebrain** is involved
4 Initiated by the response of a **receptor** to a **stimulus**	Initiated from the **brain** under **conscious** control
5 Effectors are **muscles** or **glands**	Effectors are **muscles only**

3.7.5 NERVES

Nerves are made of *bundles* of nerve cells, or **neurones**, surrounded by *connective tissue*. Each neurone is a highly modified cell capable of transmitting **electrical impulses**. A neurone can act like a charged battery, converting *chemical* energy into *electrical* energy. **Afferent**, or **sensory** neurones transmit impulses **from receptors to the central nervous system. Efferent**, or **motor** neurones transmit impulses **to effectors from the central nervous system** (see Section 3.7.1). The neurones are not physically connected but are separated by minute gaps or **synapses**. When an impulse travels from one neurone to the next, the synapse is bridged by a chemical, a **neurotransmitter, acetylcholine.**

Structure and function of neurones

Table 3.27 Structure and function of a neurone

Part of neurone	Function and action
Receptive dendrites	Receive stimuli (at receptors) or impulses (from neighbouring neurones)
Myelin sheath	Acts as an insulator, preventing loss of electrical energy
Neurilemma	Cell membrane of the neurone
Dendron	Carries the impulse to the cell body
Node of Ranvier	Narrow, non-insulated part of the neurone which tends to boost the strength of the impulse as it passes along
Cell body	Part of the neurone containing the nucleus (the control centre)
Axon (nerve fibre)	Carries the impulse away from the cell body
Terminal dendrites	Pass on the impulse to the next neurone after secreting neurotransmitter
Schwann cells	Secrete the neurilemma
Motor end plate	Passes on the impulse to the effector

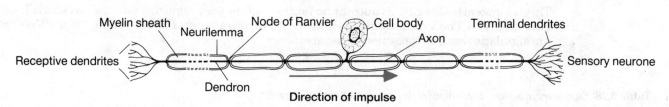

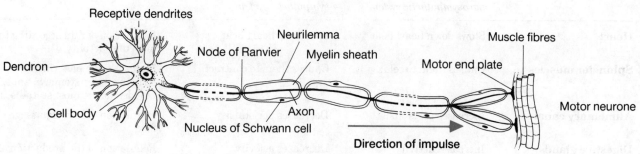

Fig. 3.52 Neurons

3.7.6 NERVE IMPULSES

Method of impulse travel—a brief, simplified explanation

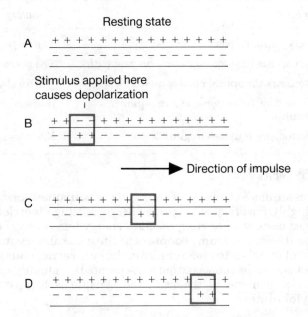

Fig. 3.53 Progressive stages in the movement of a nerve impulse

The surface of the nerve fibre is **positively** charged. Stimulating the surface *mechanically, electrically* or *chemically* causes the positive charge to be temporarily reversed. This is the process of **depolarization**, and a wave of depolarization sweeps over the surface, along the length of the nerve, as a **nerve impulse**. Only a small portion of the nerve fibre becomes depolarized, and it is made to **repolarize** rapidly (in 1/1000 second) so that it is ready to conduct another impulse. Depolarization and repolarization occur as a result of the distribution of **potassium** and **sodium** ions on either side of the membrane of an axon.

Speed and **strength** of a nerve impulse are **constant**. The nerve fibre obeys the **'all-or-none'** rule, i.e. the strength of the stimulus is either sufficient to cause depolarization completely or not at all. **Severe pain** depends on a **large number** of fibres being stimulated at once, whereas **mild pain** occurs if **fewer** fibres are stimulated. Human nerve fibres can transmit over **300 impulses per second** and the speed at which a nerve impulse travels can be up to **150 m/sec**.

Synapses are gaps between the endings of nerve fibres. They measure only .000002 cm wide, and the impulse bridges the gap via a **chemical transmitter** produced at the end of a nerve fibre on arrival of the impulse. One such substance is *acetylcholine.*

3.7.7 THE AUTONOMIC NERVOUS SYSTEM

This is a system that regulates **automatic** functions of the body requiring no *conscious* effort. There are two parts: **1 The sympathetic system** and **2 The parasympathetic system**. Their effects are **antagonistic** (work in opposition to one another).

Table 3.28 Summary of actions controlled by the autonomic nervous systems

Organ under control	Effect of parasympathetic system	Effect of sympathetic system	Result
Heart	Slows down heart beat	Speeds up heart beat	Regulation of rate according to muscular activity
Sphincter muscles	Causes them to relax	Causes them to contract	Materials can pass through structures, e.g. stomach, anus, bladder, at the most suitable time
Alimentary canal	Increases peristalsis	Decreases peristalsis	Regulation of rate of passage of food
Digestive glands	Increases activity	Decreases activity	Regulation of the production of digestive enzymes

Organ under control	Effect of parasympathetic system	Effect of sympathetic system	Result
Blood vessels	Dilates those of the alimentary canal and associated glands. Constricts those of the heart	Constricts those of the alimentary canal and associated glands. Dilates those of the heart	Adjustment of blood flow to suit the demands of the body
Iris	Contracts	Dilates	Regulation of light entering the eye
Ciliary muscles	Contracts	Relaxes	Controls accommodation of the eye
Tear glands	Inhibits action	Increases action	Control of tear production, e.g. to clean the eye membranes
Bronchial muscles	Contracts muscles	Relaxes muscles	Control of air flow in and out of lungs

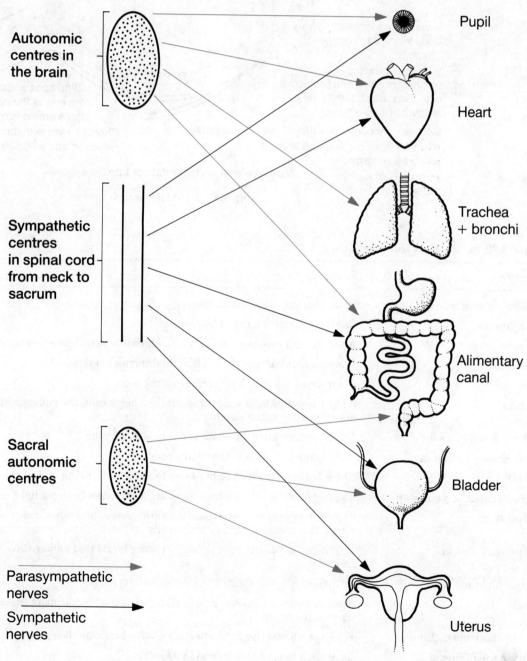

Fig. 3.54 Diagram to show the distribution of the autonomic nervous system

3.7.8 THE EYE

Structure and function

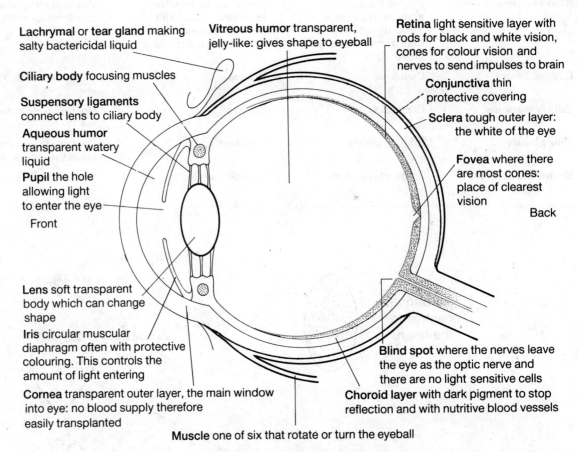

Lachrymal or tear gland making salty bactericidal liquid

Ciliary body focusing muscles

Suspensory ligaments connect lens to ciliary body

Aqueous humor transparent watery liquid

Pupil the hole allowing light to enter the eye

Front

Lens soft transparent body which can change shape

Iris circular muscular diaphragm often with protective colouring. This controls the amount of light entering

Cornea transparent outer layer, the main window into eye: no blood supply therefore easily transplanted

Vitreous humor transparent, jelly-like: gives shape to eyeball

Retina light sensitive layer with rods for black and white vision, cones for colour vision and nerves to send impulses to brain

Conjunctiva thin protective covering

Sclera tough outer layer: the white of the eye

Fovea where there are most cones: place of clearest vision

Back

Blind spot where the nerves leave the eye as the optic nerve and there are no light sensitive cells

Choroid layer with dark pigment to stop reflection and with nutritive blood vessels

Muscle one of six that rotate or turn the eyeball

Fig. 3.55 A section through the eye

Table 3.29 Structure and function of the eye

Part of eye	Function
Sclera (sclerotic coat)	Protection and muscle attachment
Conjunctiva	Protection against entry of bacteria
Cornea	A transparent extension of the sclera which allows transmission of light
Choroid	Prevents internal reflection of light and carries blood vessels
Iris	Controls the amount of light entering the eye
Retina	A light sensitive layer made of specialized nerve cells, the **rods** (for black and white vision) and **cones** (for colour vision)
Ciliary body (muscle)	Muscles which alter the shape of the lens for focusing
Suspensory ligaments	They connect the lens to the ciliary body
Pupil	The hole through which light passes from the front to the back of the eye
Fovea centralis (yellow spot)	The region of the retina where there are most cones: the most light sensitive spot
Blind spot	The region where nerves connecting with the rods and cones leave the eye as the **optic nerve**. It is devoid of light sensitive cells
Aqueous humour	A transparent (allows light through) watery liquid that helps to give the front of the eye its shape
Vitreous humour	A transparent jelly which gives the eyeball its shape
Lens	Made of layers of soft transparent material; it can become more or less biconvex to focus light on the retina
Lachrymal (tear) gland	Produces a protective antibacterial liquid to lubricate the eye
Muscles (6 of these)	They allow the eye to be moved in its socket

Accommodation

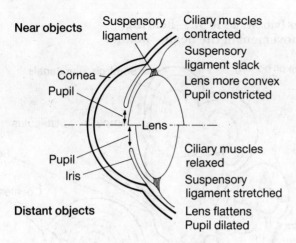

Fig. 3.56 Accommodation

Fig. 3.57 A graph of accommodation against age

The **lens** of the eye is **biconvex**, the anterior surface being slightly less curved than the posterior. It is attached at the margin to the inside of the sclerotic coat by means of the **suspensory ligaments**. The *curvature* of the lens, and thus its *focal length*, can be altered by the contraction of the **ciliary muscles**. This change in shape of the lens—the action of **accommodation**—results from a re-arrangement of the lens' *internal fibres*, and is *automatic*, allowing the eye to focus on **near** or **distant** objects.

When the eye is accommodated for *distant* objects the ciliary muscles are *relaxed* and the suspensory ligaments pull on the lens, *reducing* its curvature. The process of accommodation for *near* objects consists of *contraction* of the ciliary muscles, which takes the tension off the lens and allows it to become more curved. The range of accommodation depends on the power of the muscles and the elasticity of the lens. These factors become reduced with age (see Fig. 3.57).

Correction of long sight and short sight

In some people the eyes are not of perfectly normal shape, e.g. the anterior–posterior axis is either *shorter* or *longer* than normal. In these cases rays of light are brought to a focus *behind* or *in front of* the retina. The problem can be solved with the use of **spectacles** with either *convex* or *concave* lenses.

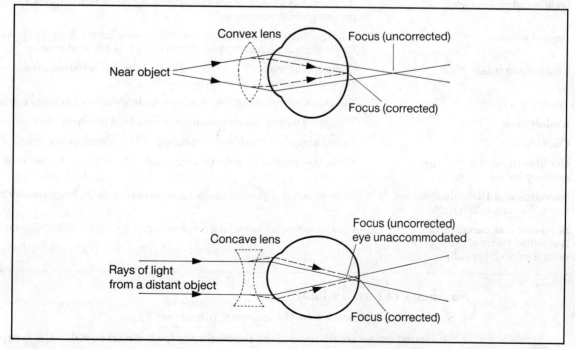

Fig. 3.58 Long sight and its correction. Short sight and its correction. (The dotted lines show the rays of light after correction by each type of lens)

3.7.9 THE EAR

Structure and functions

Two functions:
1 **Perception of sound waves** (vibrations in air)—**hearing**
2 **Detection of gravity** and **movement of the head—balance**

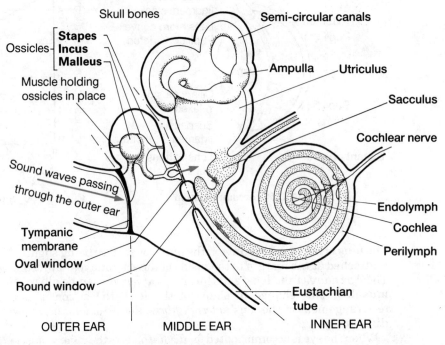

Fig. 3.59 The human ear

Table 3.30 Structure and function of the ear

Part of ear	*Function*
Skull bones (tympanic bulla)	For protection of the delicate structures of the middle and inner ear
Tympanic membrane (ear drum or tympanum)	It vibrates in response to sound waves striking its surface and causes the ossicles to vibrate
Ossicles (3 of these)	Transmission of vibrations across the air-filled middle ear
Oval window	It vibrates as a result of the stapes striking its surface and sets up vibrations in the perilymph of the inner ear
Round window	It bulges outwards every time the oval window bulges inwards, thus compensating for pressure changes set up in the perilymph by the oval window
Eustachian tube	Connects the middle ear to the back of the throat; equalizes pressure on both sides of the ear drum and so allows it to vibrate
Perilymph	The liquid surrounding the membranous labyrinth of the inner ear (see below)
Endolymph	The liquid within the membranous labyrinth of the inner ear
Cochlea	Coiled part of the inner ear containing cells sensitive to vibrations of the perilymph
Cochlea nerve (leads to the auditory nerve)	Sends the impulse from the sensitive cells of the cochlea to the brain
Sacculus and Utriculus (parts of the membranous labyrinth)	Contain sense organs which can detect rotation of the head: filled with endolymph
Semi-circular canals and Ampullae (parts of the membranous labyrinth)	Contain sense organs which can detect gravity: filled with endolymph

Summary of how we hear

1 Sound waves are received by the **external pinna** (ear flap).

2 The sound waves are directed along the **auditory (outer ear) canal** to the **tympanum**.

3 The tympanum vibrates and passes the vibrations across the middle ear via the **ossicles** to the **oval window**.

4 The oval window vibrates with the same frequency as the tympanum; it magnifies the vibrations 22 times.

5 The vibrations of the oval window are transmitted through the liquid **perilymph** in the **cochlea** and stimulate **sensitive cells**.

6 Because liquids are incompressible, the **round window** vibrates to compensate for the movement of the oval window, thus allowing for pressure changes in the perilymph.

7 Stimulation of the sensitive cells causes **nerve impulses** to be sent to the brain via the **auditory nerve**. Here they are interpreted as the sensation of sound.

Balance

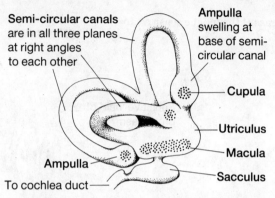

The position of the head relative to gravity is detected

Fig. 3.60 How we balance. A diagrammatic cross section of the organs of balance in the inner ear

The **ampullae** at the base of the semi-circular canals contain small discs of cells with sensory 'hairs' which project into the fluid **endolymph** inside. Attached to these 'hairs' is a mass of jelly-like material (**cupula**), which is made to move when the head is suddenly rotated. The wall of each ampulla moves with the head but the endolymph lags behind owing to its inertia, thus moving the cupula and bending the sensory hairs. As the hairs become bent, electrical impulses are set up which pass to the brain along the *auditory nerve*. The brain thus detects information from the ampullae about changes in **rotational** movement of the head. The **macula** in the **utriculus** (see Fig. 3.59) is similar to the cupula, but it is a **gravity** receptor rather than a *rotatory* receptor. From the two sets of messages, which are continuously being received by the brain, we are able to control *muscular movement* necessary to keep the body *upright*.

3.7.10 TASTE AND SMELL

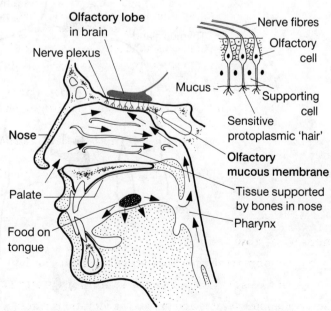

Fig. 3.61 The olfactory organ showing details of the sensitive cells

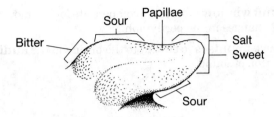

Fig. 3.62(a) The areas of the tongue sensitive to different tastes

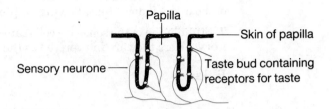

Fig. 3.62(b) A taste papilla from the back of the tongue

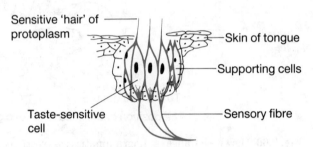

Fig. 3.63 An enlarged diagram of a taste bud

3.7.11 CHEMICAL COORDINATION–THE ENDOCRINE GLANDS AND THEIR SECRETIONS

Endocrine glands, unlike *exocrine glands* (e.g. salivary glands), have no ducts. Their secretions, the **hormones**, pass directly into the **blood system** and are carried to different parts of the body where they control various aspects of metabolism. Each hormone is **specific** in its action: it affects only **one** type of tissue or organ.

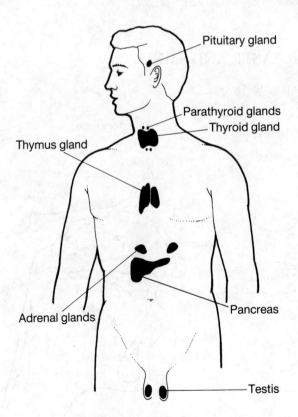

Fig. 3.64 The endocrine glands

Table 3.31 The endocrine glands and their secretions

Endocrine gland	Hormone	Function
Pituitary	Prolactin	Stimulates milk production by mammary glands
	Growth hormone	Stimulates general body growth
	Thyroid-stimulating hormone	Regulates the action of the thyroid
	Adrenal-stimulating hormone	Regulates the action of the adrenals
	Gonad-stimulating hormone	Regulates the development of reproductive organs
	Oxytocin	Stimulates the muscles of the uterus during birth
	Vasopressin (ADH)	Regulates the amount of water excreted in urine
	Lipotropin	Increases the rate of use of stored fat
Thyroid	Thyroxine	Controls the rate of growth and the rate at which glucose is used to release energy
Parathyroids	Parathormone	Regulates the rate at which the body uses calcium
Pancreas	Insulin	Stimulates the conversion of glucose to glycogen
		Stimulates the oxidation of glucose to release energy
		Inhibits the production of glucose from amino acids in the liver
Gonads	Testosterone	Regulates the development of secondary sexual characteristics
	Oestrogen	Stimulates the thickening of the uterus wall during ovulation
	Progesterone	Prepares the uterus for pregnancy
Adrenals	Adrenaline	Raises the pulse rate and the volume of blood pumped by the heart with each beat
		Increases rate and depth of respiration
		Constricts the blood vessels in the alimentary canal and skin and dilates those in the muscles
Thymus*	(not known)	Involved in development of immunity in the newborn. May also regulate the onset of sexual maturity

*The function of the thymus gland in adults is unclear

3.7.12 INTERACTION OF NERVOUS AND CHEMICAL COORDINATION

Messages are sorted out in the brain (1). The pituitary (2) can release hormones to affect the thyroid (3) and adrenals (4). 5, 6, 7. Nerve fibres to the eye, face muscles, and pharynx. 8. Nerves to the larynx, heart and intestines. 9. Nerves to the heart (10), blood vessels (11), adrenals (12), intestine (13), and bladder (14)

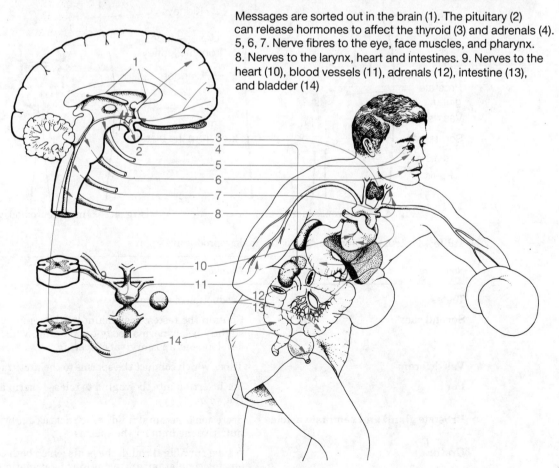

Fig. 3.65 How nervous reflexes can affect parts of the body. Messages are integrated in the brain

THEME 4 HUMAN REPRODUCTION AND THE CONTINUITY OF LIFE

4.1 Human Reproduction and Development

4.1.1 SEXUAL REPRODUCTION

Sexual reproduction is the typical method of producing **offspring** among *multicellular* animals, and though the details of the process differ in the various groups of animals, there is a general plan. The main feature of sexual reproduction is the *fusion* of two special cells, the male and female **gametes**, or more importantly, of their *nuclei*, so that the offspring receive genetic material (**chromosomes**) from both parents. This bringing together of two sets of different chromosomes allows for **genetic variation** (see Section 4.2.4). The female gamete is the **egg** (ovum) and the male gamete the **sperm**. Gametes are produced in special organs, the **gonads**, which in females are the **ovaries** and in males the **testes**.

In all mammals the *fusion* of sperm and egg, **fertilization**, takes place inside the *female*. For this to happen, the sperm must be deposited in the female in such a position that it can swim to the egg. **Mating**, **intercourse** and **copulation** are all names used to describe the act in which the **penis** of the male is inserted into the **vagina** of the female and sperms are ejaculated near the neck of the womb, the **cervix**. The penis is usually soft and flaccid but during copulation it is firm enough to penetrate the vagina. When the male becomes sexually aroused there occurs an increase in *blood flow* to the sponge-like tissues surrounding the urethra of the penis. This causes the penis to become erect. Ejaculation of **semen** (a mixture of sperms and nutritive liquid through which they swim) takes place as a *reflex action* resulting from stimulation of nerve endings in the tip of the penis. About *1.5 cm³* of semen is produced at each ejaculation. This contains about *100 million sperms*. The sperms swim through the uterus to the **fallopian tubes**, where they may come in contact with an egg (if one has been released by the ovaries). Only one sperm need reach an egg for fertilization to take place.

4.1.2 THE REPRODUCTIVE SYSTEM

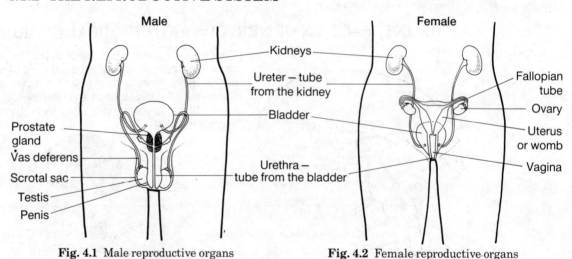

Fig. 4.1 Male reproductive organs   **Fig. 4.2** Female reproductive organs

Table 4.1 Structure and function of the male reproductive organs

Structure	Function
Testes	Production of sperms
Scrotal sacs	Contain the testes; they maintain the temperature of the testes slightly below normal body temperature which is necessary for development and survival of sperm
Vas deferens	Tubes which conduct the sperms to the urethra by peristalsis
Penis	For insertion into the vagina to release sperm at the cervix of the womb
Prostate gland and seminal vesicles	Secretion of seminal fluid, which acts as a lubricant and nutritive medium for the sperms
Urethra	A tube running through the penis which both carries sperms (during copulation) and urine (during urination)

Table 4.2 Structure and function of the female reproductive organs

Structure	Function
Ovaries	Production of eggs (ova)
Uterus	Plays a part in development of the embryo and formation of the placenta
Cervix	The opening to the uterus for the passage of sperm during copulation. The baby emerges through the cervix during birth
Vagina	For the reception of the penis during copulation For the passage of the baby during birth
Fallopian tubes (oviducts)	Provide the ideal environment for fertilization to take place Conduct the fertilized egg to the uterus
Urethra	For the passage of urine from the bladder

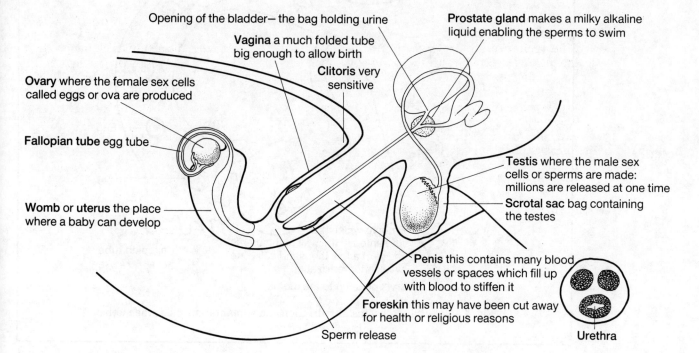

Fig. 4.3 Copulation—the discharge of male gametes near the cervix

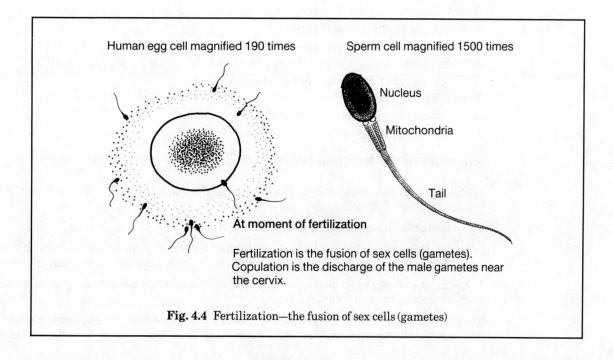

Fig. 4.4 Fertilization—the fusion of sex cells (gametes)

4.1.3 THE FATE OF AN EGG

Females are born with ovaries containing thousands of special sex cells, **oogonia**, each of which has the potential of developing into an egg. However, only a small proportion of the oogonia will be used as gamete-forming cells during the reproductive life of a woman. Development of eggs depends on the production of **hormones** by the **pituitary** and the **ovaries**. When the female becomes sexually mature these hormones control the production and release of eggs from the ovaries at regular **monthly** intervals. This continues until she is pregnant or until the age of about 45 years, when egg production ceases. Most of the eggs produced are never fertilized and, at monthly intervals, are discharged with part of the *lining of the uterus* via the vagina. This discharge is called the **menstrual flow** and it continues to pass from the vagina for about *five* days. After this, the uterus gradually develops a new lining so that it can accommodate an embryo should fertilization occur.

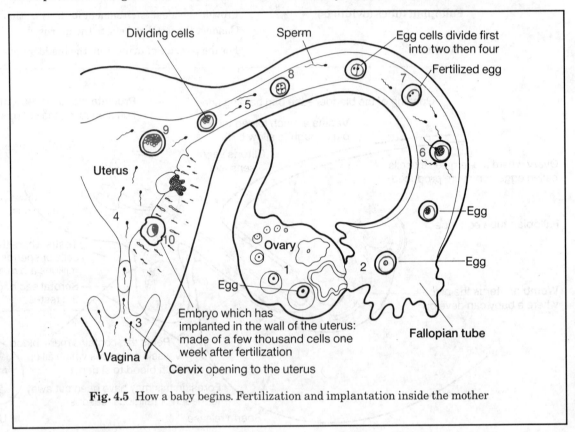

Fig. 4.5 How a baby begins. Fertilization and implantation inside the mother

1 Ovary produces egg
2 Egg released into fallopian tube
3 At about the same time, sperms enter vagina
4 Sperms swim up through uterus
5 Sperms swim along fallopian tube
6 Sperms make contact with the egg
7 Single sperm and egg fuse—fertilization
8 Fertilized egg, now divided into 4 cells, is conducted towards uterus
9 Fertilized egg about to implant in wall of uterus
10 Implantation complete, the placenta starts to develop

Summary of the hormonal control of the female reproductive cycle

1 Pituitary gland secretes **follicle-stimulating hormone (FSH)** which causes the eggs to grow inside **Graafian follicles** within the ovaries.

2 Graafian follicles secrete the hormone **oestrogen**.

3 Oestrogen causes the lining of the **uterus** to become *thick* and *glandular.* It also *stops FSH production* and causes the production of another pituitary hormone, **luteinizing hormone (LH)**.

4 LH causes an **egg** to be shed from an ovary and causes the corresponding Graafian follicle to grow from the corpus luteum (yellow body).

5 The corpus luteum is an **endocrine gland**, secreting a hormone, **progesterone**. Progesterone prepares the uterus for reception and development of the embryo and *stops the secretion of LH.*

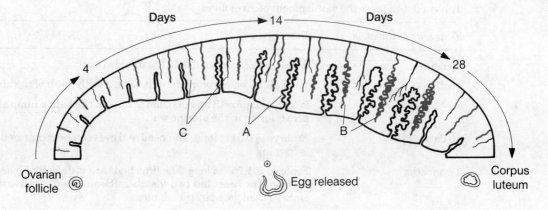

Days ——→ 14 —— Days

4   28

C   A   B

Ovarian follicle   Egg released   Corpus luteum

A The glands grow larger   B The arteries dilate   C The veins increase in size

Fig. 4.6 Diagram to illustrate the gradual thickening of the lining of the womb in preparation for the nourishment of a fertilized egg

6 IF NO FERTILIZATION OCCURS, the corpus luteum *disintegrates* and the inability to produce progesterone causes a menstrual flow. The cycle re-starts with the production of *FSH* from the pituitary once more.

7 IF FERTILIZATION OCCURS, the developing **embryo** and **placenta** produce **oestrogen** and **progesterone** to maintain the uterus in a suitable state for the continued growth of the foetus.

4.1.4 STAGES IN THE DEVELOPMENT OF AN EMBRYO

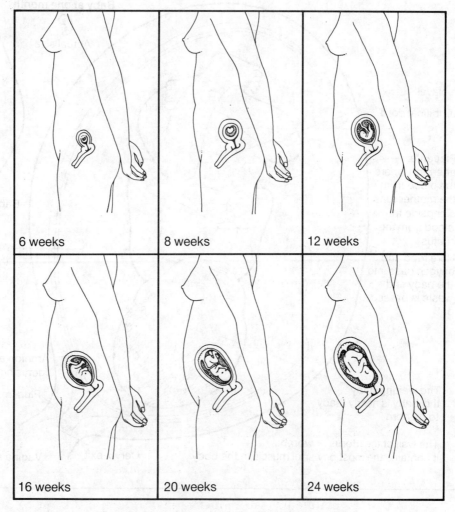

6 weeks   8 weeks   12 weeks

16 weeks   20 weeks   24 weeks

Fig. 4.7 Stages in the growth of a baby in the uterus

Table 4.3 Stages in the development of an embryo

Time after fertilization	Description
50 hours	A ball of cells just visible to the unaided eye
10 days	The ball becomes completely embedded in the wall of the uterus
10–14 days	With rapid growth and division of cells in the ball, a lump about 0.25 cm across forms in the uterine wall
30 days	Embryo is 0.5 cm long. The head and eyes can be recognized. The spinal cord is forming
1½ months	Embryo is 1.25 cm long. The limb buds are visible. Bones are beginning to develop. The heart has two chambers. Some blood vessels are formed. The embryo is enclosed by the amnion
2 months	Placenta has formed. Note that the maternal and foetal circulations are separate
3 months	The foetus weighs 14 g. All the body organs are formed
4 months	The foetus weighs 113 g and increases rapidly in weight from this stage
5 months	Limb movements can be felt in the womb. The embryo (foetus) is covered in a fine hair, lanugo, and a thin film of fat (sebum) coats the skin
6 months	Air sacs (alveoli) develop in the lungs. The nostrils open. Weight is about 1 kg
7 months	The foetus has turned so that its head is above the cervix
8 months	Weight is about 2 kg. Fingernails have formed
9th–10th month	Lanugo disappears. Weight about 3.5 kg. Length about 50 cm at birth

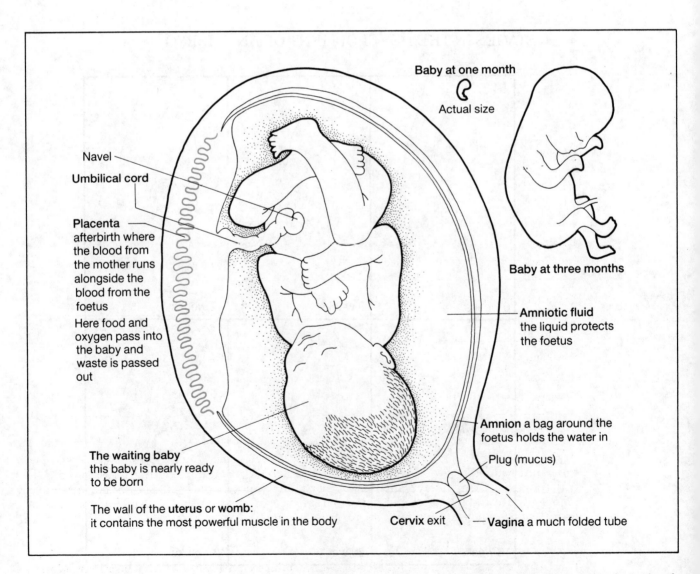

Fig. 4.8 The waiting baby. The baby lies curled up so it protects itself but can move and even sucks its thumb

4.1.5 CARE OF THE MOTHER DURING PREGNANCY

Pregnant women should pay particular attention to **diet, rest, smoking habits** and **alcohol intake**.

Diet

The growing embryo requires large quantities of **calcium**, for *skeletal* growth, *iron*, for the manufacture of *red blood cells*, and **vitamins**, which help the various *enzymes* in the processes leading to growth and development.

Rest

During the later stages of pregnancy the foetus reaches such proportions that it causes *crowding* and *pressure* on the **abdominal organs**, such as the *bladder*, and on major blood vessels and nerves. The weight of the foetus makes any exertion difficult and the woman becomes out of breath more readily than usual. She therefore requires longer rests to recover. Increased internal pressure may cause **muscular cramp, varicose veins** and the **need to pass urine more frequently**. These symptoms cause inconvenience but disappear after the birth of the baby.

Smoking

Tobacco smoke and the effects of inhaling it **reduce the efficiency of the blood to carry oxygen**. During the development of the foetus—particularly in the later stages when the rate of growth of the *brain* and *nervous system* is maximum—a considerable amount of oxygen must be supplied to the placenta. The effects of smoking on the foetus may be to **reduce the normal growth rate**, leading to stunting of *physical* and *mental* development.

Alcohol

If alcohol is taken in *excess* by the mother, its concentration in her bloodstream will reach a level that is dangerous to the foetus. Alcohol can pass across the **placenta** and damage the **nervous system** and the **liver** of the developing baby.

4.1.6 USE AND ABUSE OF DRUGS DURING PREGNANCY

Table 4.4 Drugs which should not be taken

Drug	Use	Effect on foetus
Chloroquine	Malaria	Eye abnormalities
Heroin	Drug abuse	Depressed respiration and withdrawal symptoms after birth
Live vaccines, e.g. smallpox, rubella	Immunization	Viral infection
LSD	Drug abuse	Chromosome damage
Nicotine	Smoking	Poor growth

Table 4.5 Drugs best avoided if possible

Drug	Use	Effect on foetus
Streptomycin (an antibiotic)	To combat bacterial infections	Possible deafness
Sulphurazole	To combat bacterial infections	Anaemia
Tetracycline (an antibiotic)	To combat bacterial infections	Yellowing of teeth

4.1.7 BIRTH

At the end of pregnancy the foetus moves so that its head points **downwards** at the cervix. The **muscular wall of the uterus** undergoes a series of *powerful contractions* and the baby is forced, head first, through the dilated cervix and vagina. Shortly after birth, the **placenta** is forced out in a similar manner. The **umbilical cord** is cut and tied off as soon as possible, and the part remaining on the baby withers and falls off within a few days, leaving the **navel** as a permanent scar.

4.1.8 PARENTAL CARE

For the first months of a baby's life its food consists of **milk** secreted by its mother's **mammary glands** (breasts). During the first 3 days following birth the mammary glands produce **colostrum**, which is a yellowish fluid containing antibodies (see Section 2.2.12) that protect the baby from many diseases during its early development. Colostrum also contains nutritive proteins, but in different proportions to those found in normal mother's milk. **Bottle-fed babies** are usually given food based on **cow's milk**.

Table 4.6 Comparison of the composition of cow's milk and human milk

Constituent	Cow's milk (per litre)	Human milk (per litre)
Water	860 g	876 g
Protein	34 g	12 g
Fat	42 g	36 g
Carbohydrate	48 g	70 g
Vitamin C	15 mg	52 mg
Vitamin A	0.4 mg	4.5 mg
Vitamin D	0.0002 mg	0.0003 mg
Sodium	0.6 g	0.15 g
Potassium	1.4 g	0.6 g
Magnesium	1.3 g	0.35 g
Calcium	1.2 g	0.3 g
Phosphorus	1.0 g	0.15 g
Energy	2730 kJ	2739 kJ
pH	6.8	7.3

Some advantages of breast feeding

1 There is a **special relationship built up between mother and baby** because of close physical contact lasting up to 3 hours per day.

2 The *sucking* action of the baby stimulates **contraction of the uterus wall** and helps to bring the mother's shape back to normal following birth.

3 There are **nutritional advantages** of human milk over cow's milk. **Antibodies** in the mother's colostrum are very important for the health of the newborn. Some babies become *allergic* to cow's milk, and others suffer because of an unsuitable balance of necessary minerals in cow's milk. The high protein of cow's milk can absorb too much acid from the baby's stomach. The acid normally helps digestion and kills certain harmful bacteria.

4.1.9 GROWTH OF THE INDIVIDUAL

Growth is an **irreversible increase in size** of an organism involving the synthesis of **protoplasm**. It begins at the moment of *fertilization*, continues through *gestation* (the period spent in the womb), and goes on until the end of *adolescence*. After that time, all parts of the body change and develop in significant ways. In many cases there is no further growth. Some parts of the body, such as the brain,

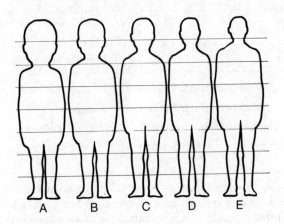

Fig. 4.9 How body proportions change during growth. (A) A newborn baby, the head is about one quarter of the total body length; (B) An infant; (C) Approaching puberty; (D) An adolescent; (E) An adult. The rest of the body has now grown more than the head, which accounts for one eighth of the body length

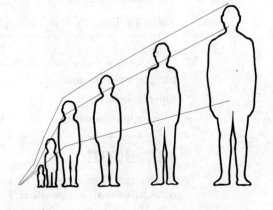

Fig. 4.10 Growth from birth to adulthood proceeds along a curve, not a straight line

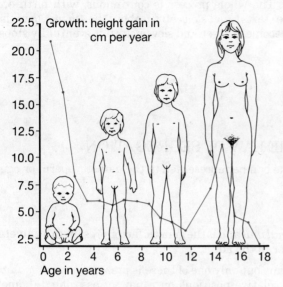

Fig. 4.11 A graph showing the number of centimetres the average girl grows in a year. After a rapid start, the rate declines until the adolescent growth spurt

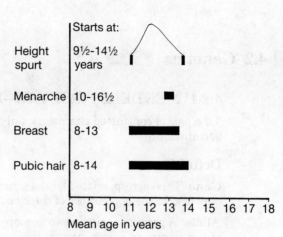

Fig. 4.13 The age range at which various systems start to grow in girls at puberty and the average period of growth

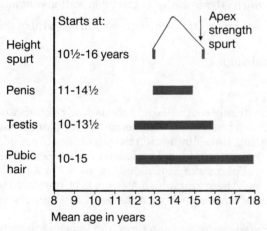

Fig. 4.12 The age range at which various systems start to grow in boys at puberty and the average period of growth

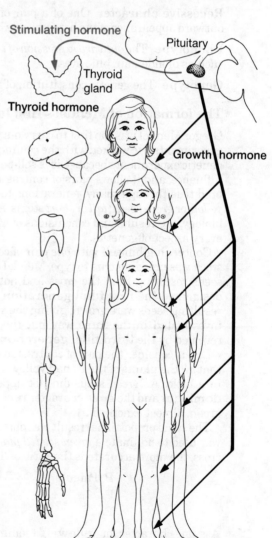

Fig. 4.14 Hormones and growth. Two important hormones influence growth. *Thyroid hormone*, released under stimulus from the pituitary, acts on the brain, teeth, bones and metabolism. *Growth hormone* secreted by the pituitary exerts an effect on the growth of all body systems

regress until the end of life. The importance of growth before birth is illustrated by the fact that the fertilized egg divides *44 times* between conception and its appearance as a baby. From then until adulthood only *four* more divisions occur. The whole process is continuous, with birth occurring merely as a landmark. Indeed, **growth rate** starts to get *slower* from about the *4th month* in the womb and, apart from a spurt in *adolescence*, it becomes slower and slower until it eventually stops.

4.2 Genetics

4.2.1 MENDEL'S FIRST LAW—THE LAW OF SEGREGATION

'Of a pair of contrasted characters, only one can be represented in the gamete (sperm or egg) by its germinal unit.'

Definitions

Gene This corresponds to Mendel's *germinal unit* and is the genetic factor present in a gamete which may lead to the appearance of the character in the adult.

Allele A gene can exist in two or more forms but only one of these is present in a *chromosome*. Two of the forms, or *alleles*, occupy the same relative positions on a pair of associated (homologous) chromosomes. One allele may be *dominant, recessive* or *equal* to the other in the pair of chromosomes, this determining the outward expression of the genes.

Heterozygote An individual receiving *unlike* genes from its parents.

Dominant character One of a pair of contrasted characters which expresses itself in the outward appearance of a heterozygote.

Recessive character One of a pair of contrasted characters which *does not* express itself in the outward appearance of the heterozygote but which is transmitted to later generations *without change*.

Phenotype The *outward expression of the genes*, i.e. an organism with certain observable characters, such as blonde hair, blue eyes.

Genotype The genetic constitution of an individual.

The formation of Mendel's first law

Gregor Mendel was the first to carry out scientifically controlled and statistically significant genetic experiments. He worked with the common garden pea plant, *Pisum sativum*. This plant is suitable for genetic experiments because it is self-pollinating, thus eliminating the possibility of outside genetic influence, and it shows pairs of contrasting characters. Mendel was able to select pea strains which bred true through many generations to several particular variations, e.g. *round* or *wrinkled* seeds; *yellow* or *green* seeds; *tall* or *short* stems. Although these examples may seem to be unrelated to human biology, the results and conclusions of Mendel's work have formed the basis for subsequent work in every aspect of genetics.

Concerning himself with *one* pair of contrasted characters at a time, and knowing that the parent stock was breeding true to type, Mendel crossed pairs of plants showing these contrasts. He grew the seeds resulting from the cross and noted the form of the characters in the offspring, which are designated the **first filial generation** (the F_1). The F_1 plants were allowed to self-pollinate. The resulting seeds were grown, giving the **second filial generation**, the F_2. Further generations were investigated in the same way but the behaviour of these particular characters was sufficiently revealed by the **third filial generation**, the F_3.

Let us consider the pair of contrasted characters, *yellow* and *green* seeds: Mendel's results showed that *all* the plants of the F_1 had yellow seeds but in the F_2, both yellow and green seeds were present in a ratio. As *green* seeds did not appear again until the F_2, the *yellow* character can be called **dominant** and the *green* character **recessive**. The actual numbers in the F_2 were 6022 yellow : 2001 green, almost exactly 3 : 1.

The same proportional result was obtained irrespective of whether pollen from a *yellow-seeded plant* was used to pollinate a *green-seeded plant* or vice-versa. The larger the number of plants used in the cross, the more accurate is the ratio of 3 : 1.

P (Parents)	Yellow	×	Green
F_1		Yellow (selfed)	
F_2	3 Yellow	:	1 Green

Assume character for **yellow**=**Y** (dominant)
Assume character for **green**=**y** (recessive)
Genes present in the adults are shown by **two symbols** because each develops from a *zygote* (the result of fusion of two gametes).

Parents: YY (yellow) × yy (green)

gametes	Y	Y
y	Yy	Yy
y	Yy	Yy

F_1
All yellow (Yy)
as effect of
Y dominant over y

F_1 selfed:

gametes	Y	y
Y	YY	Yy
y	yY	yy

F_2
3 yellow : 1 green
(YY, Yy, yY) (yy)

Human examples

Many *human* characteristics follow this simple Mendelian pattern of inheritance, with some characters being **dominant** and the others **recessive**. The study of human genetics is difficult because even the largest family is small compared with the thousands of pea plants which were used by Mendel for his statistical analyses. The *larger* the numbers used for genetical studies, the closer the agreement with the expected ratios.

Dominant human characters include *hare lip, negroid hair, the ability to taste phenylthiourea* and *the ability to roll one's tongue.* **Recessive characters** include *red hair, colour blindness* and *left handedness.* However, dominance is not always so clear cut. In some cases it is **incomplete**, for example the character for *eye colour* or for some *blood groups.* If each parent is **homozygous** for *brown eyes,* all the children will have *brown eyes,* but if the parents are **heterozygous** for *brown eye colour,* their children may have various shades such as *hazel* and *light brown.* The character for *blue eyes* is recessive so that if both parents have blue eyes, their children will also have blue eyes.

Another problem in studying human genetics is the impossibility of distinguishing people *homozygous* for some genes from those who are *heterozygous* for the same genes. It is impossible to tell if a brown-eyed man is a *pure strain* or a *hybrid* for the character merely by looking at the colour of his eyes. If a *brown-eyed man* and a *blue-eyed woman* have children, provided both parents are *homozygous, all* the children will have *brown eyes,* but if the parents are *heterozygous, one in four* children are likely to have *blue eyes.*

Let B=brown eyes and b=blue eyes

Brown eye colour is **dominant** to blue eye colour

The heterozygous parents are each Bb

From the cross Bb×Bb

the F_1 will be

gametes	B	b
B	BB	Bb
b	bB	bb

The blue-eyed child is bb.

Sometimes a particular character in an individual is controlled by more than two genes. The **ABO blood group system** (see Section 3.5.7) is controlled by three genes, A, B and O. An individual will inherit only two of these genes, one from each parent. A and B have the *same degree of dominance* and each is dominant to O. Therefore, people with AA or AO genotypes belong to group A. Those with BB or BO belong to group B. Where A and B are present, the person is group AB, and persons of genotype OO belong to group O. The genes are inherited according to Mendel's laws. That is, if parents have the genotypes AA and BO, they will be group A and group B, respectively. Their children's possible genotypes could be predicted thus:

Parents   AA × BO

gametes	A	A
B	AB	AB
O	AO	AO

50% group AB

50% group A

F_1

4.2.2 SEX DETERMINATION

The sex of humans and other mammals is determined by **X** and **Y chromosomes**. These **sex chromosomes** can be distinguished from other chromosomes, **autosomes**, because the *Y chromosome* is much **shorter** than the *X chromosome* with which it is paired. A **man** has both **X** and **Y** chromosomes. A **woman** has **2X** chromosomes.

Male XY

gametes	X	Y
X	XX	XY
X	XX	XY

Female XX

F_1 50% female   50% male

4.2.3 SEX LINKAGE

Certain genes are associated with the *sex* of an individual because they happen to occur on the **X** chromosome. **Males** (XY) only have one X chromosome and therefore any *recessive* genes carried on the region that does not pair up with the Y chromosome cannot be masked. In **females** (XX), a *recessive* gene on one X chromosome can be masked by a corresponding *dominant* gene on the other X. For a recessive character to appear in a female, she would have to be *homozygous* (double recessive) for that gene. Recessive forms of the sex-linked genes therefore express themselves more frequently in males than in females. **Colour blindness** and **haemophilia** (see Section 2.2.17) are examples of sex-linked genes.

4.2.4 VARIATION

Two types: **continuous** and **discontinuous**.

   Continuous variations show an *even gradation* within a population. **Height** in humans is a good example. If in a population the height of each adult is measured and a **histogram** constructed of the number of individuals whose height falls within a given range, each range decided upon being equal, it will show a curve of **normal distribution** (Gaussian curve) (see Fig. 4.15(a)).

   Variation is **inheritable** only if it is due to **genes** (see Section 4.2.5). Height in man is only *partially* genetically controlled; any effects caused by the **environment** cannot be inherited. In the case of height many genes contribute to the character, for example, those controlling the production of *growth hormones* and those controlling the rate of *protein metabolism*. The environmental factors involved may be equally diverse, for example, the effects of *starvation, malnutrition, disease,* and *lack of exercise*.

   Discontinuous variation within populations can be seen where the individuals fall into two or more *distinct* groups with respect to a particular character. It usually occurs where there is a completely dominant and recessive character within a pair of contrasted genes. Height in pea plants, investigated by Gregor Mendel (see Section 4.2.1), is an example of discontinuous variation. This particular plant character is controlled by a single pair of genes and the environment has very little overall effect on it within a large population.

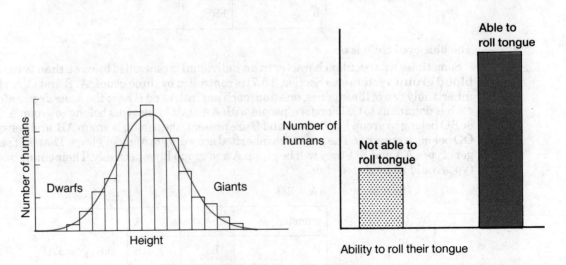

Fig. 4.15(a) Continuous variation (curve drawn from histogram)

Fig. 4.15(b) Discontinuous variation

4.2.5 CHROMOSOMES AS CARRIERS OF HEREDITARY FACTORS—DNA

When a cell is not undergoing division (and the vast majority of cells do not divide again once they have been formed), the **nucleus** appears, under the microscope, as a uniformly **greyish dot**. However, during **cell division**, the contents of the nucleus take on a very different appearance. They become organized into a number of *rod-shaped threads*. These are called **chromosomes** (from *chromos*, meaning coloured, and *soma*, meaning body, because they can be stained with dyes and show up within the cells as discrete units). Each species of animal and plant has a *fixed* number of chromosomes in each nucleus of each of its cells. Between species chromosomes differ in *number* and *shape*: the closer the relation between species, the more similar are the chromosomes. Man has **46 chromosomes** in each of his cells, except the **gametes**, which have **23** (see section on Meiosis, p. 104). In the nucleus of a cell that is not dividing, the chromosomes are still present, even though they do not stain. They are actually dispersed as a very fine network throughout the nucleus.

Chromosomes carry **genes** along their length. Genes are made of a unique chemical, **deoxyribonucleic acid**, or **DNA**. The DNA molecule is extremely large. It is roughly the shape of a long *ladder* that has been twisted into a *spiral*. It has been estimated that a molecule of DNA is 2000 to 3000 times longer than it is thick and is made of well over 10 000 smaller molecules. It is built in the following way: There are essentially identical halves, each comprising a twisted chain of sugar (deoxyribose) molecules linked together by phosphate molecules—this forms the backbone of the ladder—and each carrying a particular chemical base. Links between neighbouring bases hold the two chains together (and form the rungs of the ladder). The only difference between each half of the DNA molecule is the particular assortment of chemical bases.

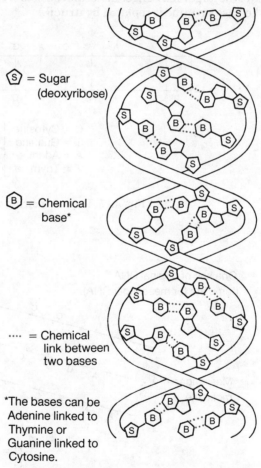

$\textcircled{S}$ = Sugar
(deoxyribose)

$\textcircled{B}$ = Chemical
base*

.... = Chemical
link between
two bases

*The bases can be
Adenine linked to
Thymine or
Guanine linked to
Cytosine.

Fig. 4.16 DNA structure

Each gene is composed of a DNA molecule with its own characteristic *arrangement of bases*. It takes only *one* base to be altered to change the particular gene. There is an almost *unlimited* number of possible arrangements if you consider that a strand of DNA can be over 10 000 base units long. Therefore, there is an almost unlimited number of possible genes in plants and animals.

The function of DNA

DNA determines which *chemical reactions* take place in a cell and at what speeds. It does this by dictating which *proteins* are manufactured in the cell. About 2000 proteins are known from living cells, and many of them are able to act as *catalysts* in the chemical activity of the cell: these proteins are the **enzymes**. Chemical reactions cannot occur at any appreciable rate in cells unless they are catalysed. Therefore, by controlling *protein synthesis*, DNA controls the life of the cell.

4.2.6 HOW PROTEINS ARE MADE IN CELLS

Proteins are made up of building blocks (molecules) known as **amino acids**, which consist of *carbon, nitrogen* and *hydrogen* atoms arranged such that there are *basic* and *acidic* portions of the molecules. In proteins, amino acids are linked together in chains, the acid group of one amino acid attaching to the basic group of the next. DNA is able to regulate how the amino acids are arranged. There are about *20* different amino acids and each protein has its own characteristic *types* and *arrangement* of amino acids. Similarly, the types and arrangement of the *bases* in the DNA molecule act as a **code** that determines which amino acids are linked together.

$$\text{Amino acid} \underset{A}{\overset{\text{Link}}{\rule{3cm}{0.4pt}}} \text{Amino acid} \underset{B}{\overset{\text{Link}}{\rule{3cm}{0.4pt}}} \text{Amino acid}\ C$$

The following is a very simplified account of how DNA is used for making proteins:

1 The long molecule of DNA (remember it is like a twisted ladder) **unwinds** and **splits** along its length between the bases.

2 One *half* of the molecule now acts as a *template* for the formation of a **messenger molecule**, which is made by new bases from the nucleus lining up opposite their *complementary* partners in the original half of the DNA, e.g. Cytosine (C) with Guanine (G), and forming a single strand. The result is that the **code** present in DNA is reproduced in the messenger molecule. (The sugar molecules forming the backbone of the larger messenger molecule consists of **ribose** not deoxyribose, and in ribonucleic acid (**RNA**) the base thymine is replaced by **uracil**.)

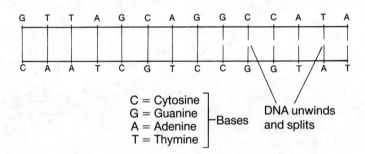

Fig. 4.17 The base pairing of a DNA molecule

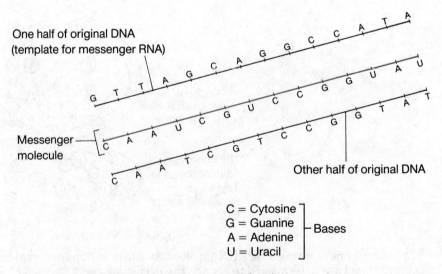

N.B. No thymine is found in the messenger. Another base, **uracil**, is present instead.

Fig. 4.18 The 'transcription' of the DNA code onto a messenger molecule

3 The messenger molecule then passes through the *nuclear membrane* to the **ribosomes** (see Section 1.1).

4 The *code* on the messenger molecule then determines which *amino acids* from the *cytoplasm* of the cell become linked together and therefore the type of protein produced.

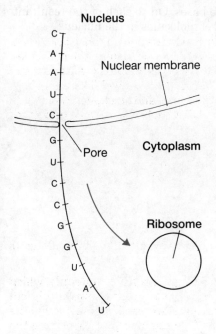

Fig. 4.19 Messenger RNA passes to ribosome

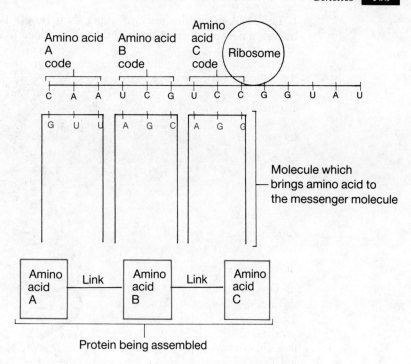

Fig. 4.20 DNA code transcribed into amino acid chain

4.2.7 CELL DIVISION

Mitosis

Chromosomes are made of many DNA molecules lying side by side. Any division of a cell into two must include a division of the chromosomes and if the resulting *daughter cells* are to be identical, then the division of the chromosomes must be precise. This is achieved in **mitosis**, which occurs in all cells within growing tissues.

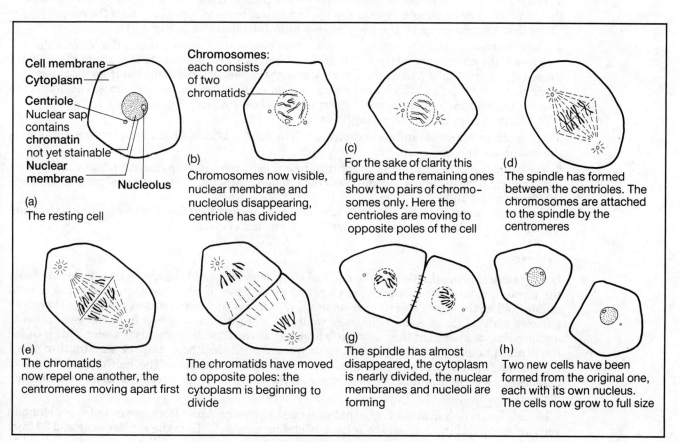

Fig. 4.21 Stages in mitosis

1 The DNA molecules *unwind* along their length between the bases. On to each of the resultant halves, a new *complementary* second half is added from the pool of molecules in the nucleus.

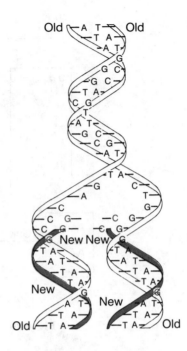

Fig. 4.22 Division of DNA. During the division of a cell to form two daughter cells, the double helix of DNA divides and forms two daughter helices. This it does by unwinding itself; each strand then acts as the template for the formation of a new strand

The outcome is the **doubling** of the chromosomes into two strands, the **chromatids**, which lie side by side. There is one part of the chromosome that does *not* become duplicated in this way; it is the **centromere**.

2 Their duplication having been completed, the chromosomes *shorten* and *increase in thickness.*

3 The **nucleolus** and **nuclear membrane** disintegrate and the chromosomes spread throughout the *cytoplasm.* The **centriole** divides and the two halves move to opposite ends of the cell.
These first 3 stages comprise the **prophase** of mitosis (stages a–c in Fig. 4.21).

4 The chromosomes move together and arrange themselves in a *single plane* in the *centre* of the cell. As a result, the centromeres of the different chromosomes are at an equal distance from either end of the cell (d). In plant cells, *fibrous threads* appear in the cytoplasm, radiating out from the two halves of the centriole, or **poles**, which are present, one on each side of the chromosomes. This forms the spindle. The fibrous threads are not obvious in animal cells undergoing mitosis.
This stage is often called the **metaphase**.

5 The centromeres *divide* and one *complete set* of chromatids is pulled back towards each pole. This is the **anaphase** ((e)–(f)).

6 The two sets of chromatids organize themselves as *two nuclei.* In each case, a *nuclear membrane* re-forms and then the *nucleolus* appears. Next the cytoplasm separates into two equal parts to complete the division ((g)–((h)).
The *significance* of mitosis is the formation of *two new cells* which are *identical* to one another, and to their parent cell, in every respect except in the amount of cytoplasm.

Meiosis

During **sexual reproduction**, if the egg had 46 chromosomes and the sperm had 46 chromosomes the zygote (produced by fusion of the gametes) would have 92 chromosomes, double the normal number. When the zygote grew into an adult via the embryo and foetus stages, then it would produce gametes with 92 chromosomes. So there would be a *progressive doubling* from one generation to another. But we know that the number of chromosomes in a species remains *constant.* This is called the **diploid** number, and for this number to remain unaltered there must be a **reduction** of the diploid number by a *half* every time gametes are formed by cell division. The 'half' diploid number of chromosomes is the **haploid** number and *gametes* acquire this as a result of **meiosis** (reduction division).

Meiosis occurs *only* in *diploid* cells that give rise to gametes. Apart from sperm and egg all human cells are diploid. Human diploid cells have 46 chromosomes—23 from the mother's egg and 23 from the father's sperm—that are arranged as 23 pairs.

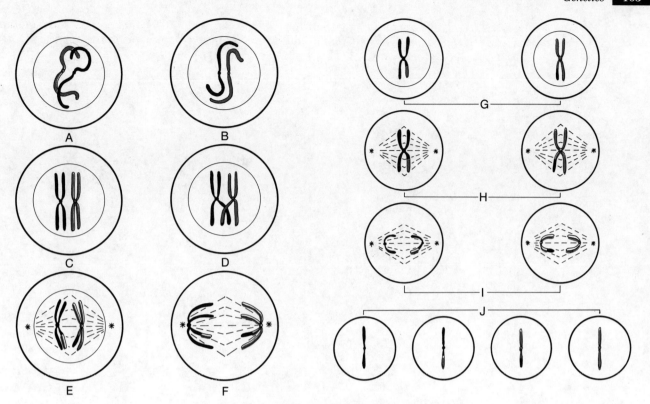

Key: Maternal chromosome is red; Paternal chromosome is black; Diploid number = 2

Fig. 4.23 Meiosis in a gamete-forming cell

1 Each *chromosome* moves towards, and begins to pair with, its partner. The pairing process results in a very *close contact* along the whole of the length of the chromosomes (B). Thus the first stage of *meiosis* differs from that in mitosis. At the start of mitosis the chromosomes consist of two chromatids which are formed by duplication, but in meiosis whole *pairs* of chromosomes come together.

2 While in this close union, the chromosomes *shorten* and *thicken*, and each becomes *duplicated* into **two chromatids** (C). At this stage the *nuclear membrane* begins to disintegrate.

3 Along the length of the pairs of chromosomes, individual **chromatids cross** one another in complex ways. As a result of this, chromatids **exchange** various sections (D). The force of attraction that up to this point has held the pairs of chromosomes together now ceases to operate fully, and the pairs of chromosomes begin to *separate* (E). (In Fig. 4.23 for simplicity only one cross-over is shown.)

4 The *chromosomes separate completely* and move to *opposite* poles of the cell (F). The *cytoplasm divides* (G). At this point, each daughter cell still has the *diploid* number of chromosomes, but because of *crossing over* of sections of the chromatids, **genes** from one partner have been mixed with genes from the other partner.

5 Each new cell undergoes a *mitotic* division. The chromosomes, each consisting of *two complete chromatids* (even though parts have been exchanged), line up along the centre of the new cell (H). One set of chromatids passes to each pole of the cell. Each new set of chromosomes starts to form a nucleus (I).

6 A division of the cytoplasm occurs and nuclear membranes re-appear. As a result, **four gametes**, each with the *haploid* number of chromosomes, have been formed from an original *diploid* cell (J).

  The *significance* of meiosis is:

(a) The formation of cells with **half** the normal number of chromosomes.

(b) **Mixing of genes** between pairs of chromosomes contributing to **variation** within the chromosomes.

TEST YOURSELF

Introduction

There now follows a series of questions, some of which are taken from actual GCSE 1988 papers, and others which have been prepared in the style appropriate to GCSE Human Biology. The questions have been selected to assess a variety of skills including:
1 Knowledge with understanding *(K)*
2 Skills and processes *(P)*
   (a) Application of knowledge   (b) Interpretation of data   (c) Observation

The questions are divided into groups that correspond to the headings of the sections previously covered and each group begins with multiple choice items. Following these are questions which usually require short answers or ask you to label diagrams. At the end of each question, there is an indication of the mark out of 100 that you can expect from answering the questions correctly. (Marks for multiple choice questions are either ½ or 1 mark for each correct response depending on the examination board.) If the question assesses knowledge with understanding, it is marked with a '*K*'. If it assesses skills and processes, it is marked with a '*P*'.

ADVICE ON ANSWERING QUESTIONS

If the questions are multiple choice
1 Remember that, unless otherwise stated in the beginning of the question, there will only be one correct answer.
2 If you are asked to underline the correct answer or tick an appropriate box, never underline or tick more than one of the alternatives.
3 Read the stem (beginning of the question) very carefully.
4 Try to form an answer in your mind.
5 Look for the alternative in the multiple choice which matches your answer.
6 Check the other alternatives to make sure that they are wrong.
7 If another alternative appears to be correct, check your original idea.

If the questions require very short answers
1 If you are not sure how much information to supply, give more rather than less.
2 Keep your answer as concise as possible. An examiner may not be able to see that you have the right idea of the answer if it is written in an overcomplicated way.

Finally, while using this Test Yourself section, do not consult the answers at the end until you are certain that you have done your very best to complete the questions on your own.

ASSESSMENT OBJECTIVES AND CONTENT OF A SYLLABUS

The table below shows mark allocations for the assessment objectives and the content. Each individual syllabus gives details of the way its assessment objectives and content feature in the overall assessment scheme. It is therefore wise to obtain the most up-to-date syllabus for the examination group for which you are entering the examination. A charge is made for the cost of the syllabus.

Assessment objectives

Content	Knowledge and understanding	Skills and processes (including experimental and observational skills)	Mark allocations in complete assessment
Diversity of organisms			between 5% and 10%
Relationships between organisms and with the environment			between 25% and 40%
Organization and maintenance of the individual			between 25% and 40%

Content	Knowledge and understanding	Skills and processes (including experimental and observational skills)	Mark allocations in complete assessment
Development of organisms and the continuity of life			between 15% and 25%
Mark allocations in complete assessment	of the order of 45%	not less than 40% (at least 20% to experimental and observational skills)	

At least 15 per cent of the marks in any complete examination must be allocated to topics related to the personal, social, economic and technological applications of biology in modern society, with the greater emphasis being given to technological considerations.

Questions

THEME 1 MAN'S POSITION IN THE LIVING WORLD

1 (a) Which of the following is not part of an animal cell?
   A a nucleus **B** a cell membrane **C** cytoplasm **D** a cellulose wall *(K)*

(b) Enzymes:
   A are biological catalysts
   B work independently of pH
   C are not involved in respiration
   D do not alter the rate of a chemical reaction *(K)*

(c) One difference between green plants and animals is that green plants have chlorophyll. For which of the following processes is it essential to plants?
   A digesting food
   B making mineral salts available
   C making carbohydrates
   D speeding up respiration *(K)*

(d) which of the following is a tissue?
   A muscle **B** a leucocyte **C** the stomach **D** the skeleton *(K)*

(e) Which of the following is not a characteristic of all living things?
   A respiration **B** excretion **C** nutrition **D** hearing *(K)*

(f) Which of the following is needed for all forms of life?
   A oxygen **B** water **C** chlorophyll **D** starch *(K)*

(g) Man is a mammal because:
   A he moves in search of his food
   B he is a vertebrate
   C he has hair
   D he is warm-blooded *(K)*

(h) Some living cells were broken into fragments and arranged into two groups:
   Group I—all fragments lacked a nucleus
   Group II—all fragments possessed a nucleus
   Each group was maintained under uniform conditions and examined at regular intervals.

	Group I	Group II
Fragments examined	200	200
Surviving 24 hours	160	158
Surviving 48 hours	120	148
Surviving 72 hours	60	144
Surviving 96 hours	6	144

The best conclusion that can be made from this investigation is that:
   A the nucleus is normally necessary for the continued life of the cell
   B nucleated and non-nucleated cell fragments have an equal chance of survival
   C cell fragments cannot live long
   D the removal of the nucleus injures the cytoplasm of the cell fragments *(P)*

2 The graph opposite shows how enzyme action is affected by pH.
   (a) State the pH at which Enzyme 1 reacts fastest. *(P)(1)*
   (b) Describe **two** other differences between the action of Enzyme 1 and Enzyme 2. *(P)(2)*

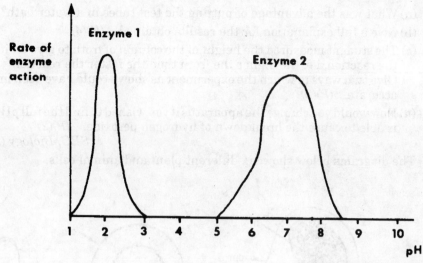

WJEC, Biology (Human), Paper 2, 1990

3 Catalase is an enzyme which promotes the breakdown of hydrogen peroxide to release oxygen. It is not an enzyme of the digestive system but it is present in many living cells. The diagram shows an experiment set up by a student as part of a study of this enzyme. The contents of each test tube had a different pH value as shown. A piece of fresh liver was then added to each tube.

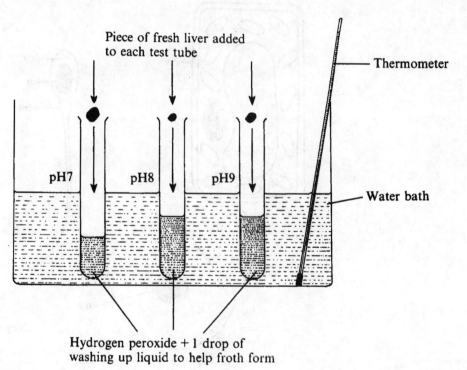

The diagram below shows the results just a few seconds later.

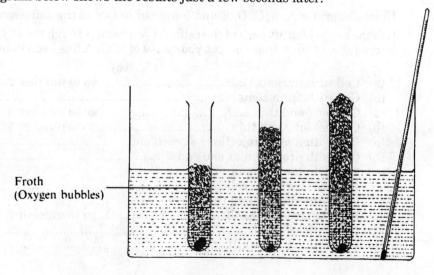

(a) What was the advantage of putting the test tubes in a water bath? *(P)(1)*

(b) Give a full explanation for the results obtained. *(K)(4)*

(c) The student measured the height of the column of froth to give an indication of the speed of the reaction, i.e. the higher the froth then the faster the reaction.
Give **two** ways in which the experiment as shown could have been improved to make it more accurate. *(P)(2)*

(d) How would you change the apparatus if you wished to find the full pH range at which catalase is able to cause the breakdown of hydrogen peroxide? *(P)(2)*

SEG, Biology (Human), Paper 2, 1991

4 The diagrams below show six different plant and animal cells.

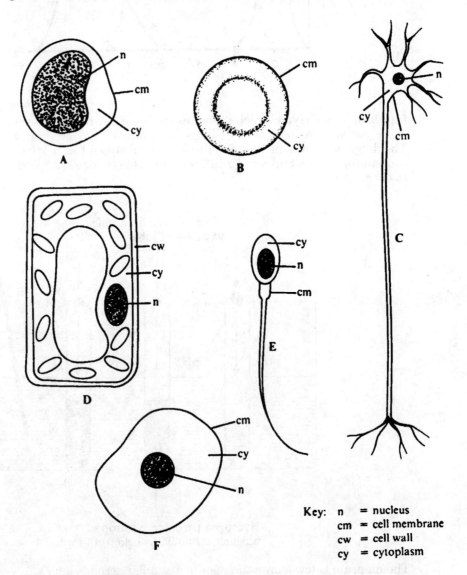

Key: n = nucleus
      cm = cell membrane
      cw = cell wall
      cy = cytoplasm

Note: Diagrams A, B, C, D, E and F are not drawn to the same scale.

Use the key to identify each of the cells. As you work through the key for each cell, tick the boxes in the table to show how you got your answer. Cell A has been done for you.

Key

1 (a) Cell with nucleus ....go to number 2
  (b) Cell without nucleus...**Red blood cell**
2 (a) Cell long and thin ....go to number 3
  (b) Cell not long and thin ....go to number 4
3 (a) Cell with many projections at each end ....**Nerve cell**
  (b) Cell with projection at one end ....**Sperm cell**
4 (a) Cell with nucleus more than
       half the size of the cell...**White blood cell**
  (b) Cell with nucleus less than
       half the size of the cell ....go to number 5
5 (a) Cell with cell wall ....**Plant palisade cell**
  (b) Cell without cell wall...**Cheek cell**

Key part used

Cell	1 (a)	1 (b)	2 (a)	2 (b)	3 (a)	3 (b)	4 (a)	4 (b)	5 (a)	5 (b)	*Name of cell*
A	✓			✓			✓				White blood cell
B											
C											
D											
E											
F											

(P)(5)

LEAG, Biology (Human), Paper 1, 1991

5 (a) The diagrams below show three cells A, B and C. The cells are not drawn to the same scale.

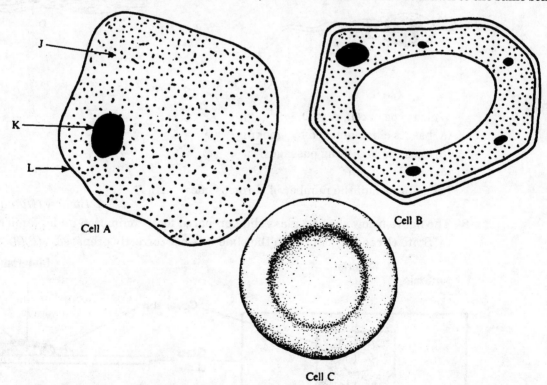

Cell A

Cell B

Cell C

  (i)   Name the parts labelled J, K and L. *(K)(3)*
  (ii) Which cell is a plant cell? *(K)(1)*
  (iii) Give **three** differences, that you can see in the diagrams, between cell B and cell C. *(K)(3)*

(b) Bone cells are round and have a central nucleus. Extending from the edge of the cell are branched strands of cytoplasm that are longer than the diameter of the cell.
  (i)   Use this information to draw a diagram of a bone cell. *(P)(3)*
  (ii) The heart is an organ with thick walls of muscle tissue and a space containing blood cells. Use this information to explain the difference between a cell, a tissue and an organ.*(K)(3)*

NISEAC, Biology (Human), Paper 2, 1991

6 Complete the table to show **two** important differences between a human epithelial cell and a leaf mesophyll cell.

	Human cell	*Leaf cell*
(i)		
(ii)		

(K)(4)
SEG, Biology (Human), 1991

7 The diagrams below show four types of human cell. (Not to scale)

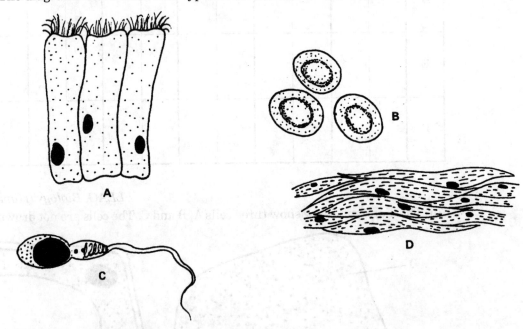

Which type of cell, A to D,
(a) has its cilia damaged by smoking?
(b) lines the breathing passages?
(c) carries oxygen?
(d) contains half the number of chromosomes? *(K)(4)*

NEA, Biology (Human), Paper 1, 1990

8 The figure below shows a glass slide prepared for examination under a microscope.
(a) State **three** ways in which the slide was not correctly prepared. *(P)(3)*

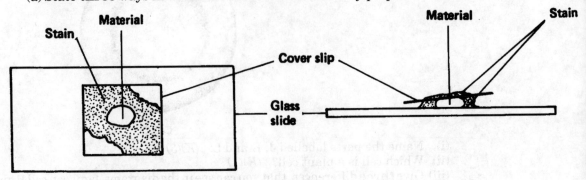

(b) When using a microscope, a student found a number of problems. Suggest a reason for each of the following problems.
(i)   Spots appeared in the field of view which moved when the eyepiece lens was turned.
(ii) Despite a good clean slide and clean microscope lenses, the view was blurred.
(iii) Only half the field of view was seen. *(P)(3)*

MEG, Biology (Human), Paper 5, 1991

9 The diagrams below show a leaf on a plant which was left in bright light for two days.

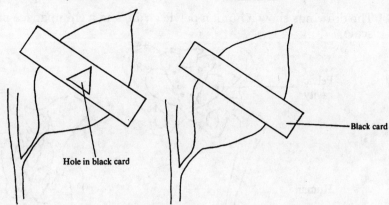

(a) (i) On the diagram below shade areas of the leaf which would contain starch after two days. *(K)(2)*

Top surface

(ii) Why was the card put on the bottom surface of the leaf? *(K)(1)*

(b) (i) Name the process in the leaf which makes starch. *(K)(1)*

(ii) Light is needed for starch to be made. Name **one** chemical which is also needed. *(K)(1)*

LEAG, Biology (Human), Paper 1, 1991

10 The diagrams show an experiment which was set up and the results.

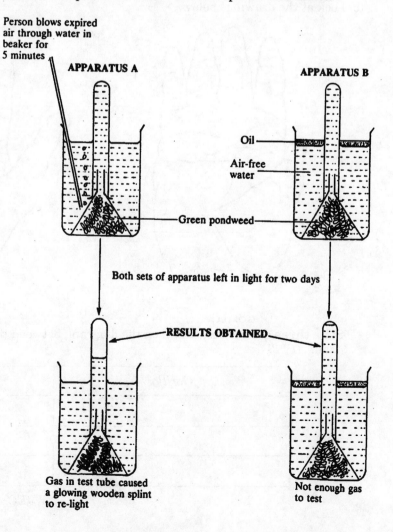

Suggest an explanation for the results obtained. *(K)(4)*

SEG, Biology (Human), Paper 1, 1990

11 The drawings show a human pelvic girdle and a chimpanzee pelvic girdle. They are drawn to scale

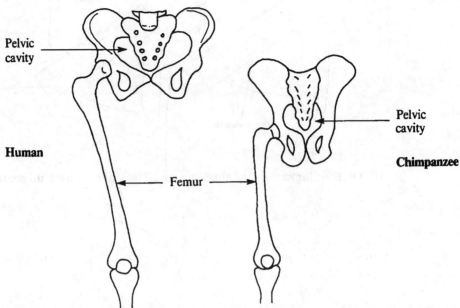

(a) (i) Make **two** observations on the difference between the human femur and the chimpanzee femur.

(ii) Make **one** observation on the difference between the human pelvic cavity and the chimpanzee pelvic cavity. *(P)(3)*

(b) Give **one** reason why man and the chimpanzee are classed as

(i) mammals,

(ii) primates. *(K)(2)*

(c) Look at the drawings below.

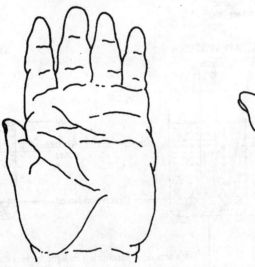

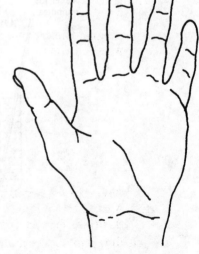

GORILLA   MAN

State **three** differences, shown on the diagram, between the gorilla's hand and the human hand. *(P)(3)*

	Gorilla	Man
(i)		
(ii)		
(iii)		

WJEC, Biology (Human), Paper 1, 1990

THEME 2 MAN AND HIS ENVIRONMENT

2.1 Interdependence

1 (a) The feeding relationship in a pond can be represented by the diagram below.

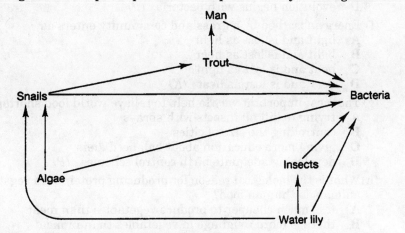

What is the name given to this feeding relationship?
A food web **B** food pyramid **C** consumer chain **D** food chain *(K)*

(b) Consider the feeding relationship represented below.

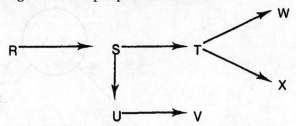

The letters represent organisms. Which of the following population changes in the other organisms would be most likely to directly result in an increase in the population of T?
A a decrease in the population of S
B a decrease in the population of U
C a decrease in the population of V
D a decrease in the population of W *(P)*

(c) The diagram below represents the passage of energy through a biological community. The arrows show the direction of movement of energy from one group of organisms to another.

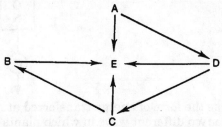

(i) Would green plants be represented by A, B, C or D? *(P)*
(ii) A collective name for the organisms represented by E is
    A producer **B** primary carnivore **C** decomposer **D** herbivore *(K)*

(d) The diagram below can be used to represent the numbers per unit area in a community. It shows that
A there are fewer herbivores than carnivores
B as food chains progress, fewer organisms are involved
C there are more animals than plants
D food chains always have four organisms in the chain *(P)*

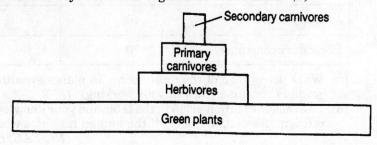

(e) The destruction of all bacteria would be catastrophic for all life on earth because
  A   bacteria are the hardest organisms to kill
  B   the organisms that feed on bacteria would starve
  C   soil nutrients would remain in undecayed organisms
  D   evolution begins with bacteria   *(P)*

(f) Energy absorbed by a grassland community enters as
  A   light and is lost as light
  B   light and is lost as heat
  C   heat and is lost as light
  D   heat and is lost as heat   *(K)*

(g) The most important way to help to relieve world food shortages is by
  A   trying to kill all insects with sprays
  B   controlling the size of cities
  C   giving more education about balanced diets
  D   developing adequate birth control schemes   *(P)*

(h) What is the biological reason for producing protein-rich vegetables in preference to rearing animals for human food?
  A   it is much cheaper to produce vegetables than meat
  B   there is more roughage in vegetables than in meat
  C   vegetables contain less fat than meat does
  D   less energy and fixed nitrogen are lost in producing vegetables   *(P)*

2   (a) The diagram below shows the transfer of energy through a simple food web.

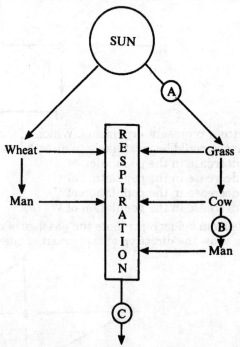

(i)   Name the form of energy transferred at A, B and C. *(K)(3)*
(ii) Give **two** different ways in which plants are adapted to ensure they receive sufficient light energy for photosynthesis. *(K)(2)*
(iii) Plant breeders have developed crop plants which can use a greater percentage of the sun's energy for photosynthesis. What are the advantages of developing such crop plants? *(K)(3)*

(b) The table below shows information about consumers and the food they eat.

Feeding type	% of energy extracted from food	% of energy extracted from food and then built into body tissue
Primary consumer	40	10
Secondary consumer	70	10

(i) What percentage of the total energy in plants eventually becomes body tissue of the primary consumer? (Show your working) *(P)(2)*
(ii) Use the information given in the table and your knowledge to explain why there is more efficient use of light energy if the human race eats wheat rather than meat. *(P)(4)*

NISEAC, Biology (Human), Paper 2, 1991

3 (a) The diagram below shows part of a pond ecosystem and the surrounding farmland.

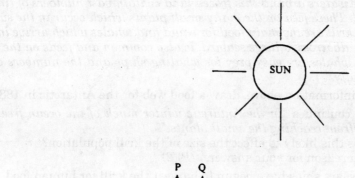

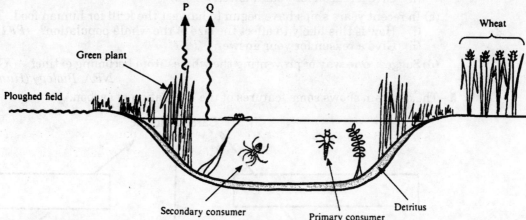

Green plant

Ploughed field

P   Q

Wheat

Secondary consumer

Primary consumer

Detritus

(i) From the diagram, use the correct words to complete the food chain. *(P)(1)*

Green plant	→		→	

(ii) Explain why green plants are called producers. *(K)(2)*

(b) A sample of water from the pond contained the following organisms (the organisms are not drawn to the same scale).

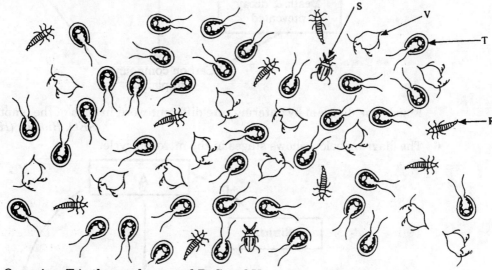

Organism T is the producer and R, S and V are consumers.
Complete the trophic levels for R, S and V.

Organism	What it feeds on	Trophic (feeding) level
R	V	
S	R	
T	███████	1st
V	T	

(P)(3)
NISEAC, Biology (Human), Paper 1, 1991

4 The following account is taken from the diary of a biologist on an Antarctic survey ship in 1885.

"The waters around this frozen land contain vast numbers of tiny shrimps known as krill. These feed on the many small plants which occur in the surface waters.
The krill are the main food for squid and whales which arrive in the summer to feed.
The albatross, a large seabird, is also common and feeds on the squid and krill.
The whales are easy prey for whaling ships and the numbers of whales are falling rapidly."

(a) From the information above, draw a food web for the Antarctic in 1885. *(P)(5)*

(b) The diary continues *"In the Antarctic winter much of the ocean freezes over and light is prevented from reaching the small plants."*
   (i)   How is this likely to affect the size of the krill population?
   (ii) Give a reason for your answer. *(P)(2)*

(c) In recent years ships have begun to harvest the krill for human food.
   (i)   How is this likely to affect the size of the whale population? *(P)(1)*
   (ii) Give a reason for your answer. *(P)(1)*

(d) Suggest **one** way of preventing the whales from becoming extinct. *(K)(1)*

NEA, Biology (Human), Paper 1, 1990

5 The diagram shows some features of the circulation of carbon.

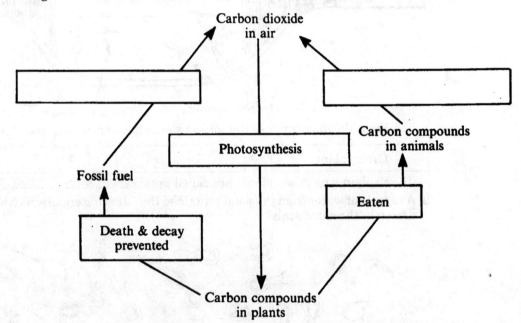

Finish this diagram by entering **one** different word in each of the empty boxes. *(K)(2)*

SEG, Biology (Human), Paper 1, 1991

6 The diagram below shows stages in the nitrogen cycle.

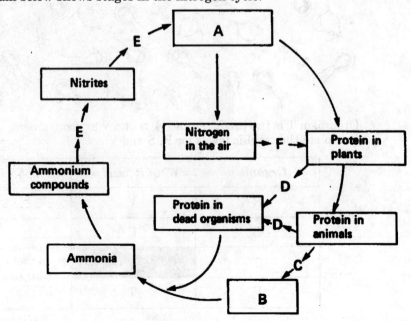

(a) Name the substances A and B. *(K)(2)*

(b) Name the processes C and D. *(K)(2)*

(c) Name the type (**not** names) of bacteria which carry out the processes at E and F. *(K)(2)*

NEA, Biology (Human), Paper 1, 1991

7 The diagram below shows apparatus which could be used to study the process by which bacteria turn wine into vinegar.

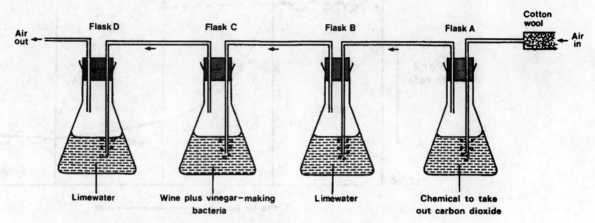

(a)(i) Why was the cotton wool used? *(P)(1)*

(ii) What will happen to the pH of the liquid in flask C? *(P)(1)*

(iii) Why does air have to be passed through flask C? *(P)(1)*

(iv) After a few days the limewater in flask B was still clear but the limewater in flask D was cloudy (milky white). Explain both of these results. *(K)(2)*

(v) Suggest another way in which the air in flask D is different from the air in flask B. Give a reason for your answer. *(K)(2)*

(b) The diagram below shows the type of apparatus used in industry to make large amounts of vinegar.

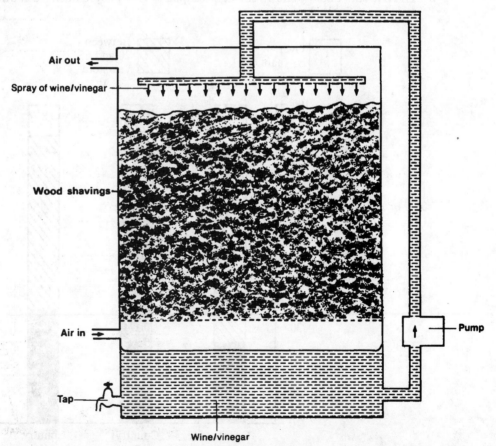

(i) Where in the apparatus will there be most vinegar-making bacteria? *(K)(1)*

(ii) Suggest why the wine/vinegar is pumped back to the top. *(K)(1)*

(iii) What is the advantage of having wood shavings for the liquid to pass over? *(K)(2)*

(iv) Apart from taste and smell, how could you test the vinegar to see if it was ready for use? *(K)(1)*

LEAG, Biology (Human), Paper 2, 1990

8   The graph below shows a pattern of population change.

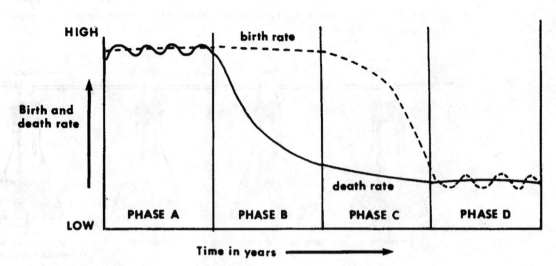

(a) Describe what happens in phase A to
    (i)   the birth rate,
    (ii) the death rate.   *(P)(3)*

(b) In which of the phases A–D is it **most** likely that a government birth control programme was introduced?   *(P)(1)*

(c) In phase B, are numbers in the population likely to be increasing, decreasing or stable?
                                                                                    (P)(1)
                                                WJEC, Biology (Human), Paper 1, 1990

9   The bar chart below shows the age composition of people in three countries. Three age groups are shown for each country.

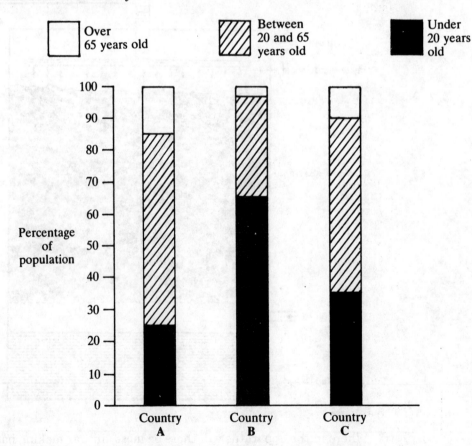

(a) Which country is most likely to have the least developed birth control? Explain the reason for your answer.   *(P)(2)*

(b) Which country is most likely to have a well developed medical service in which all patients receive proper treatment for any disease? Explain the reason for your answer.   *(P)(2)*
                                                SEG, Biology (Human), Paper 1, 1990

10 Below is a graph of the world's population since 3 000 BC.

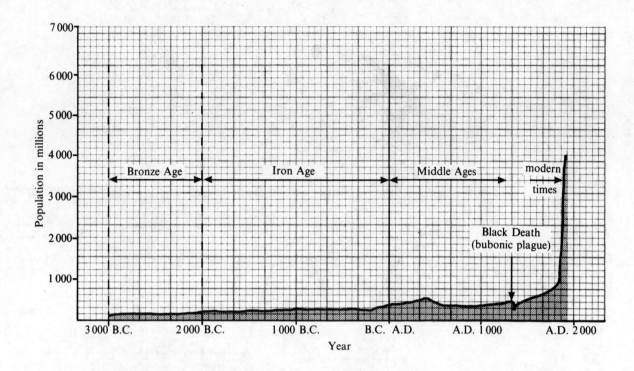

(a) Extend the graph to determine the world's population by the year 2 000 AD. *(P)(1)*

(b) Give **three** reasons for the growth in human population during the last 500 years. *(K)(3)*

(c) Name **three** different ways in which the rate of growth of the world's population might be kept in check. *(K)(3)*

NISEAC, Biology (Human), Paper 3, 1990

2.2 Disease

1 (a) After having a disease such as mumps, a person is likely to have acquired:
   A artificial immunity
   B passive immunity
   C natural immunity
   D active immunity *(K)*

(b) The use of an insecticide is most likely to reduce the number of people suffering from:
   A athlete's foot   **B** rabies   **C** diabetes   **D** malaria *(K)*

(c) Penicillin is no longer effective against some infectious diseases caused by bacteria because:
   A these diseases have been totally eliminated
   B some people are allergic to penicillin
   C the bacteria have developed resistant strains
   D there are new antibiotics to combat these diseases *(K)*

(d) The incubation period of an infectious illness follows soon after:
   A the formation of antibodies in the blood
   B the quarantine period of the illness
   C development of a high temperature
   D entry of the infective organism into the body *(K)*

(e) Dysentery and food poisoning may be spread by houseflies that land on food after they have:
   A walked over open wounds on the body
   B been sprayed with insecticides
   C settled on human faeces
   D sucked blood from an infected person *(K)*

(f) The antibiotic effect of penicillin was first discovered by
   A Jenner   **B** Lister   **C** Pasteur   **D** Fleming *(K)*

2 A person developed a severe throat infection. The doctor prescribed a course of penicillin and also sent a throat swab sample to a laboratory where the sequence of events in the flow diagram overleaf was followed.

(a) Measure the **diameter** of the clear areas surrounding each disc. *(P)(5)*

(b) In view of the results which antibiotic was the most effective? *(P)(1)*

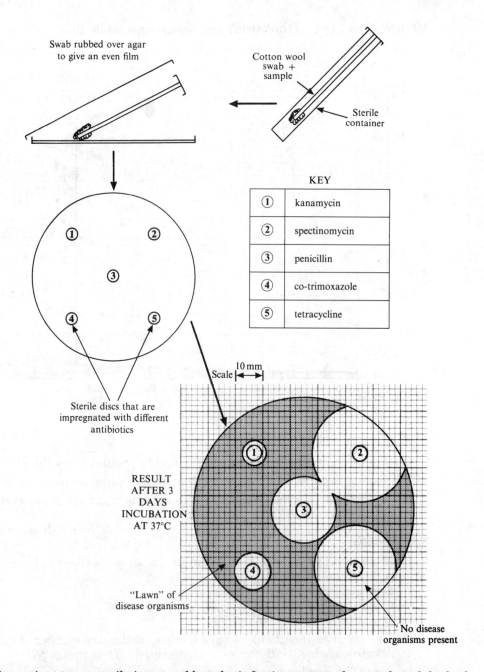

KEY

①	kanamycin
②	spectinomycin
③	penicillin
④	co-trimoxazole
⑤	tetracycline

RESULT AFTER 3 DAYS INCUBATION AT 37°C

"Lawn" of disease organisms

No disease organisms present

(c) The patient temporarily improved but the infection returned, even though he had not been exposed to reinfection. The same laboratory test was repeated and the results are shown below.

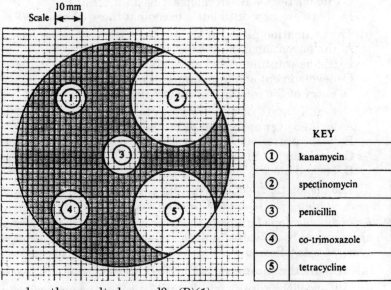

KEY

①	kanamycin
②	spectinomycin
③	penicillin
④	co-trimoxazole
⑤	tetracycline

In what way has the result changed?   *(P)(1)*

(d) Give an explanation that could account for this change in result. *(K)(2)*

(e) What treatment would you now recommend for the patient? Give **one** reason for your recommendation. *(K)(2)*

NISEAC, Biology (Human), Paper 3, 1990

3 The following questions are about organisms which are either harmful or helpful to humans.

(a) Complete the table below by selecting answers from the bottom of each column. *(K)(4)*

Disease	Organism	Transmission
Malaria		
	Bacteria	
Influenza Typhoid Herpes Athlete's foot	Fungus Protozoan Mosquito Virus	By a vector On food In water During sexual intercourse

(b) Give **one** reason why locusts are described as pests. *(K)(1)*

(c) Describe **two** ways in which bees are useful to humans. *(K)(2)*

(d) Explain how bacteria are useful in each of the following:
   (i)   sewage disposal, *(K)(2)*
   (ii) nitrogen cycle. *(K)(2)*

LEAG, Biology (Human), Paper 1, 1990

4 The diagram below shows two different responses, A and B, of human blood cells to the presence of a bacterium in the blood.

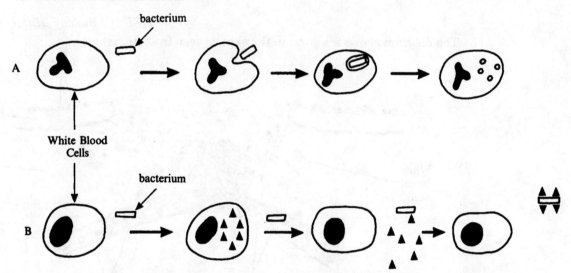

(a) Describe how each of the two responses, A and B, prevent infection. *(P)(4)*

(b) The graph overleaf shows the levels of diphtheria antibodies in blood following injections to promote active immunity to the disease.
   (i)   What was injected into the patient to promote active immunity? *(K)(1)*
   (ii) What is the difference between active and passive immunity? *(K)(2)*
   (iii) How did the body's response to the second injection differ from the response to the first injection?
         Suggest **one** reason for this difference. *(P)(2)*
   (iv) From the start of the treatment, how many days passed before the patient became immune to diphtheria? *(P)(1)*
   (v)   Hospital treatment for a bad cut includes an injection to promote passive immunity to tetanus. Explain why this injection is given rather than one to promote active immunity.
         (K)(2)

(c) Sometimes when a kidney is transplanted into the body of a patient the operation fails due to tissue rejection.
   (i)   What is tissue rejection? *(K)(1)*
   (ii) Explain why rejection occurs. *(K)(2)*

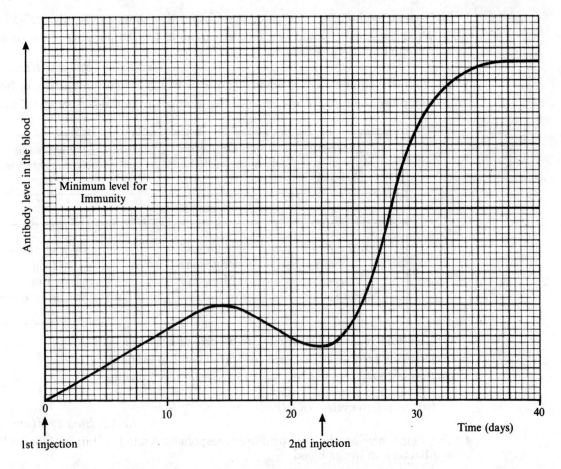

NISEAC, Biology (Human), Paper 2, 1991

5 The diagram shows a wound in the skin as seen in sectional view.

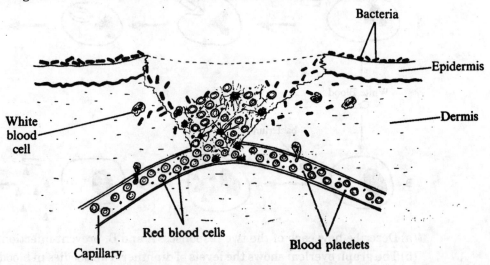

Briefly describe what this diagram shows about the way the body defends itself against the entry of bacteria. Only use information visible in the diagram. *(P)(5)*

SEG, Biology (Human), Paper 1, 1991

6 (a) The threadworm is a common parasite in children. Some events in its life cycle are shown in the diagram.
   (i) Why is the threadworm called a parasite? *(K)(2)*
   (ii) Use the information in the diagram to help identify two precautions which should be taken to avoid re-infection by worms. *(P)(2)*
   (iii) The worms can be killed by taking medicine. Why should other members of the family take the medicine as well as the infected child? *(K)(1)*
   (iv) The skin around the anus of a person with threadworms is often itchy. Scratching the area can break the surface of the skin and cause bleeding. How might this action lead to infection by bacteria? *(K)(2)*

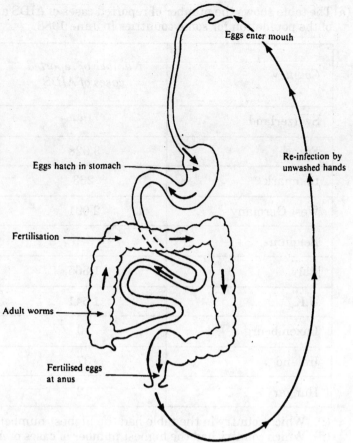

(b) Headlice are parasites found in hair.
   (i)   Give **two** signs that show a person has headlice. *(K)(2)*
   (ii) Give **one** way in which headlice are adapted to life in hair. *(K)(1)*
   (iii) Explain **one** method used to control headlice. State the method and give an explanation.
                                                                          (K)(2)

7 The data below show the ten leading causes of death in the USA in 1900 and in the 1980s.

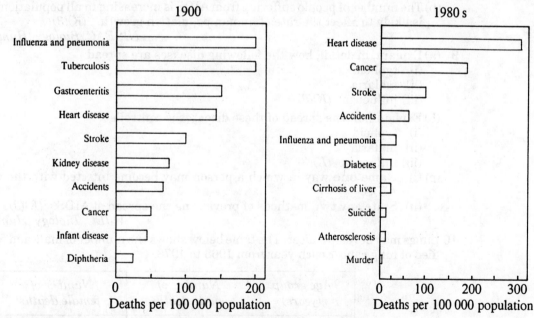

(a) State which causes of death appear on both occasions. *(P)(1)*

(b) Heart disease in the 1980s is the major cause of death. Calculate by how much it has changed since 1900. *(P)(1)*

(c) What is the approximate total number of deaths in 1900 from the **top three** causes? *(P)(1)*

(d) Calculate the percentage of deaths from heart disease and stroke together in the 1980s.
                                                                          (P)(2)

(e) Suggest why tuberculosis and diphtheria no longer appear in the 1980s 'top ten'. *(K)(1)*

(f) Suggest why diabetes now appears in the 1980s 'top ten'. *(K)(1)*

                                              WJEC, Biology (Human), Paper 1, 1991

8 (a) The table shows the number of reported cases of AIDS and the number of cases per million of the population for some countries in June 1988.

Country	Number of reported cases of AIDS	Number of cases per million of the population
Switzerland	439	67
France	3 628	65
Denmark	263	52
West Germany	2 091	34
Belgium	340	34
Italy	1 865	32
U.K.	1 541	27
Luxembourg	10	25
Ireland	37	11
Hungary	12	1

(i)   Which country in the table had the highest number of reported cases of AIDS? *(P)(1)*
(ii) Which country had the highest number of cases of AIDS per million of the population? *(P)(1)*
(iii) Are the answers to (a)(i) and (a)(ii) the same? Explain your answer. *(P)(2)*
(iv) A prediction that there would be 3 000 cases of AIDS in the UK by June 1988 did not come true. Suggest **two** reasons for this. *(K)(2)*
(v) What do the initials AIDS stand for? *(K)(2)*
(vi) What type of organism causes AIDS? *(K)(1)*

(b) The number of people suffering from AIDS is increasing in all populations. Explain how this is likely to affect the rate of human population growth. *(K)(3)*

NISEAC, Biology (Human), Paper 2, 1990

9 (a) Explain, in detail, how the following diseases are spread:
(i)   typhoid
(ii) malaria
(iii) influenza *(K)(6)*

(b) Explain how the spread of these diseases is controlled:
(i)   typhoid
(ii) malaria
(iii) influenza *(K)(3)*

(c) (i) Name **one** way in which a person may become infected with the virus which causes AIDS.
(ii) State any **two** methods of preventing the spread of AIDS. *(K)(3)*

WJEC, Biology (Human), Paper 1, 1990

10 Lungs may develop cancer. The table below shows the number of male and female humans who died of lung cancer each year from 1968 to 1978.

Age group (years)	Number of male deaths	Number of female deaths
1-4	12	6
5-24	85	34
25-44	4 300	1 700
45-64	107 000	27 000
Over 65	162 000	39 000

(a) Which sex is most affected by lung cancer? *(P)(1)*

(b) Which age group has the greatest annual death rate? *(P)(1)*

(c) What is the ratio of deaths between males and females for the 1–4 year age group? *(P)(1)*

(d) Explain why children of 1–4 years of age develop lung cancer. *(K)(2)*

NISEAC, Biology (Human), Paper 1, 1990

11 The diagram below shows the percentage of people who die each year in Britain from various causes.

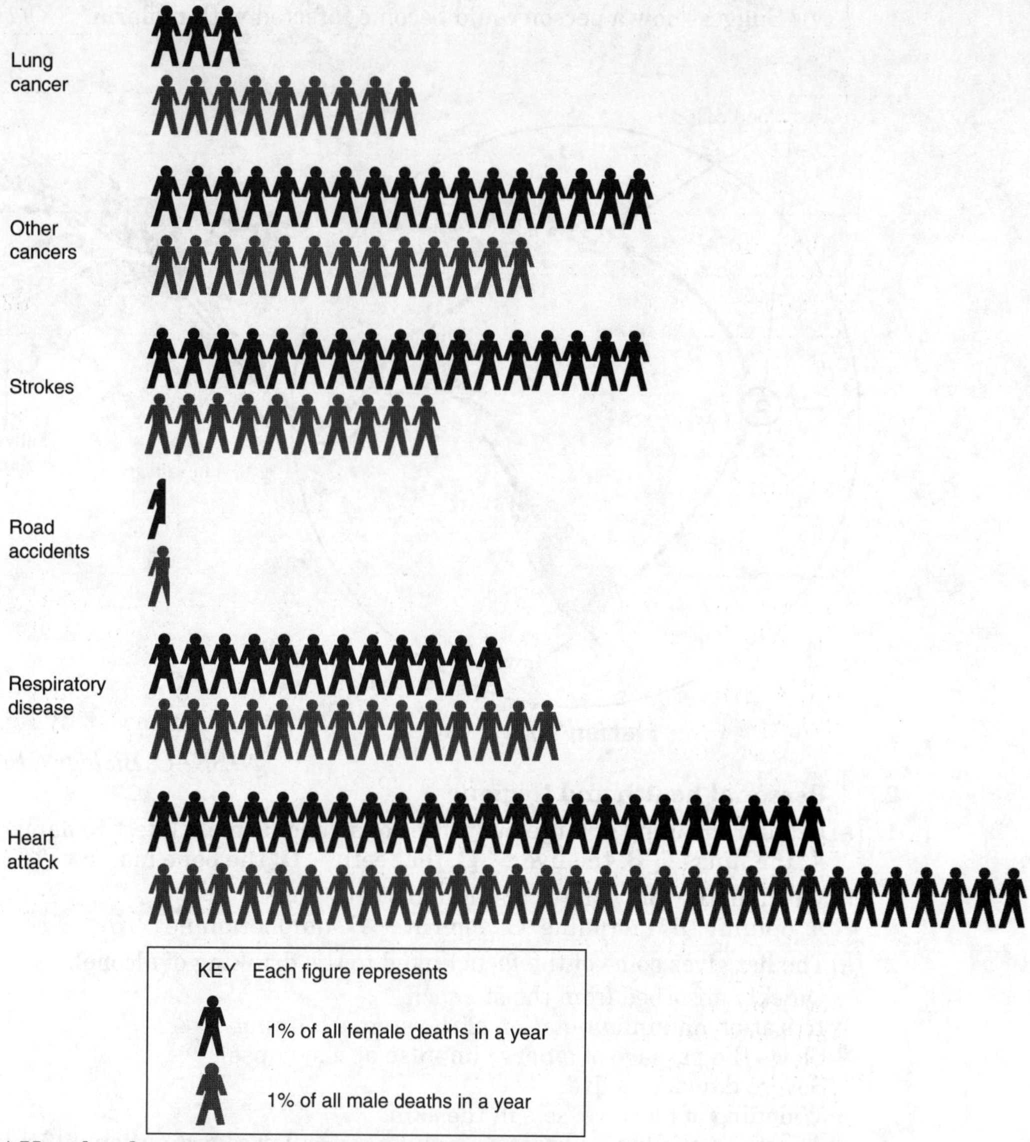

(a) Use the chart to answer the following questions.

   (i)   What is the commonest cause of death in females? *(P)(1)*

   (ii) What percentage of males die from lung cancer? *(P)(1)*

(b) Suggest **one** reason why more men than women die from lung cancer. *(K)(1)*

(c) Which part of a balanced diet helps to prevent cancer of the bowel (large intestine)? *(K)(1)*

NEA, Biology (Human), Paper 1, 1990

12 (a) Complete the table using the words from the list below.

       Bacterium   Fungus   German measles   Protozoan   *Rubella*   *Salmonella*

Type of organism	*Name of organism*	*Disease caused*
	Trichophyton	Athlete's foot
	Plasmodium	Malaria
		Food poisoning
Virus		

(K)(6)

(b) The diagram below shows a simplified life cycle for the malarial parasite. Different stages are labelled A, B, C, D and E. Use the information in the diagram to help you answer the following questions.

(i) Which state, A, B, C, D or E, in the life cycle of the parasite, passes from the insect into man? *(P)(1)*

(ii) Name the type of insect that transmits malaria. *(K)(1)*

(iii) What happens to the parasite between stage C and stage D? *(K)(1)*

(iv) Suggest how the parasite gets from B to C in the human body. *(K)(1)*

(v) Suggest how a person could become infected with malaria. *(K)(1)*

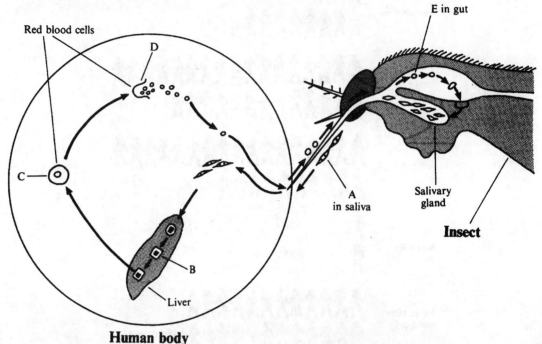

NISEAC, Biology (Human), Paper 1, 1990

2.3   Personal health and hygiene

1 (a) Regular drinking of large quantities of alcohol is most likely to damage
   A the lungs   **B** the liver   **C** the teeth   **D** the bone marrow   *(K)*

(b) Which of the following is a stimulant drug?
   A opium   **B** morphine   **C** aspirin   **D** amphetamine   *(K)*

2 (a) The list gives some of the facts linked to the drinking of alcohol.

Quickly absorbed from the stomach
Irritation and inflammation of the stomach lining
Slows the passage of a nerve impulse at a synapse
Severe damage to liver
Widening of blood vessels in the skin
Affects cerebellum of brain so making muscular co-ordination difficult
Affects cerebrum so changing behaviour
Protein or vitamin malnutrition

Use some of the information in this list to explain why a person who has drunk too much alcohol is unsafe to drive a car. *(P)(3)*

(b) Give **one** serious effect which the overuse of antibiotics as a medicine can have on a person.
(K)(1)

SEG, Biology (Human), Paper 1, 1990

3 The drawings below show different postures.

A

B

(a)(i) Which diagram, A or B, shows the correct way of picking up a heavy load?

   (ii) Give **one** reason for your answer. *(K)(2)*

(b) This drawing shows a man with bad posture.

Give **two** ways in which he is standing badly. *(K)(2)*

WJEC, Biology (Human), Paper 1, 1991

4 (a) Many different substances are used as additives to food for purposes such as flavouring, preserving, colouring and preventing oxidation. These additives are shown on the label on the product. They are often shown as a letter E followed by a number.

The list below shows some E numbers which are used as food additives. The name of each is also given. Which **one** of them would you expect to be used as a preservative?

Briefly explain the reason for your choice.

    E122 (carmosine)   E406 (agar)

    E280 (proprionic acid)   E440 (pectin) *(K)(3)*

(b)(i) Name **one** food which can be preserved by the addition of large amounts of sugar.

   (ii) Explain why this food will stay in a fresh condition for several weeks even after the container has been opened to the air. *(K)(4)*

(c) Milk can be preserved by pasteurisation (heated to 80 °C for 30 seconds) or by ultra-heat treatment (heated to 132 °C for 1 minute). The following experiment was done to compare the effectiveness of these two methods of preservation. The milk which was placed in the three test tubes was one day old.

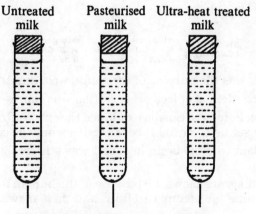

Equal amount of blue indicator dye added to each tube. Dye becomes colourless when oxygen is absent.

The results were:

Time from start of experiment (hours)	Colour of milk		
	Untreated milk	*Pasteurised milk*	*Ultra-heat treated milk*
0	blue	blue	blue
1	white	blue	blue
3	white	white	blue

(i) Untreated milk contains micro-organisms. Explain as fully as possible the results produced by this experiment.

(ii) Which is the most effective treatment for preserving milk? *(K)(6)*

(d) In some places which sell read-to-eat food, items such as meat pies are often kept for long periods in a heated display cabinet ready to serve. Suggest **one** possible danger for a person eating such food. *(K)(2)*

SEG, Biology (Human), Paper 1, 1991

5 Peter and Susilla carried out an investigation to compare different methods of food preservation. They prepared a meat broth by dissolving a meat extract in water.
The broth was divided equally and placed into three sterile test tubes and treated as shown. They were then sealed with sterile cotton wool and tinfoil, and stored as shown in the diagram below.

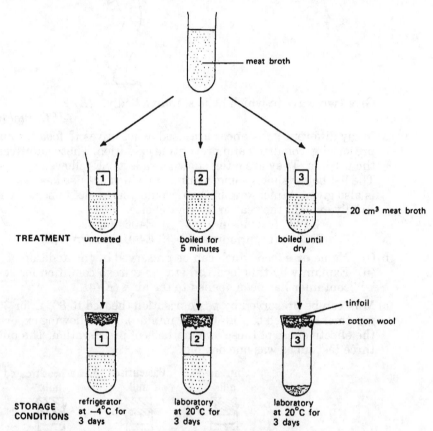

(a) What was the purpose of the cotton wool and the tinfoil? *(P)(1)*

(b) Which method of food preservation was represented by tube 2? *(K)(1)*

(c) When Peter and Susilla examined the tubes after three days, they realised that they should have set up a control tube. Describe what the control tube should have been. *(P)(3)*

(d) Explain why the broth in tube 1 was still fresh after three days. *(K)(1)*

NEA, Biology (Human), Paper 1, 1990

6 (a) The diagram shows the position of the human foot bones whilst wearing high-heeled shoes. Examine the picture carefully, and then answer the questions that follow.

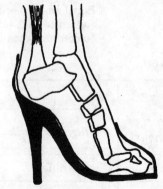

(i) Suggest **two** ways in which high-heeled shoes can damage the feet. *(K)(2)*

(ii) What damage can wearing high-heels cause to the wearer's body other than to the feet?
  (K)(2)

(iii) Why is it important for young children to wear shoes that fit correctly? *(K)(2)*

(b) When lifting a heavy object, the back should be kept as straight as possible. This can be achieved by bending the knees, grasping the object firmly and straightening the legs. Explain how a failure to do this can damage the vertebral column and spinal cord. *(K)(3)*

SEG, Biology (Human), Paper 3, 1990

7 In the first few weeks after birth babies are fed mainly on milk.
The table below shows the concentration of some of the nutrients found in human milk and in cows' milk.

Nutrient	*Concentration (g per 100 g milk)*	
	Human milk	*Cows' milk*
Protein	1.25	3.50
Milk sugar	7.50	4.50
Fat	3.50	4.00
Water	87.00	87.00

(a) Suggest **one** way in which cows' milk could be changed to make it more similar to human milk. *(P)(1)*

(b) Milk does not contain much vitamin C. Suggest **one** way in which young babies could easily be given extra vitamin C. *(K)(1)*

(c) Explain why babies fed on human milk suffer from fewer infections than babies fed on bottled milk. *(K)(2)*

(d) Give **two** other reasons why breast milk is better than bottled milk for feeding a young baby. *(K)(2)*

NEA, Biology (Human), Paper P, 1990

8 The diagram shows the effect of different temperatures on bacteria.

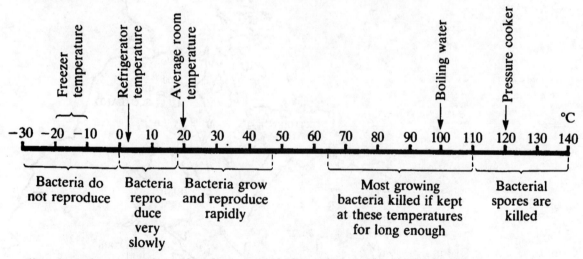

Use the information from this diagram to help explain each of the following.

(a) Milk which has been pasteurised (heated to about 70 °C) stays fresh for a few days but eventually goes sour. *(P)(2)*

(b) UHT milk has been heated to 135 °C. It remains drinkable for a very long time. *(P)(2)*

(c) A freezer preserves food for much longer than a refrigerator. *(P)(2)*

SEG, Biology (Human), Paper 1, 1990

Theme 2.4 Public health

1 (a) Which of the following processes is not necessary in the purification of water for drinking purposes?
A filtration **B** sedimentation   **C** fluoridation   **D** chlorination *(K)*

(b) Which of the following breaks down organic matter in sewage?
A chlorine   **B** viruses   **C** oxygen   **D** bacteria *(K)*

(c) The purpose of the U-bend in a toilet is:
A to prevent rats climbing up from the sewers
B to prevent bacteria from entering the sewers
C to stop unpleasant smells rising from the sewers
D to keep the pipes lubricated *(K)*

(d) Which of the following does the National Health Service pride free to *all* adults?
   A spectacles
   B false teeth
   C vaccination against influenza
   D hospital treatment for illness   *(K)*

(e) If you wanted to reduce the long-term unsightliness of a refuse dump, which of the following would you be most keen to prevent being dumped?
   A wooden and cardboard boxes
   B tins and plastic containers
   C sheets of newspaper and magazines
   D tree prunings and hedge trimmings   *(K)*

(f) The activated sludge process is a method of:
   A sewage treatment
   B water purification
   C refuse disposal
   D land drainage   *(K)*

2 (a) The map below shows the discharge of two chemical pollutants into the Irish Sea.
   (i)   What is the total annual discharge of mercury into the Irish Sea?   *(P)(1)*
   (ii) Give **one** problem caused by the discharge of mercury into water.   *(K)(1)*

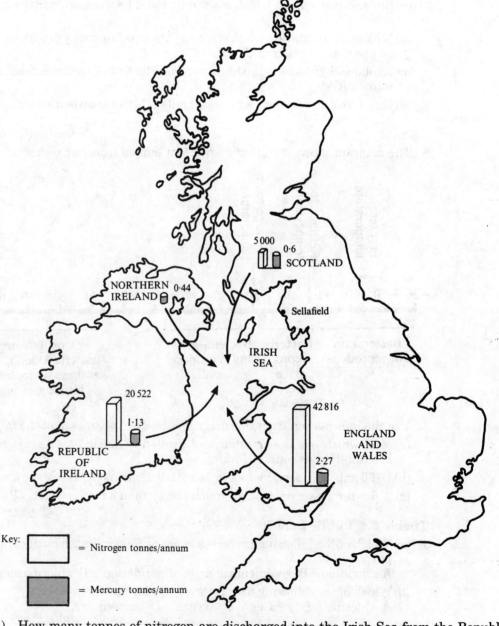

5 000   0·6   SCOTLAND

NORTHERN IRELAND   0·44

Sellafield

IRISH SEA

20 522   1·13

42 816

REPUBLIC OF IRELAND

ENGLAND AND WALES   2·27

Key:
☐ = Nitrogen tonnes/annum
▦ = Mercury tonnes/annum

(b) (i)   How many tonnes of nitrogen are discharged into the Irish Sea from the Republic of Ireland?   *(P)(1)*
   (ii) What is the main source of nitrogen pollution?   *(K)(1)*
   (iii) Suggest **two** ways of reducing this pollution.   *(K)(2)*

(c) Below is a chart showing the radioactive liquid discharge from the Sellafield nuclear reprocessing plant between 1975 and 1985.

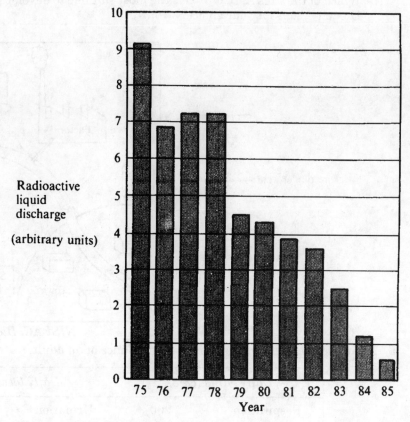

(i) Describe the trend in discharges from 1979 to 1985. *(P)(2)*

(ii) How many times greater was the radioactive liquid discharged in 1979 than in 1985? (Show your working) *(P)(2)*

(iii) What is the mean discharge per annum of radioactive liquid from 1979 to 1982 inclusive? *(P)(1)*

(iv) Give **two** effects of radioactive waste on the environment. *(K)(2)*

(v) Give **two** ways of disposing of radioactive waste. *(K)(2)*

NISEAC, Biology (Human), Paper 2, 1991

3 The diagram shows stages in the treatment of sewage.

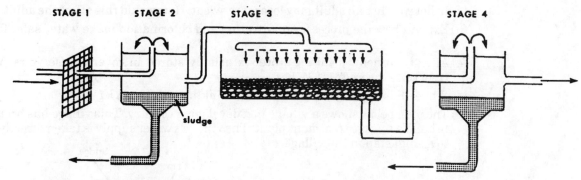

(a) Water is the main component of sewage. Name **two** other substances found in sewage. *(K)(1)*

(b) Explain what happens in Stage 1. *(K)(1)*

(c) To what use can the sludge be put in Stage 2? *(K)(1)*

(d) Explain fully how the sewage is treated in Stage 3. *(K)(3)*

WJEC, Biology (Human), Paper 1, 1990

4 (a) The list below includes substances that occur naturally:

timber   water   coal   oil   metal ores

(i) List **three** which are used as fuels. *(K)(1)*

(ii) Name **one** of these substances which man will eventually use up. *(K)(1)*

(iii) Name **two** air pollutants that are formed when coal or oil is burnt. *(K)(2)*

(iv) Explain how acid rain is formed. *(K)(2)*

(v) Give **two** effects of acid rain on the environment. *(K)(2)*

(b) The map below shows part of a town and the surrounding area. The parts shown are not drawn to the same scale.
Which of the sites A, B, C or D is the most suitable to develop as a new housing estate? Give **three** reasons for your choice. *(P)(3)*

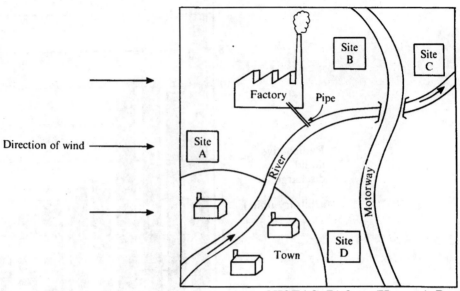

Direction of wind

NISEAC, Biology (Human), Paper 1, 1990

5 The table below shows the daily water balance of an adult.

Daily gains (cm3)		Daily losses (cm3)	
Respiration	200	Urination	1500
Food and drink	2300	Breathing	500
		Sweating	300
		Egestion (Defaecation)	200

(a) Work out how much water an adult loses in a day. *(P)(1)*

(b) If more water was taken in with food and drink, which one of the daily losses would increase? *(P)(1)*

(c) In hot weather an adult may lose more sweat. How would this affect the adult's urine? *(P)(1)*

(d) Explain how the processes of filtration and chlorination make water safer for drinking. *(K)(2)*

(e) After treatment, drinking water is usually stored in covered reservoirs. Why are these reservoirs covered? *(K)(1)*

(f) Why is fluoride sometimes added to drinking water? *(K)(1)*

(g) The plan below shows a village in a developing country. This village has been given a grant to build a sewage treatment plant. The village's water supply is taken directly from the river to a single tap in the village.

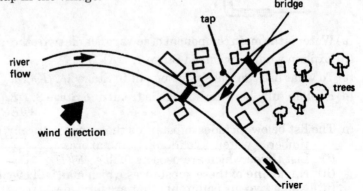

(i) Mark with a letter S on the plan a place on the river where it would be safe to build a sewage treatment plant. *(P)(1)*

(ii) Explain your answer. *(P)(2)*

NEA, Biology (Human), Paper Q, 1990

6 Since about 1850 there has been a very large increase in the world human population. Briefly suggest how each of the following has helped to cause this increase in the number of people in the world.

(a) The use of chlorine in treating drinking water. *(K)(2)*

(b) The 'green revolution' in agriculture with the use of fertilisers and carefully selected plants and farm animals producing high yields. *(K)(3)*

SEG, Biology (Human), Paper 1, 1990

7 Read through this recent newspaper article and answer the questions below.

River of Stinking Shame

From its source in the giant mountains of Czechoslovakia to its mouth in the North Sea, the River Elbe is an environmental disaster. Years of industrial pollution have left the Elbe ecologically dead, with the lowest concentration of oxygen in any of the nine major rivers running into the North Sea. In Czechoslovakia it picks up huge quantities of nitrates from artificial fertilisers used in farming. Chlorine pours in as it flows through East Germany's heartland and 27 tonnes of mercury are dumped each year. By the time the river reaches the sea, it is releasing annually about 182 tonnes of copper, 219 tonnes of lead, 1 835 tonnes of zinc, 12 000 tonnes of phosphates and 150 000 tonnes of ammonium salts.

(a) State how much mercury is dumped per year. *(P)(1)*

(b) Write down **eight** different pollutants deposited in the River Elbe. *(P)(2)*

(c) Why should artificial fertilisers contain nitrates? *(K)(1)*

(d) Explain what 'ecologically dead' means, and how the river has become ecologically dead. *(K)(2)*

WJEC, Biology (Human), Paper 2, 1991

THEME 3 HUMAN STRUCTURE AND FUNCTION

3.1 The skeleton and movement

1 (a) Cartilage in a synovial joint serves to:
   A give the body its shape
   B protect the muscles at the joint
   C reduce friction
   D allow for extra movement *(K)*

(b) In which of the following parts of the body is a hinge joint found?
   A the shoulder   B the knee   C the hip   D the skull *(K)*

(c) The structures which attach muscles to bones are called:
   A tendons   B nerves   C ligaments   D cartilages *(K)*

(d) When we chew, the lower jaw is moved by the contraction of muscles. These muscles are:
   A circular   B smooth   C radial   D voluntary *(K)*

(e) Which type of joint allows movement in more than one plane?
   A hinge   B gliding   C ball and socket   D saddle *(K)*

(f) When the arm is flexed:
   A the biceps relaxes and the triceps expands
   B the biceps expands and the triceps relaxes
   C the biceps expands and the triceps contracts
   D the biceps contracts and the triceps relaxes *(P)*

2 (a) The diagram below shows an elbow joint.

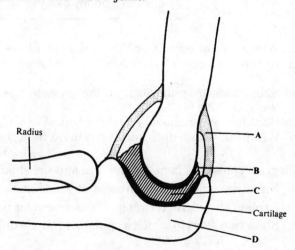

   (i) Name the parts A, B, C and D. *(K)(4)*

(ii) Name **two** features of the joint which reduce friction. *(K)(2)*

(iii) Explain how muscles cause the arm to bend at the elbow. *(K)(3)*

(iv) What is the function of ligaments? *(K)(1)*

(b) As a result of age, calcium is withdrawn from bones.

Equal lengths of young adult bone and older adult bone were put into dilute acid for 1, 2 or 3 days.

Identical lengths of young adult and older adult bone were put into water.

The pieces of bone were then clamped to a bench and a 2 kg mass was tied to each free end.

The drawings below show what happened but are **not** in the correct order.

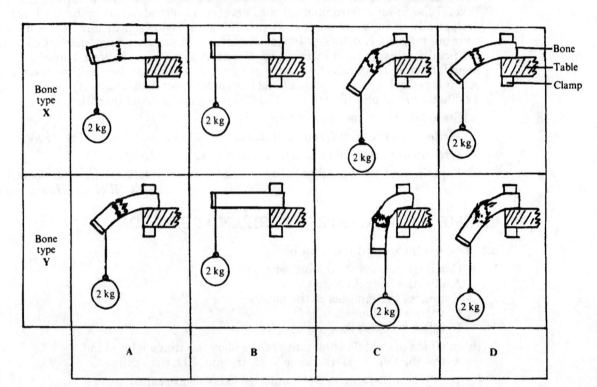

(i) Copy the key below on to your answer paper. Put the correct letter, A, B, C or D, for each pair of diagrams into the key.

Key	Letter
Controls	
Bones in acid for 1 day	
Bones in acid for 2 days	
Bones in acid for 3 days	

(P)(4)

(ii) Which type of bone, X or Y, was the older bone? Give a reason for your answer. *(P)(2)*

(iii) Give **one** reason why the bones did not break completely after being placed in acid. *(K)(1)*

(iv) Substances are removed from the bones by the acid. Name **one** substance removed by the acid. *(K)(1)*

(v) How does this removal affect the bones? *(K)(1)*

(vi) Which substance does burning remove from the bone? *(K)(1)*

LEAG, Biology (Human), Paper 3, 1990

3 The diagram shows the bones of the arm and the shoulder joint.

(a) (i) Name the types of joint present at X and at Y. *(K)(2)*

(ii) Explain why a greater range of movements is possible at joint X than at joint Y. *(K)(4)*

(b) (i) State **two** ways in which a sphincter muscle differs from a skeletal muscle, such as the biceps. *(K)(2)*

(ii) Identify, as exactly as possible, the position of **one** sphincter muscle in the body. *(K)(1)*

(iii) What is the function of the sphincter muscle you have identified? *(K)(1)*

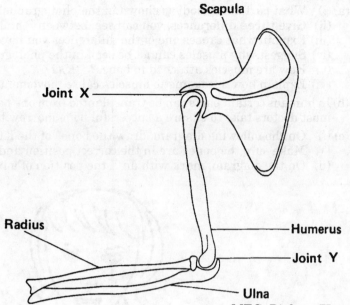

MEG, Biology (Human), Paper 3, 1990

4 Label the parts A, B, C and D on the diagram of the synovial joint. *(K)(5)*

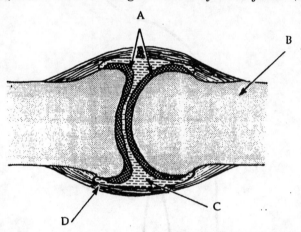

WJEC, Biology (Human), Paper 1, 1991

5 The X-ray photograph P shows part of the limb of a child. Photograph Q shows the same part of an adult limb.

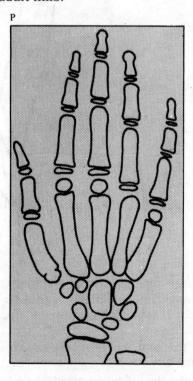

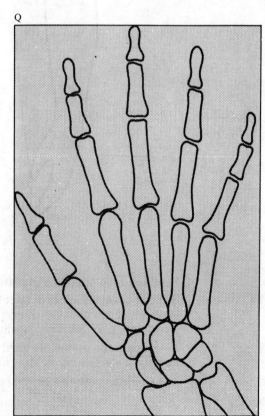

(a) (i)   What part of the body is shown in the photographs? *(K)(1)*
    (ii) Give **three** differences, you can see, between P and Q. *(P)(3)*
    (iii) Explain what causes one of the differences you have noted. *(K)(2)*
    (iv) Suggest why muscles cannot be seen in the photographs. *(K)(1)*
    (v)   How are muscles attached to bones? *(K)(1)*
    (vi) Explain how antagonistic muscles cause movement. *(K)(3)*

(b) In humans certain parts can be transplanted from one person to another. What precautions
    must doctors take to ensure a successful bone marrow transplant? *(K)(2)*

(c) (i)   On the following diagram, draw the bones of the left arm.
          Make sure the bones are in the correct position and are in proportion. *(K)(3)*
    (ii) On the diagram, mark with an X the position of a ball and socket joint. *(K)(1)*

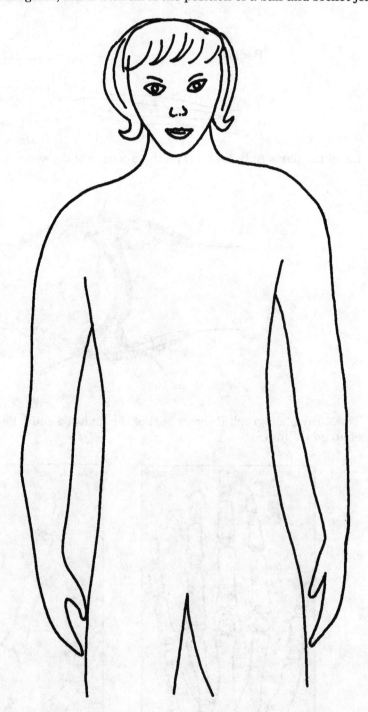

(d) Read the following paragraphs.

Some years ago doctors did not like performing joint replacement operations on people under
50 years of age because the replacement only lasted 15 years. Today, age is not considered
a restriction for joint replacement.

In the past the materials used for the joint replacements have been heavy, solid steels but
now light steels and plastics are used.

Use the information above to answer the following questions.

(i) What conclusions can you come to about replacement joint operations? *(P)(2)*

(ii) What restrictions would prevent hip replacement operations being performed on young children? *(K)(1)*

NISEAC, Biology (Human), Paper 3, 1991

6 The diagram shows bones and muscles in the human leg.

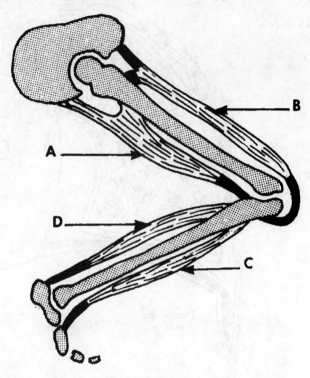

(a) State which muscle would contract to straighten the leg. *(K)(1)*

(b) When muscles A and C contract, state what happens to B and D. *(K)(1)*

(c) Label any tendon shown on the drawing. *(K)(1)*

WJEC, Biology (Human), Paper 1, 1990

3.2 The respiratory system

1 (a) The approximate percentage of oxygen in expired air is

    A 0.04   **B** 4   **C** 16   **D** 21 *(K)*

(b) Air will enter the lungs when the:

    A diaphragm is raised

    B volume of the thorax is decreased

    C ribs and sternum are lowered

    D volume of the thorax is increased *(K)*

(c) The epiglottis:

    A closes the oesophagus during breathing

    B prevents the trachea from collapsing

    C closes the trachea when swallowing

    D closes the nasal cavity when swallowing *(K)*

(d) The products of tissue respiration are:

    A carbon dioxide and nitrogen

    B carbon dioxide and water

    C carbon monoxide and water

    D nitrogen and water *(K)*

(e) The membranes surrounding the lungs comprise:

    A the pericardium

    B the periosteum

    C the pleura

    D the perichondrium *(K)*

(f) The processes of respiration and burning are similar but only respiration

    A releases energy

    B produces waste gases

    C uses up fuel

    D occurs within cells *(K)*

2 The diagram below shows the human thorax and some parts concerned with the breathing mechanism.

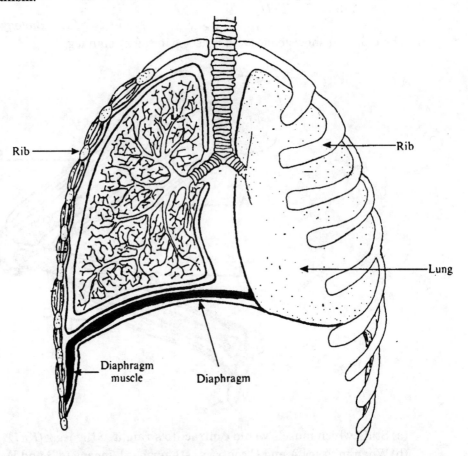

(a) Complete the table to show what happens to each of the labelled structures when air is **breathed in**. Cross out the word which is **incorrect**.

Structure	What happens
Lung	expands/contracts
Rib	raised/lowered
Diaphragm muscle	contracts/relaxes
Diaphragm	raised/lowered
Thorax	volume increases/decreases

(K)(5)

(b) A sample of exhaled air was tested to find the percentage of oxygen and carbon dioxide present. The results are shown below.

Volume of air sample $= 15.0 \text{ cm}^3$
Volume of air without carbon dioxide $= 14.4 \text{ cm}^3$
Volume of air without carbon dioxide and oxygen $= 12.0 \text{ cm}^3$

Use these results to calculate the percentage of carbon dioxide and the percentage of oxygen in the air sample. (Show your working) *(P)(4)*

(c) (i) Name a chemical used to absorb carbon dioxide. *(K)(1)*
(ii) Name a chemical used to absorb oxygen. *(K)(1)*
(iii) Explain why the sample of air tested in (b) is exhaled and not atmospheric air. *(K)(1)*

NISEAC, Biology (Human), Paper 2, 1990

3 (a) Aerobic respiration can be shown by the following equation.

Glucose + Oxygen → Carbon dioxide + Water + _____

Finish this equation by filling the space shown by the line. *(K)(1)*

(b) The diagram shows a small part of a lung.

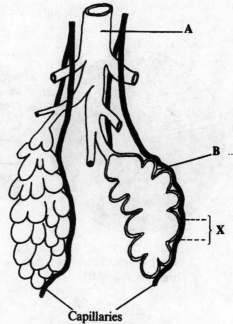

Capillaries

(i) Label parts A and B on the diagram. *(K)(2)*
(ii) Give **one** way in which the structures labelled B help the lungs to work efficiently.
(K)(1)

SEG, Biology (Human), Paper 1, 1990

4 The diagram below shows a section through some alveoli (air sacs) from the lungs.

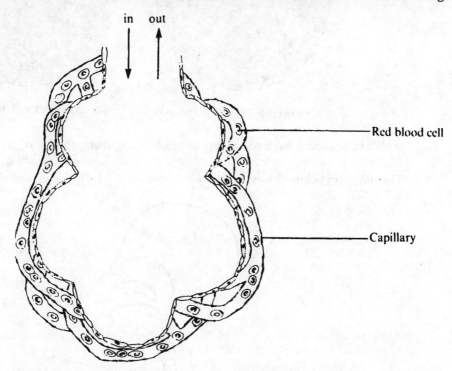

(a)(i) Place an arrow on the diagram to show where oxygen can enter the blood stream. *(K)(1)*
(ii) Name a gas which leaves the blood capillaries and goes into the alveoli. *(K)(1)*
(iii) By what process do gases pass into and out of the capillaries? *(K)(1)*

(b) The pie charts overleaf show the composition of air breathed in and out by two people A and B. Both people were breathing at the same rate.

One of the people had worked as a coal miner for many years. Coal dust slows down the rate at which oxygen is absorbed.
(i) What percentage of oxygen was taken into the lungs of both people? *(P)(1)*
(ii) What was the percentage of oxygen breathed out by person A? *(P)(1)*
(iii) What was the percentage of oxygen breathed out by person B? *(P)(1)*
(iv) Which person, A or B, had worked as a coal miner? Use the data in the pie charts to give a reason for your answer. *(P)(2)*
(v) Name **one** other dust, apart from coal dust, which can damage the lungs and name **one** disease that it causes. *(K)(2)*

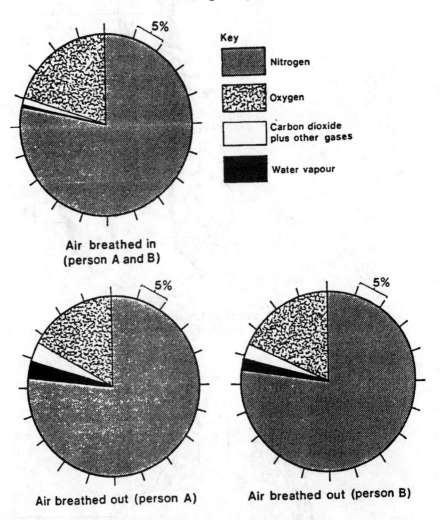

Percentage of gases in air

Key

Nitrogen

Oxygen

Carbon dioxide plus other gases

Water vapour

Air breathed in
(person A and B)

Air breathed out (person A)

Air breathed out (person B)

(c) What are some harmful effects of smoking cigarettes? *(K)(4)*

LEAG, Biology (Human), Paper 2, 1990

5 The diagram below shows a vertical section through the head and chest of a man.

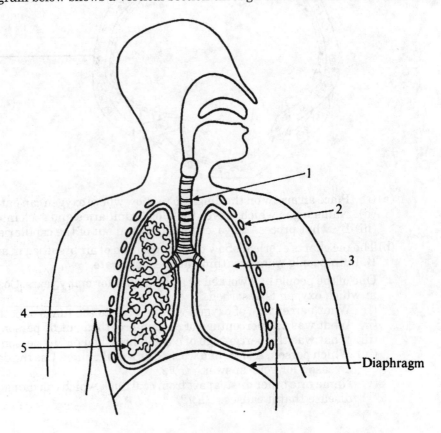

The list below gives the names of some of the structures in this part of the body.

LIST

Alveolus	Bronchus	Epiglottis	Heart
Intercostal muscle	Larynx	Lung	Pleural membrane
Rib	Thorax	Trachea	

(a) Name the numbered parts in the diagram. *(K)(5)*

(b) Draw arrows on the diagram to show the path air takes when it is breathed in. *(K)(1)*

(c) The diaphragm is shown in its position when air has been breathed out. Draw, on the diagram, the position of the diaphragm when air has been breathed in. *(K)(1)*

(d) What happens to the rib cage when air is breathed in? *(K)(1)*

(e) Which numbered part contains residual air when air is breathed out? *(K)(1)*

NISEAC, Biology (Human), Paper 1, 1990

3.3 Food and nutrition

1 (a) If you wished to show that honey contains a reducing sugar, which of the following procedures would you carry out?
   A add Sudan III
   B boil with Benedict's or Fehling's solution
   C add iodine solution
   D heat with Millon's reagent *(K)*

(b) Anaemia can be caused by a deficiency of:
   A carbohydrates   B hormones   C vitamin C   D a mineral salt *(K)*

(c) Roughage in our diet is not digested, but it is useful because:
   A it helps prevent constipation
   B it supplies vitamin B
   C it supplies calcium
   D it provides extra carbohydrates *(K)*

(d) Which of the following nutrients provides the most energy per gram?
   A carbohydrates   B fats   C proteins   D vitamins *(K)*

(e) Carbohydrates may be stored in the muscles and liver as:
   A glucose   B glycerol   C glycogen   D cellulose *(K)*

(f) Iodine is essential in the diet because it:
   A helps to prevent tooth decay
   B is an antiseptic
   C is needed to produce thyroxine
   D is needed to produce vitamin D *(K)*

2 (a) The following information was printed on the outside packaging of a breakfast cereal.

Ingredients	:	100% wholewheat
Nutritional information	:	per 100 g of product
Energy	:	1 440.0 kJ
Fat	:	2.2g
Protein	:	10.4g
Carbohydrate		
starch	:	73.7g
sugar	:	1.0g
fibre	:	9.5g

   (i)   What part of the wheat plant cells provided the fibre in the cereal? *(K)(1)*
   (ii) Explain why, when you eat cereal, the cells of your body receive less than one third of the total energy contained in the cereal. *(K)(3)*
   (iii) From what source do wheat plants ultimately obtain their energy? *(K)(1)*
   (iv) Explain why the figure for starch is much greater than the figure for sugar. *(K)(2)*
   (v)   What is the main source of energy in the cereal? *(K)(1)*

(b) The graph overleaf shows the result of an experiment in which the rate of digestion of starch was measured for different levels of amylase concentration. The temperature was maintained at 15 °C throughout the experiment.
   (i)   At what % amylase concentration did the rate of starch digestion reach its maximum level? *(P)(1)*
   (ii) What is the effect of increasing the amylase concentration beyond the point at which maximum digestion occurred? Suggest a reason for your answer. *(P)(3)*
   (iii) On the same set of axes above, draw a curve which could be expected if the experiment was repeated at 25 °C, with all other factors remaining constant. *(P)(2)*

(c) Describe, in detail, how you would carry out an experiment to measure the rate of digestion of starch at different levels of amylase concentration.   *(K)(5)*

(d) What is the optimum pH for the digestion of starch by salivary amylase?   *(K)(1)*

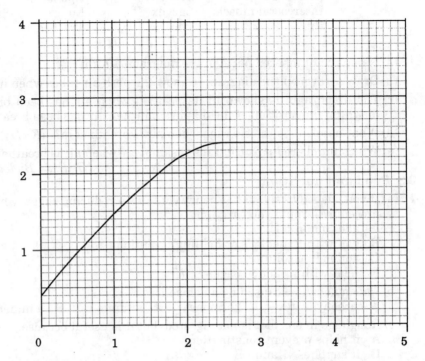

NISEAC, Biology (Human), Paper 3, 1990

3   The table below shows the composition of four different foods.

Food	Carbohydrate g per 100 g	Protein g per 100 g	Fat g per 100 g
A	0	17.1	0.9
B	0	0.4	82
C	48.5	8.2	1.7
D	2.3	1.0	0

(a) Identify **each** food by putting a letter A, B, C or D in each box.

	Letter
Bread	
Fish	
Cabbage	
Butter	

(P)(4)

(b) Calculate how much protein there is in a snack consisting of 200 g food C and 50 g food B. (Show your working) *(P)(3)*

WJEC, Biology (Human), Paper 1, 1990

4 The bar chart shows the carbohydrate, fat, protein and water content of cheese.

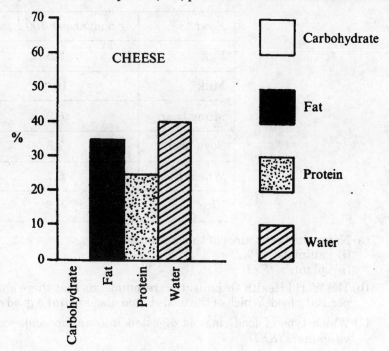

The information below was obtained from labels on the wrapper of a loaf of white bread and a box of breakfast cereal.

White bread		*Breakfast cereal*	
Constituents	*(g per 100 g food)*	*Constituents*	*(g per 100 g food)*
Protein	7	Fat	1
Carbohydrate	52	Protein	13
Fat	2	Carbohydrate	68
Salt	1	Fibre	15
Water	38	Water	3

(a) Use information from these tables to draw similar bar charts for the carbohydrate, fat, protein and water contents of these two foods. Use the axes below and the same key.*(P)(5)*

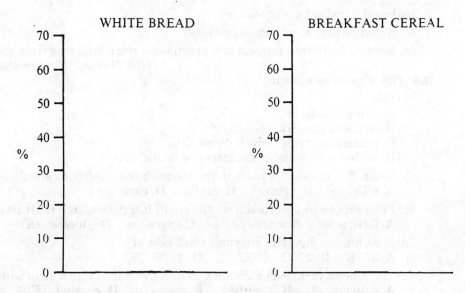

(b) Describe a safe method you could use to find out if the carbohydrate in the breakfast cereal included sugar. *(K)(5)*

SEG, Biology (Human), Paper 2, 1991

146 Test yourself

Test yourself

5 The figures below show the amount of an amino acid called leucine in different types of food.

Food	g leucine per 100 g food
Egg	8.8
Milk	10.0
Mung bean	6.9
Soya bean	7.8
Wheat flour	6.7
Rice	8.5

(a) Name the best source of this amino acid in
   (i) animals, *(P)(1)*
   (ii) plants. *(P)(1)*

(b) The World Health Organisation recommends that there should be more than 7.0 g leucine per 100 g food. Which of the foods listed above is **not** a good enough source of leucine? *(P)(2)*

(c) Which type of food class is digested into amino acids—carbohydrates, fats, proteins or vitamins? *(K)(1)*

(d) Give **one** way in which amino acids are used in the body. *(K)(1)*

WJEC, Biology (Human), Paper 1, 1991

6 The table below shows the composition of four foods.

Food	Content per 100 g food					
	Fat g	Protein g	Carbohydrate g	Iron mg	Vitamin C µg	Vitamin D µg
A	2.4	0.0	18.5	5.4	30	0.01
B	0.0	3.6	12.2	1.3	22	1.7
C	4.2	0.1	0.0	0.5	60	12.0
D	6.4	7.5	15.5	0.0	5	22.4

Which of the foods, A to D,
(a) would be best at preventing scurvy?
(b) has the highest energy value?
(c) would be best at preventing rickets?
(d) would a doctor recommend to a pregnant woman suffering from anaemia? *(K)(4)*

NEA, Biology (Human and Social), Paper 1, 1990

3.4 The digestive system

1 (a) Bile:
   A emulsifies fats
   B contains urea from the liver
   C contains enzymes which digest fat
   D makes conditions in the intestine acidic *(K)*

(b) When digestion takes place in the stomach the conditions should be:
   A alkaline   **B** neutral   **C** acidic   **D** basic *(K)*

(c) Before it can be absorbed from the small intestine starch must be broken down to:
   A fatty acids   **B** amino acids   **C** glycogen   **D** glucose *(K)*

(d) Most human digestive enzymes work best at:
   A 37 °C   **B** 27 °C   **C** 17 °C   **D** 47 °C *(K)*

(e) The process of digestion enables us to convert food into a form which can be:
   A dehydrated   **B** absorbed   **C** excreted   **D** egested *(K)*

(f) Amino acids are produced as a result of the breakdown of:
   A fats   **B** sugars   **C** proteins   **D** vitamins *(K)*

2 (a) The diagram shows the teeth on the left side of the mouth of a human adult.

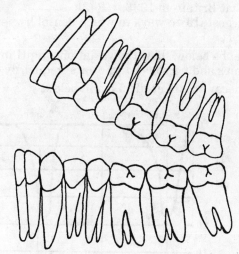

   (i)   On the diagram label the crown and the root of one molar tooth. *(K)(2)*
   (ii) Write the letter I on all the incisor teeth and the letter C on all the canine teeth in the diagram. *(K)(2)*
   (iii) Use the information in the diagram to predict the number of teeth in the whole mouth. *(P)(1)*
   (iv) Name **two** structures that pass through the root of each tooth into its pulp cavity. *(K)(2)*

(b) (i) Explain why teeth decay. *(K)(3)*
    (ii) The diagrams below show three stages in the decay of teeth.

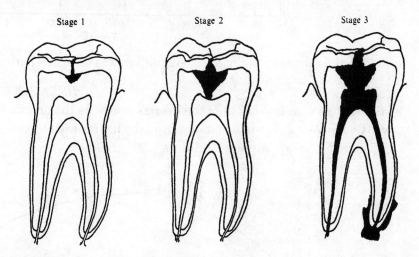

Stage 1   Stage 2   Stage 3

   Explain why the person with this decaying tooth felt pain at stage 2 and 3 but not at stage 1. *(K)(2)*

(c) The graph below shows data about the dental health of children in Northern Ireland and Great Britain in 1983.

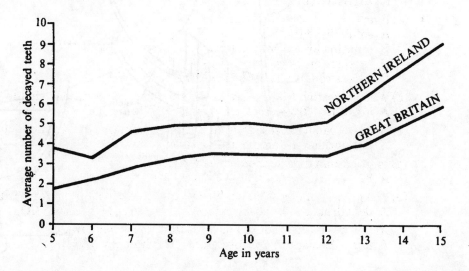

    (i)   Use the graph to comment on the dental health of children in Northern Ireland and Great Britain in 1983. *(P)(2)*

    (ii) Suggest **three** ways in which dental hygiene can be improved in Northern Ireland.

(K)(3)

(d) The graphs below show the variations in pH in the mouth of a person (A) who only eats at mealtimes and person (B) who eats frequently during the day.

Tooth decay occurs at pH 5.5 and below.

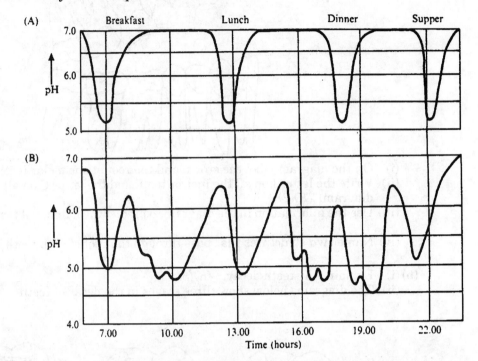

What do the graphs suggest about differences in eating patterns, pH and tooth decay?

(P)(3)

NISEAC, Biology (Human), Paper 3, 1991

3 Substances pass into or out of the liver as shown by the arrows on the diagram below.

(a) Choose **one** different substance from the list for each label:

    starch   urea   protein   glucose   bile *(K)(3)*

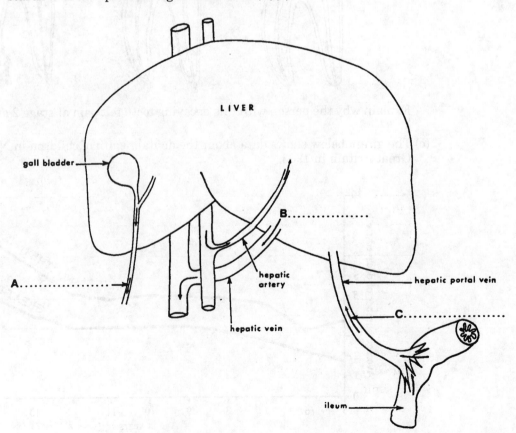

(b) Name **one** substance that is detoxified in the liver. *(K)(1)*

WJEC, Biology (Human), Paper 1, 1990

4 A student set up the following apparatus.

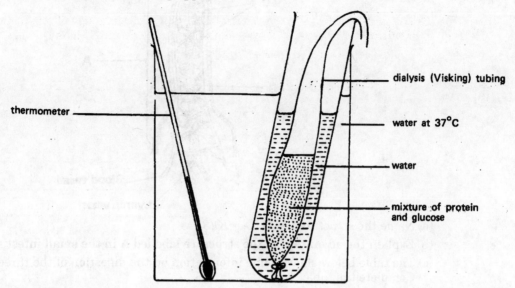

(a) After 30 minutes the student removed a sample of water from the boiling tube and tested it for glucose.
  (i) Which piece of apparatus would you use to remove the sample of water? *(K)(1)*
  (ii) Describe how you should test the sample of water for glucose and describe the expected result. *(K)(3)*

(b) The student also tested the water in the boiling tube for protein. This test was negative. Explain why no protein was found. *(K)(2)*

NEA, Biology (Human and Social), Paper 1, 1990

5 A student tested a sample of milk for protein, reducing sugar (glucose), fat (lipid) and vitamin C. She did the same tests on a sample of distilled water. She set up the experiment shown below and left it for 2 hours at 37 °C. She tested the milk and water again. Her results are shown in the table.

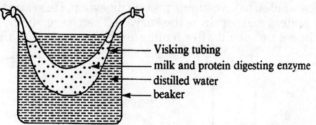

Table of results   ✓ = positive result   ✕ = negative result

Test carried out	At start		After 2 hours	
	milk in visking tubing	water in beaker	milk in visking tubing	water in beaker
Protein	✓	✕	✕	✕
Glucose (reducing sugar)	✓	✕	✓	✓
Fat (lipid)	✓	✕	✓	✕
Vitamin C	✕	✕	✕	✕

Write a **full** explanation of the results for
(a) protein,
(b) glucose (reducing sugar),
(c) fat (lipid),
(d) vitamin C. *(K)(7)*

WJEC, Biology (Human), Paper 1, 1991

6   The diagram below shows a section through a structure found in the wall of the small intestine.

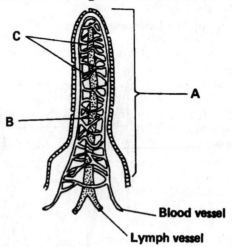

(a) Name the structures A, B, C. *(K)(3)*

(b) Explain the advantage of the structure labelled A in the small intestine. *(K)(2)*

(c) The table below shows some information on the digestion of the three main types of food. Complete the table.

Food	Enzyme involved in digestion	Product of digestion	Carried away in
Carbohydrate		Reducing sugar	Blood vessels
Fats, oils			
Protein	Protease		

(K)(6)
MEG, Biology (Human), Paper 2, 1991

7   Huw wanted to investigate protein digestion. He set up tube A as shown below, using egg white for protein and pepsin as the enzyme. Then he remembered that the stomach contents are acid, so he set up tube B after 5 minutes. Fifteen minutes after that he looked at both tubes.

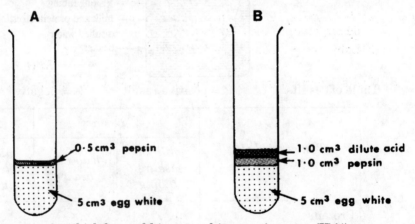

(a) List **four** ways in which he could improve his experiment. *(K)(4)*

(b) What colour would you see if you tested the egg white with Biuret solution? *(K)(1)*
WJEC, Biology (Human), Paper 1, 1990

3.5 The circulatory system

1   (a) Universal recipients (Group AB) can receive blood from any other group because:
    A they do not suffer from anaemia
    B they receive more blood that other people
    C their blood contains no A or B antibodies
    D their blood contains no A and B antigens *(K)*

    (b) Most carbon dioxide is carried to the lungs:
    A dissolved in the plasma
    B as sodium bicarbonate
    C in the white blood cells
    D in the platelets *(K)*

(c) Fibrinogen is necessary for:
  A keeping the colour of blood
  B the formation of haemoglobin
  C the clotting of blood
  D removing carbon dioxide from blood *(K)*

(d) Some babies are born with a hole between the right and left atria (auricles) of the heart. These babies often have a bluish tinge to their lips, fingers and cheeks. This is because:
  A much of the blood bypassed the lungs
  B no blood can pass to the lungs to be oxygenated
  C blood leaks out of the heart through the hole and causes bruises
  D the blood only circulates between the heart and the lungs *(K)*

(e) During exercise which of the following factors is least likely to increase?
  A pulse rate
  B stroke volume of the heart
  C digestion of food
  D breakdown of glucose *(K)*

(f) The highest concentration of oxygen in the blood is found in the small veins of the:
  A brain   **B** heart   **C** lungs   **D** liver *(K)*

2 The diagram shows a simple plan of the circulation of blood round the body.

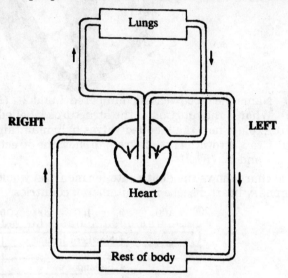

(a) Use a pencil or crayon to shade in on the diagram all the blood vessels which carry deoxygenated blood. *(K)(2)*

(b) Label the pulmonary vein on this diagram. *(K)(1)*

SEG, Biology (Human), Paper 1, 1990

3 The diagram shows the build-up of fatty deposit on the inside of an artery.

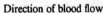

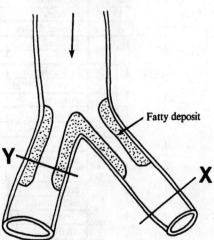

This is the view of the artery cut across at X.

Draw how you would expect to see the artery cut across at Y. Draw your diagram to scale. *(P)(3)*
WJEC, Biology (Human), Paper 1, 1991

4 (a) The diagram shows a ventral view of a section of a mammalian heart and the major blood vessels connected to it.

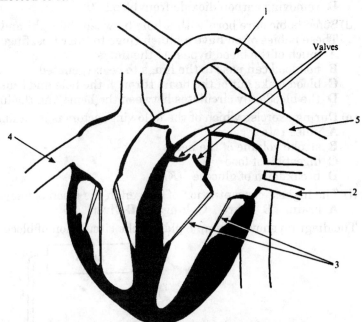

(i)   Name the blood vessels numbered 1 and 2. *(K)(2)*
(ii) What is the function of the structures labelled 3? *(K)(1)*
(iii) Explain how the labelled valves help maintain blood flow in one direction only. *(K)(2)*
(iv) Draw arrows on the diagram to show the direction of blood flow in the vessels numbered 4 and 5. *(K)(2)*

(b) The chart shows the death rate for men and women, between the ages of 40 and 69, from coronary heart disease in a number of countries.

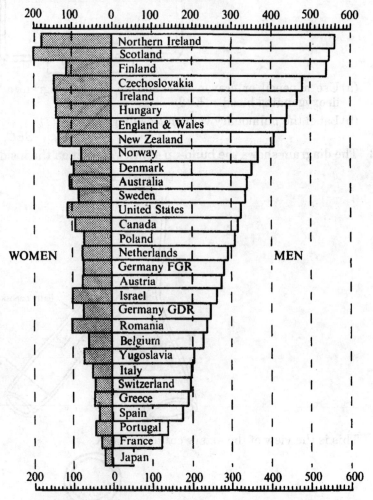

Number of deaths per 100 000 of the population

(i) How much greater is the death rate for males, between the ages of 40 and 69, from coronary heart disease in Northern Ireland than in Portugal? *(P)(1)*

(ii) All the countries in the British Isles are in the top seven in the chart. Suggest **one** reason why Britain has such a high death rate from coronary heart disease. *(K)(1)*

(c) Graph A below shows the relationship between the death rate for coronary heart disease and the blood cholesterol level. Graph B shows the relationship between cholesterol levels and age, for men and women.

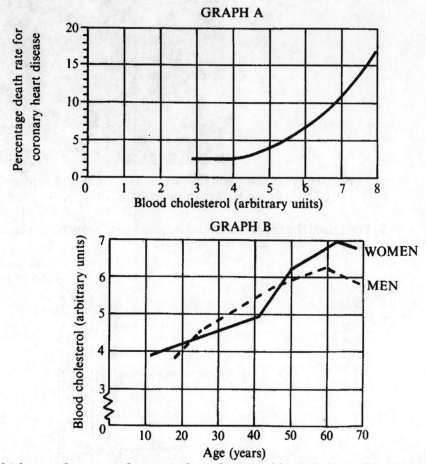

GRAPH A

Percentage death rate for coronary heart disease

Blood cholesterol (arbitrary units)

GRAPH B

Blood cholesterol (arbitrary units)

WOMEN

MEN

Age (years)

(i) At which ages do men and women show the same blood cholesterol level? *(P)(2)*

(ii) Use the information in the graphs to explain why the death rate for men, from coronary heart disease, is higher than the death rate for women, between the ages of 25 and 45. *(P)(2)*

(iii) Use the graphs to determine the level of blood cholesterol that would keep the death rate, from coronary heart disease, at a minimum. *(P)(1)*

(iv) What does your answer to (c)(iii) suggest about cholesterol as the only cause of coronary heart disease? *(P)(1)*

(d) The photographs below show sections through an artery of a healthy individual (A) and an artery from a patient who died from coronary heart disease (B).

Section of Artery A.

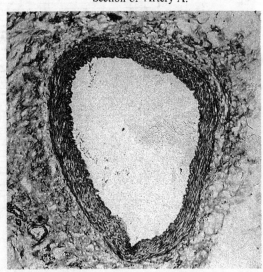

Section of Artery B.

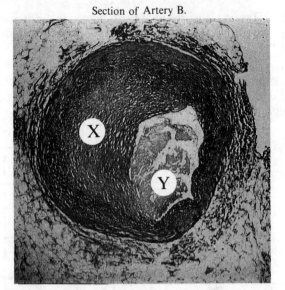

Suggest what the parts labelled X and Y are and explain how their presence could have brought about a coronary thrombosis. *(K)(3)*

NISEAC, Biology (Human), Paper 3, 1991

5   Peter used the apparatus below to investigate stretching (elasticity) in a main artery and main vein.

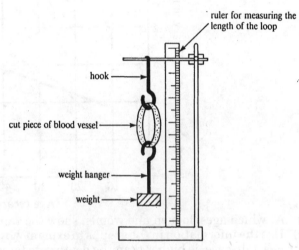

The graph below shows the results obtained for Test 1.

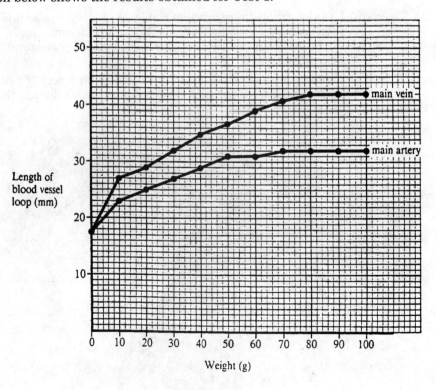

Length of blood vessel loop (mm)

Weight (g)

(a) (i) What was the **greatest** length recorded for the artery? *(P)(1)*
(ii) What weight was responsible for this? *(P)(1)*

(b) (i) What was the **greatest** length recorded for the vein? *(P)(1)*
(ii) What weight was responsible for this? *(P)(1)*

(c) On removing the weights, the blood vessels spring back. Peter measured the lengths of the loops after the weights were removed and recorded the results in the table.
(i) Use the graph to complete the results table. *(P)(1)*

Test 2 results

	Length of blood vessel in mm	
	Main artery	Main vein
Before the first weight added		
After all the weights were removed	21	30

(P)(1)

(ii) State which blood vessel **almost** returns to its original size. *(P)(1)*
(iii) Which blood vessel has the greater elasticity? *(P)(1)*
(iv) The diagrams below show cross sections of the artery and vein.

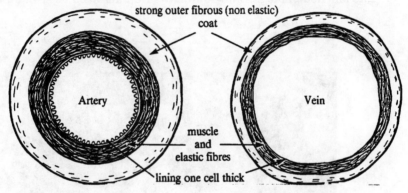

Use the diagrams to explain the results Peter obtained for
(I) Test 1 *(P)(1)*
(II) Test 2 *(P)(1)*
(III) State whether the artery or vein is best suited to cope with blood at high pressure. *(P)(1)*

WJEC, Biology (Human), Paper 2, 1991

6 The Biotech Enzyme Company has developed a new enzyme which can be used to treat blood clots in the human body.

The enzyme is supplied to hospitals in a solution. The solution contains 100 units of enzyme per 100 cm³ liquid.

The solution is kept in a refrigerator at 4 °C until needed.

In solution the enzyme only keeps for two weeks.

A scientist at the hospital wondered if the enzyme would keep longer if it were bought as a powder.

(a) Explain how the scientist could do a fair and accurate test to find out if this was true. (The active enzyme will break down a blood clot in a test tube within 5 minutes at 35 °C.) *(K)(5)*

(b) The results show that the enzyme does keep longer as a powder.

Suggest **two** other advantages of ordering powdered enzyme rather than enzyme solution. *(K)(2)*

NEA, Biology (Human and Social), Paper 1, 1990

7 The diagram below shows part of the human blood circulation.

(a) In the diagram, which number correctly shows the left atrium and which number shows the right ventricle? *(K)(2)*

(b) Which **two** vessels, labelled A, B, C or D, are arteries? *(K)(2)*

(c) On the diagram, draw arrows in the heart to show the direction of blood flow. *(K)(2)*

(d) Explain how chamber 4 pushes blood into vessel D. *(K)(2)*

(e) Explain why the wall of chamber 3 is thinner than the wall of chamber 4. *(K)(2)*

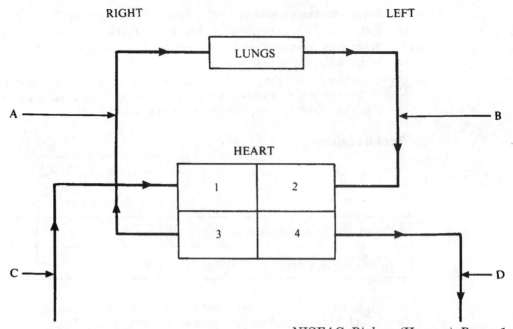

RIGHT   LEFT

NISEAC, Biology (Human), Paper 1, 1991

8 The labelled photograph below shows human blood as seen down a microscope.

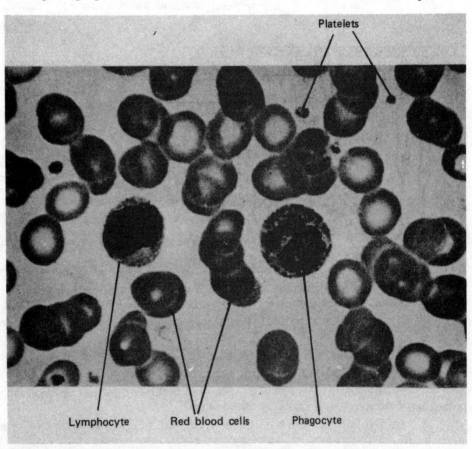

(a) (i)   Which of these types of blood cell produce antibodies? *(K)(1)*
    (ii)   Explain how antibodies help to prevent infection. *(K)(1)*
    (iii) Explain how phagocytes help to protect the body from infection. *(K)(2)*

(b) **fibrin   platelets   red blood cells   fibrinogen   plasma**

Choose words from the above list to complete the following passage about blood clotting.

When the skin is cut, substances released by the .... cause an enzyme to be activated. This enzyme changes a soluble protein called .... into ...., which is insoluble. A network of threads is formed and .... become trapped in this network and dry to form a clot. *(K)(4)*

(c) An injured person may need a blood transfusion. Explain why it is important to know both the donor's blood group and the patient's blood group. *(K)(1)*

NEA, Biology (Human), Paper P, 1990

3.6 Regulation/homeostasis

1 (a) As urine leaves the kidney and passes to the bladder:
 A its composition remains unchanged
 B glucose is removed
 C urea is added
 D water is removed *(K)*

 (b) When we are very hot, the capillaries in the skin:
 A dilate **B** collapse **C** constrict **D** darken *(K)*

 (c) A function of the human epidermis is to:
 A insulate the body with fat
 B absorb air
 C prevent entry of bacteria
 D produce sweat *(K)*

 (d) Which of the following controls the release of urine from the body?
 A bladder **B** ureter **C** urethra **D** sphincter muscle *(K)*

 (e) When you are resting, under which of the following weather conditions would sweat evaporate most rapidly?
 A hot, dry and windy
 B hot, dry and still
 C hot, humid and still
 D cold, dry and windy *(K)*

 (f) Urea is made in the:
 A skin **B** kidney **C** liver **D** bladder *(K)*

2 The diagram below shows part of the human excretory system.

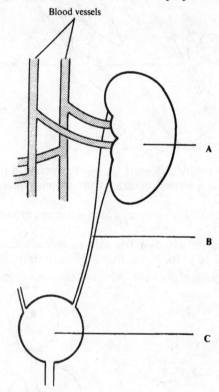

Blood vessels

 (a) Label structures A, B and C on the lines provided. *(K)(3)*

 (b) Name **two** substances in blood which are regulated by the kidneys. *(K)(2)*

LEAG, Biology (Human), Paper 1, 1990

3 The diagram below shows a kidney and its associated blood vessels. The arrow indicates the direction of blood flow.

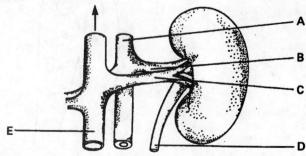

(a) (i)   Which letter indicates:
the renal artery?
the ureter?   *(K)(2)*

(ii)   State **two** differences in composition between the blood in the renal artery and that in the renal vein.   *(K)(2)*

(b) Chemical tests on urine can often give information about the way various parts of the body are working.

(i)   The presence of proteins in urine may indicate kidney disease. Why do proteins not appear in normal urine?   *(K)(1)*

(ii)   Which disease is indicated by the presence of glucose in the urine?   *(K)(1)*

(iii)   Why is glucose found in the filtrate in the Bowman's capsule but not in the urine? *(K)(1)*

MEG, Biology (Human), Paper 3, 1990

4   (a) The diagram shows a section through the skin.

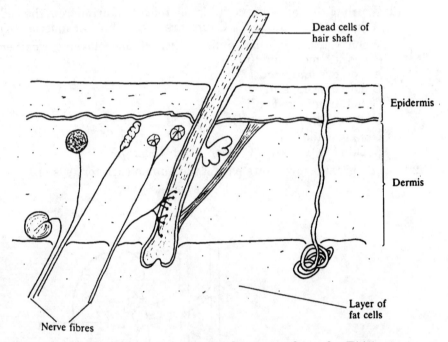

(i)   How many different types of nerve endings are shown?   *(P)(1)*

(ii)   Name a stimulus other than touch which can affect one of the receptors in the skin.   *(K)(1)*

(iii)   Describe **one** way in which a named effector in the body could respond to this stimulus.   *(K)(1)*

(iv)   Using information from the diagram to help you, explain why a person having a hair cut feels no pain, but it hurts when a hair is pulled out.   *(P)(3)*

(b) The diagram shows the position of some organs in the body.

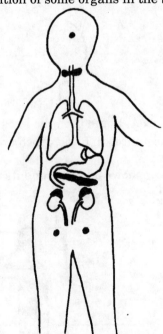

(i) On this diagram label the pituitary and adrenal glands. *(K)(2)*

(ii) Following a meal the concentration of glucose in the blood may rise. More insulin is then released by the pancreas. This causes glucose to be changed to glycogen and so the amount of glucose in the blood falls.
Explain what then happens when the concentration of glucose has returned to normal. *(K)(2)*

(iii) If a person's pancreatic duct becomes blocked the control of glucose in the body by insulin is not affected but the digestion of food becomes very difficult. Explain these observations. *(K)(2)*

SEG, Biology (Human), Paper 1, 1990

5 (a) The body temperature of a mammal remains within narrow limits in spite of changes in the environmental temperature. State **two** ways in which this "constant" body temperature is of value to mammals. *(K)(2)*

(b) The graph below shows variations in a person's body temperature over two days.

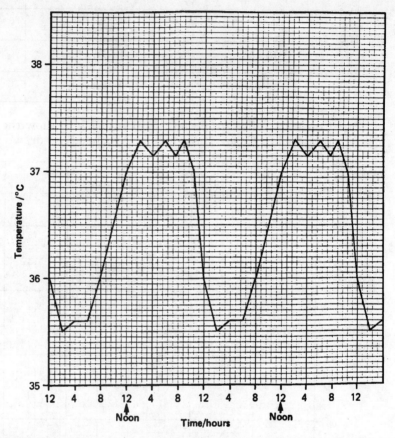

(i) Describe the pattern of overall changes in body temperature shown over a period of 24 hours. *(P)(2)*

(ii) Between which times is the person most likely to be sweating? *(P)(1)*

(iii) Explain how sweating helps to regulate body temperature. *(K)(2)*

(c) Explain why urine production decreases as sweating increases. *(K)(2)*

MEG, Biology (Human), Paper 3, 1991

6 (a) The diagram below shows a simplified human urinary system.

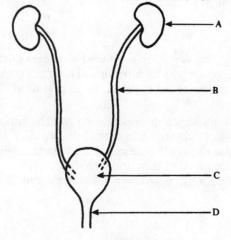

(i)   Name the parts labelled A and B. *(K)(2)*

(ii) What is the function of part B? *(K)(1)*

(b) Identical twins, Chris and Alex, were each given some liquid to drink. Chris drank 1 000 cm³ of water and Alex drank 1 000 cm³ of weak salt solution. The volume of urine produced was recorded for each boy and the results are shown in the table below.

Time (in minutes) from drinking liquid	*Cumulative volume (in cm3) of urine produced since start of experiment by*	
	Chris	*Alex*
30	350	0
60	750	0
90	950	150
120	1 050	250
150	1 100	300

(i)   Construct a line graph on the axes below to show the cumulative volumes of urine produced by Chris. The graph for Alex has been drawn for you. *(P)(3)*

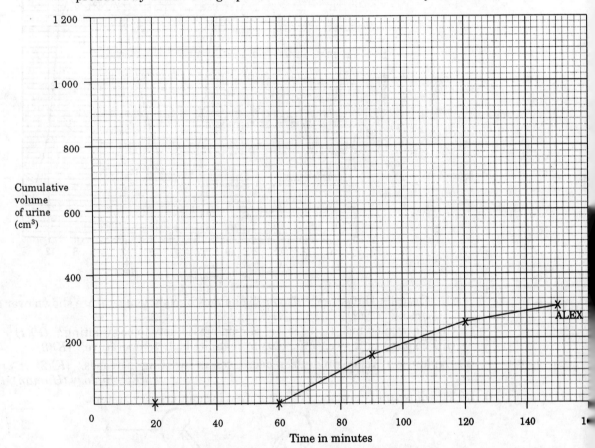

(ii) Suggest why Alex produced much less urine than Chris. *(P)(2)*

(iii) Suggest why Chris produced a larger total volume of urine than the 1 000 cm³ of water he drank at the start of the experiment. *(P)(1)*

NISEAC, Biology (Human), Paper 2, 1990

7 (a)(i)   The photograph opposite shows the human urinary system and its associated blood vessels. Identify the parts labelled X, Y and Z. *(K)(3)*

(ii) State clearly the function of the part labelled Z, and describe what features enable it to carry out this function. *(K)(3)*

(iii) Name a nitrogenous waste compound that is removed from the blood by the kidneys. *(K)(1)*

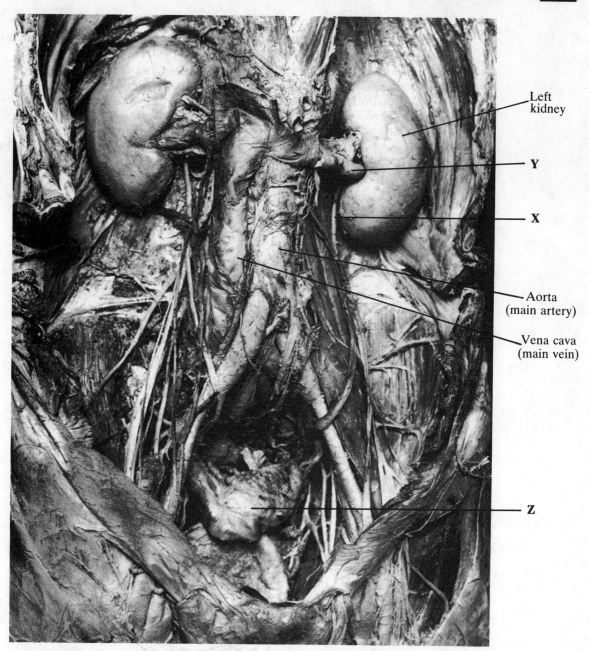

(b) The following diagram shows a simplified version of a kidney dialysis machine in use.

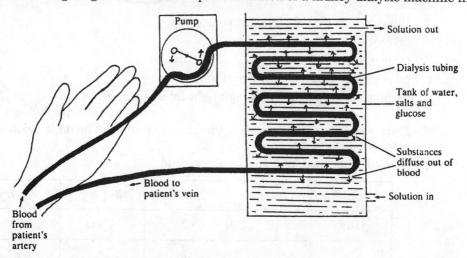

(i)   Why do red blood cells remain inside the dialysis tubing? *(K)(1)*
(ii) The solution surrounding the dialysis tubing contains a certain concentration of salts and glucose. Explain how this regulates the composition of the blood. *(K)(4)*
(iii) In what way is the dialysis tubing as shown in the diagram suited to its function? *(K)(2)*
(iv) Through which structure in the living kidney does ultrafiltration take place? *(K)(1)*

SEG, Biology (Human), Paper 3, 1990

3.7 Coordination

1 (a) As light rays pass through the eye they are bent by each of the following except:
  A the vitreous humour   **B** the iris   **C** the lens   **D** the cornea   *(K)*

(b) Conditioned reflexes differ from most other responses in that:
  A   they happen much faster than other responses
  B   the relationship of stimulus and response has been learned during one's lifetime
  C   they need taste or smell of food to start them off
  D   they do not involve nerves in their action   *(K)*

(c) The axons of many nerve cells are covered with a myelin (fatty) sheath which:
  A   prevents impulses from going too fast
  B   insulates the cell from neighbouring nerve cells
  C   prevents bacterial infection
  D   keeps the cells at a constant temperature   *(K)*

(d) The spinal cord:
  A   allows the spine to be flexible
  B   supports the weight of the back
  C   allows the passage of nerve impulses to and from the brain
  D   protects the spine from damage   *(K)*

(e) The medulla oblongata of the brain controls:
  A balance   **B** hearing   **C** learning   **D** breathing   *(K)*

(f) When the eye is focused on near objects:
  A the lens is thinner than normal
  B the ciliary muscles are relaxed
  C the pupil is very small
  D the suspensory ligaments are slack   *(K)*

2 Below is a diagram of a human eye in section.

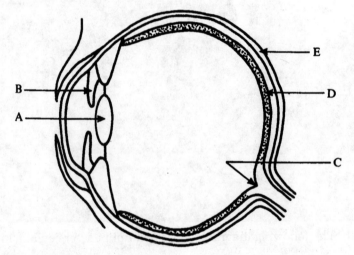

Which one of the five labelled structures
(a) contains rod and cone cells?
(b) bends the light?
(c) is attached to muscles which move the eye?
(d) protects the retina from high light intensity?   *(K)(4)*

NISEAC, Biology (Human), Paper 2, 1990

3 Some pupils were investigating their reaction times. The table below shows how long it took to catch a falling ruler.
Measurements are in 1/100ths of a second.

Pupils	1st try	2nd try	3rd try	4th try	5th try
Huw	9	9	9	6	5
Nia	7	7	4	2	2
Mari	7	8	10	9	7
Ifan	5	4	3	4	2

(a) Whose reaction time was the quickest **overall**? *(P)(1)*

(b) Whose reaction time got **worse** before getting better? *(P)(1)*

(c) State whose overall performance did **not** improve. *(P)(1)*

(d) State whose performance improved the **most**. *(P)(1)*

WJEC, Biology (Human), Paper 1, 1991

4 The body is controlled and coordinated by the nervous system and by the endocrine (hormone) system.

The diagrams show the main features of these two systems.

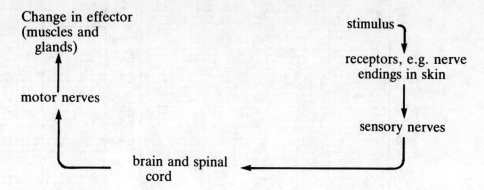

NERVOUS SYSTEM

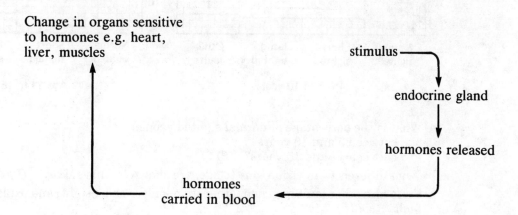

ENDOCRINE SYSTEM

Using information from the diagrams only:

(a) give **two** ways in which these systems are similar, *(P)(2)*

(b) give **one** way in which these systems are different. *(P)(1)*

SEG, Biology (Human), Paper 1, 1990

5 The following four chemicals are found in the human body:

glycogen   glucagon   adrenaline   insulin

Complete the table below by writing in the names of the correct chemicals. You may use each chemical once, more than once or not at all. The first one has been done for you.

	Name of chemical(s)
Produced by the pancreas	Insulin, Glucagon
Are hormones	
Cause glucose to be stored in the liver	
Cause glucose to be released by the liver	
Is the stored form of glucose	

(K)(4)

LEAG, Biology (Human), Paper 1, 1990

6 The diagram below shows information from a survey on the eyesight of two groups of people of different ages.

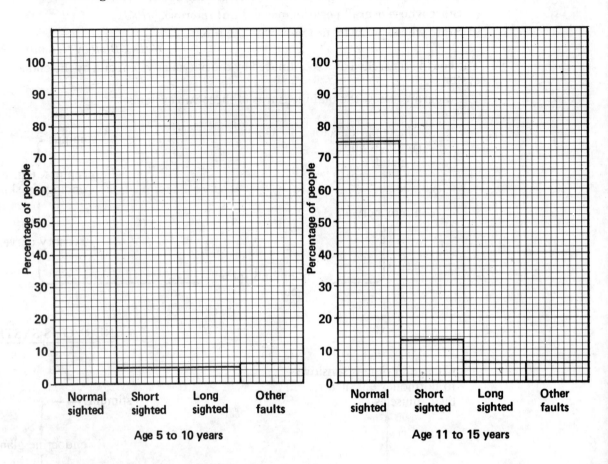

Age 5 to 10 years   Age 11 to 15 years

(a) What is the percentage of normal sighted people:
   between 5 and 10 years?
   between 11 and 15 years? *(P)(2)*

(b) What differences in vision, due to age, are shown by this survey? *(P)(4)*

(c) State **one** other fault in vision (other than long or short sight) and explain the cause of the fault. *(K)(2)*

(d) The lenses shown below are called bifocal lenses.

   The shaded part is for close-up work.

   The unshaded part is for looking at things further away.

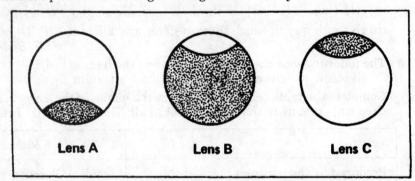

Lens A   Lens B   Lens C

State which lens would be most suitable for the following people.
(i)   An aircraft pilot who needs to read overhead instruments as well as looking forward through the cockpit window.
(ii) A musician who needs to be able to look at sheets of music and sometimes look at the conductor.
(iii) A shop assistant who needs to keep looking up at the customer and down at the till. *(P)(3)*

MEG, Biology (Human), Paper 2, 1991

7 (a) The diagram shows a section through a human eye.
   (i)   Name parts A, B and C. *(K)(3)*
   (ii) What are the functions of part X and part Y? *(K)(2)*
   (iii) Explain how tears protect the surface of the conjunctiva. *(K)(1)*

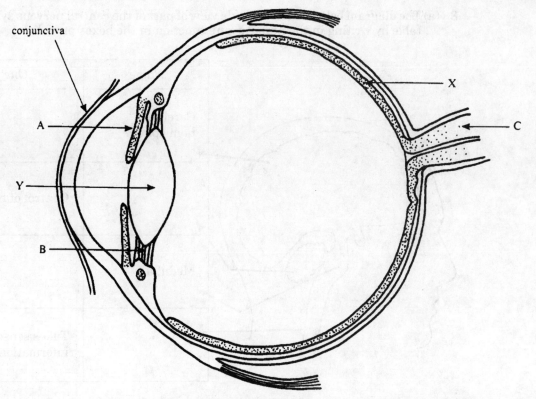

(b) The diagram below shows the path of rays of light, from a distant object, in a short sighted eye.

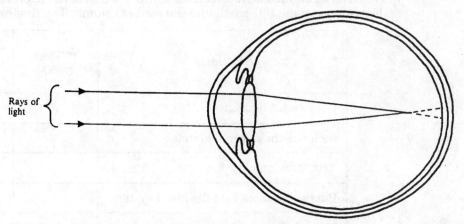

(i) Use the information in the diagram to explain why the object is not seen clearly. *(P)(1)*
(ii) Give one cause of short sight in humans. *(K)(1)*
(iii) Complete the diagram below to show how the spectacle lens focuses the rays of light onto the retina.

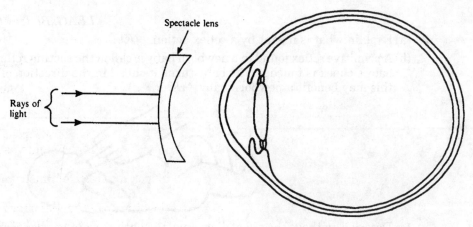

(K)(2)

NISEAC, Biology (Human), Paper 1, 1991

8 (a) The diagram below shows the side view of part of the central nervous system. Complete the table by writing in the name or **one** function in the boxes provided.

Name	One function
Cerebral hemisphere	
	Control of balance
Medulla	
	Takes sensory information to the brain

(K)(4)

(b) The table below includes statements which are true of the nervous system **or** the endocrine (hormone) system. Put a tick into the correct column. The first one has been done for you.

Statement	Nervous system	Endocrine (hormone) system
Uses motor neurones	✓	
Includes the adrenal glands		
Acts more quickly		
Puts substances into the blood system		
Uses electrical impulses		
Usually has a long lasting effect		

(K)(5)

LEAG, Biology (Human), Paper 1, 1991

9 (a) Explain what is meant by a reflex action. *(K)(2)*

(b) A primitive reflex found in a newborn baby is called the rooting reflex which occurs when the baby's cheek is touched: the baby turns its head in the direction of the touch. Suggest how this may benefit a newborn baby. *(K)(2)*

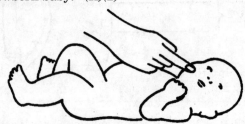

(c) Describe, without the aid of diagrams, the pathway of the knee-jerk reflex from stimulus to response. *(K)(6)*

(d) The following information was recorded at a hospital before and after a patient had brain surgery. The chart shows the size of the patient's pupils and whether or not they react to light (+ or −); it also shows the amount of limb movement (a dot is for both limbs).

TIME

PUPILS			10.00	18.00	Operation	14.00	14.30	15.00	15.30	16.00	16.30	17.00	17.30	18.00				
	right	Size (mm)	3	3		4	4	3	3	3	3	3	3	3				+ reacts
		Reaction	+	+		+	+	+	+	+	+	+	+	+				− no reaction
	left	Size (mm)	3	3		4	4	3	3	3	3	3	3	3				c. eye closed by swelling
		Reaction	+	+		+	+	+	+	+	+	+	+	+				
LIMB MOVEMENT	ARMS	Normal power	●	●		●	●	●	R	R	R	R	●	●				
		Mild weakness							L	L	L	L						
		Severe weakness																Record right (R) and left (L) separately if there is a difference between the two sides.
		Spastic flexion																
		Extension																
		No response																
	LEGS	Normal power	●	●		●	●	●	R	R	R	R	●	●				
		Mild weakness							L	L	L	L						
		Severe weakness																
		Extension																
		No response																

(i) What happens to the size of the pupils after the operation. *(P)(2)*

(ii) Which arm loses power after the operation? *(P)(1)*

(iii) Why is it necessary to record the left side of the body separately from the right side? *(P)(2)*

SEG, Biology (Human), Paper 3, 1991

10 The diagrams below compare the reaction times of two drivers A and B to a child running out into the road. One of these drivers has had a drink containing alcohol.

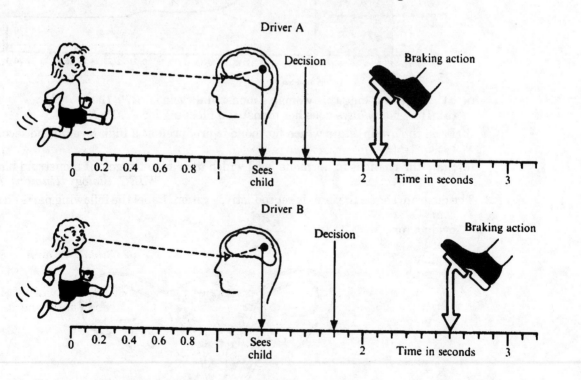

(a) After seeing the child,
  (i) how long did it take driver A to make a decision? *(P)(1)*
  (ii) how long did it take driver B to make a decision? *(P)(1)*

(b) How much longer than driver A did driver B take to apply the brakes after seeing the child? *(P)(1)*

(c) Which driver had had a drink containing alcohol? *(P)(1)*

(d) Name **two** long term effects of regularly drinking too much alcohol. *(K)(2)*

THEME 4 HUMAN REPRODUCTION AND THE CONTINUITY OF LIFE

4.1 Human reproduction and development

1 (a) Sperms are produced in greater numbers than eggs because:
    A they are small in size
    B they are viable for only a few days
    C more than one sperm fertilises an egg
    D the chances of a sperm reaching an egg are very small *(K)*

(b) Human ovulation normally occurs approximately every:
    A 14 days **B** 28 days **C** 9 months **D** 40 days *(K)*

(c) Fertilisation occurs usually in the
    A uterus **B** vagina **C** fallopian tube **D** ovary *(K)*

(d) During the development of the foetus it is protected by all of the following **except** the:
    A uterus wall
    B amniotic fluid
    C muscles of the abdomen
    D diaphragm *(K)*

(e) Which of the following is **not** transported from the mother across the placenta to the foetus?
    A urea **B** oxygen **C** glucose **D** amino acids *(K)*

(f) The fusion of an egg and a sperm is called:
    A copulation **B** implantation **C** fertilisation **D** ovulation *(K)*

2 The graph below shows changes in hormone levels throughout a woman's menstrual cycle.

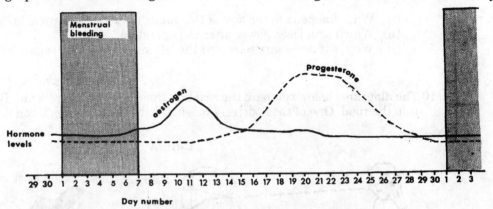

(a) (i) State how long this woman's menstrual cycle is. *(P)(1)*
    (ii) How many days does her menstrual bleeding last? *(P)(1)*

(b) From the graph, state which hormone is produced at a high level in the second half of the cycle. *(P)(1)*

(c) State the changes in hormone level which appear to trigger off menstrual blooding. *(P)(1)*

WJEC, Biology (Human), Paper 1, 1990

3 The diagram shows the female reproductive system. Label the following parts on this diagram:
    ovary
    oviduct (or Fallopian tube)
    uterus
    vagina

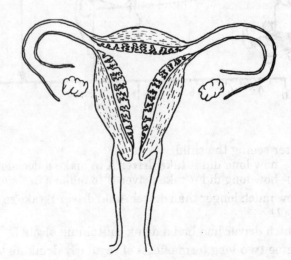

(K)(4)
SEG, Biology (Human), Paper 1, 1990

4 The diagram shows the female reproductive system in vertical section.

   (a) Label A–E on the diagram. *(K)(5)*

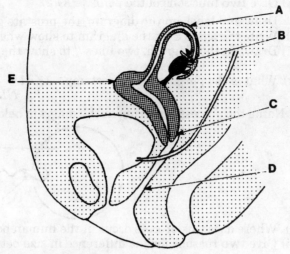

   (b) On the diagram, put an arrow and label

      (i) **P** to show where the penis is inserted during copulation.

      (ii) **F** to show where fertilisation occurs.

      (iii) **O** to show where ovulation occurs.

      (iv) **Placenta** to show where the placenta is attached during pregnancy. *(K)(4)*

   WJEC, Biology (Human), Paper 1, 1991

5 The diagram shows a foetus approximately ten weeks old.

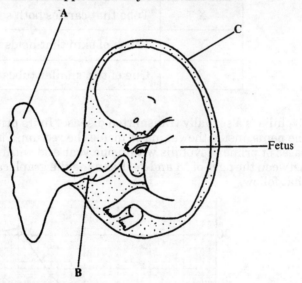

   (a) Give the names of the parts labelled A, B and C.

   (b) What is present inside part B?

   (c) It is sometimes said that part A acts as a barrier. Explain what is meant by this and give **one** example. *(K)(6)*

   SEG, Biology (Human), Paper 1, 1991

6 (a) The diagram below shows a simplified human male reproductive system.

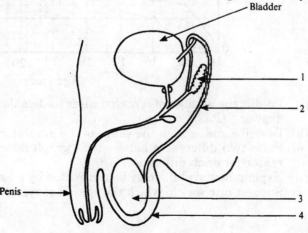

    (i)   Name the numbered parts in the diagram. *(K)(4)*
    (ii) What is the function of the bladder? *(K)(1)*
    (iii) Give **two** functions of the penis. *(K)(2)*

 (b)(i)   Draw and label, on the diagram, the prostate gland in the correct position. *(K)(2)*
    (ii) Write the letter S on the diagram to show where sperm are made. *(K)(1)*
    (iii) Draw, on the diagram, two lines // to show the part that is cut during a vasectomy. *(K)(1)*

    (iv) What is the purpose of a vasectomy? *(K)(1)*

NISEAC, Biology (Human), Paper 1, 1990

7 (a)(i) Name the process occurring in the diagram below. *(K)(1)*

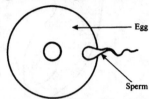

Egg

Sperm

    (ii) Where does this process occur in the human body? *(K)(1)*
    (iii) Give **two** reasons for the difference in size between the egg and the sperm. *(K)(2)*

 (b)(i)   Name a hormone that controls the development of female secondary sexual characteristics. *(K)(1)*
    (ii) Give **one** example of a human female secondary sexual characteristic. *(K)(1)*

NISEAC, Biology (Human), Paper 2, 1990

8 (a) The table describes three parts of the male reproductive system.
Identify parts X, Y and Z from their description.

X	Tube that carries both semen and urine.
Y	Pouch of skin that holds the testes.
Z	One of two similar tubes that carry sperm.

(K)(3)

(b) Syphilis is a sexually transmitted disease. In its primary stage, a painless sore appears on the penis, inside the vagina or inside the rectum. The graph shows the number of reported cases of primary syphilis within one year and within one area, for both males and females between the ages of 14 and 24. Examine the graph carefully and then answer the questions that follow.

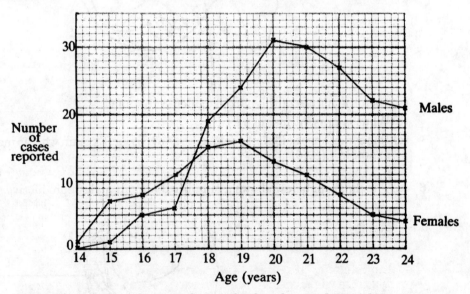

    (i)   Predict the number of reported cases for females aged 13 and give **one** reason for your answer. *(P)(2)*
    (ii) Describe and explain the shape of the graph for males. *(P)(2)*
    (iii) State **two** differences between the graph for males and that for females. Suggest a reason for **each** difference. *(P)(4)*
    (iv) Explain how syphilis may be contracted by a baby during birth. *(K)(3)*
    (v) Suggest **one** way in which the spread of syphilis could be reduced. *(K)(1)*

SEG, Biology (Human), Paper 3, 1990

9 (a) The diagrams below show some stages in an 'in vitro' fertilisation programme.

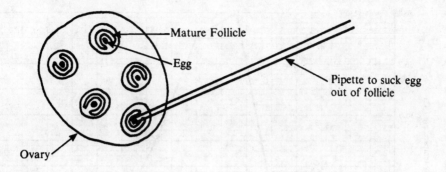

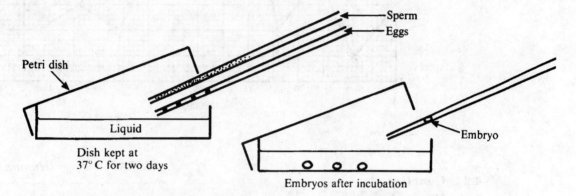

  (i)   Describe how the embryos are introduced into the body. *(K)(2)*
  (ii) Suggest why more than one embryo is introduced into the body. *(K)(2)*
  (iii) Explain the importance of incubating the embryos at 37 °C for two days before they are introduced into the body. *(K)(3)*

(b) The table below shows the reliability of a number of different methods of contraception. (Reliability is shown as the number of pregnancies in one year resulting from 1 000 women/men using that method.)

Method of contraception	*Reliability*
Male sterilisation	2.5
Female sterilisation	1.0
Intrauterine device (IUD)	7.0
Pill	3.5
Condom	9.0
Rhythm method	20.0

  (i)   Explain the difference between birth control and contraception. *(K)(2)*
  (ii) Which method, shown in the table, is the most reliable? *(P)(1)*
  (iii) Suggest why the pill is more reliable than the IUD. *(K)(2)*
  (iv) If 5 000 women were using the rhythm method of contraception, how many would become pregnant in one year? (Show your working) *(P)(1)*

(c) The reliability of the rhythm method of contraception can be improved if the woman can recognise when she ovulates. The graph overleaf shows the body temperature of a woman over 40 days.
  (i)   What was the woman's body temperature 20 days after the beginning of her menstruation? *(P)(1)*
  (ii) For how many days was the body temperature over 36.7 °C? *(P)(1)*
  (iii) Mark on your graph the point at which ovulation is most likely to have occurred. *(P)(1)*
  (iv) Explain why identification of ovulation can increase the chance of a woman becoming pregnant. *(K)(3)*

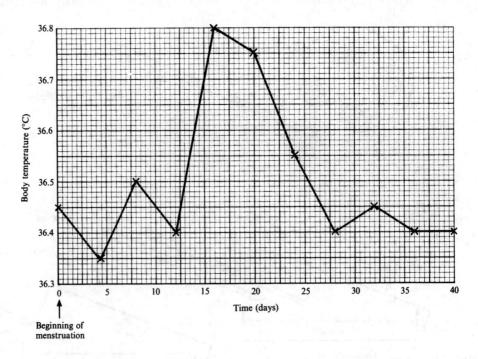

NISEAC, Biology (Human), Paper 3, 1991

4.2 Genetics

1 (a) Mitosis occurs:
  A in gametes
  B in males only
  C when there are too many chromosomes in a cell
  D whenever new body cells are produced *(K)*

  (b) A chromosome:
  A is found only in gametes
  B carries genetic information
  C is present at all times in cells
  D can migrate across the nuclear membrane *(K)*

  (c) The sex of a baby is determined by:
  A the mother's ovum
  B the number of ova produced
  C the father's sperm
  D the age of the father *(K)*

  (d) A gene is:
  A a unit of heredity
  B made up of chromosomes
  C found only in male gametes
  D produced after fertilisation *(K)*

2 The diagrams below show the divisions which occur in the nuclei of two types of human cells.

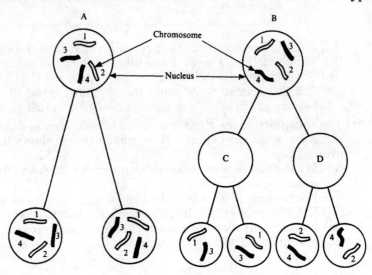

(a) Give **two** differences, you can see, between type A and type B division. Write the differences in the table below.

Difference	Type A division	Type B division
1		
2		

(P)(2)

(b) Which of the numbered chromosomes should be present in circles C and D? *(P)(2)*

(c) Where, in the human body, does type B division occur? *(K)(1)*

NISEAC, Biology (Human), Paper 1, 1991

3 Read through this data carefully, then answer the questions below.

A man is Blood Group A. This is his phenotype for blood grouping. His genotype is AO.
A woman is Blood Group B. This is her phenotype for blood grouping. Her genotype is BO.
Their children's possible genotypes are shown below.

Woman's gametes	Man's gametes	
	A	O
B	AB	BO
O	AO	OO

So, the children's phenotypes will be:
Blood Group AB
Blood Group B
Blood Group A
Blood Group O

(a) Tick (more than once if necessary) in the appropriate column if:

	dominant	recessive	co-dominant (incompletely dominant)
Allele O is			
Allele A is			
Allele B is			

(P)(5)

(b) In the box below, fill in the possible gametes and genotypes of the children of a man, genotype AO, and a woman, genotype AB.

Woman's gametes	Man's gametes	

(P)(4)

(c) Of these children, what percentage would you expect to be Blood Group A? *(P)(1)*

WJEC, Biology (Human), Paper 2, 1991

4 (a) The diagrams below show two types of human ear lobes.

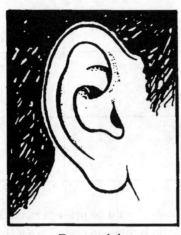

Free ear lobes

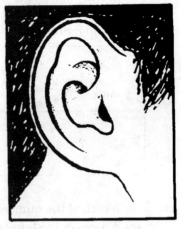

Attached ear lobes

The allele for free ear lobes (F) is dominant to the allele for attached ear lobes (f).

(i) State whether people with the following genotypes have free ear lobes or attached ear lobes:

genotype Ff

genotype ff *(P)(2)*

(ii) Gametes contain only one allele.

Complete the two circles to show the gametes that can be produced from an Ff person.

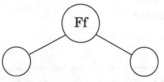

(P)(2)

(iii) Complete the cross below for a woman who is homozygous for ear lobes (FF) and a man who is heterozygous for ear lobes (Ff).

Woman's gametes	Man's gametes	

(P)(3)

(iv) What type of ear lobes do the offspring from this cross have? *(P)(1)*

(b) The sex of humans is controlled by two sex chromosomes.

The letters X and Y are used to represent the sex chromosomes.

(i) What sex is a person with two X chromosomes? *(K)(1)*

(ii) Use the letters X and Y to show the sex chromosomes in a male skin cell and a female liver cell. *(K)(2)*

NISEAC, Biology (Human), Paper 1, 1991

5 (a) The table below shows the approximate amounts of DNA in a cell

Type of cell	DNA in arbitrary units
White blood cell	104
Red blood cell	0
Sperm cell	52
Cell beginning mitosis	208
Cheek cell	104

(i)   Account for the difference in DNA between the red blood cell and the white blood cell. *(K)(1)*
(ii) Account for the difference in DNA between the sperm cell and the cheek cell. *(K)(1)*
(iii) Account for the large amount of DNA in the cell at the beginning of mitosis. *(K)(1)*

(b) A technique of 'DNA fingerprinting' has been developed to compare the genetic composition of different people.

A person's DNA is separated into 'bands' by this technique which involves using enzymes to split DNA.

The diagram below shows the bands of DNA for eight people, A to H.

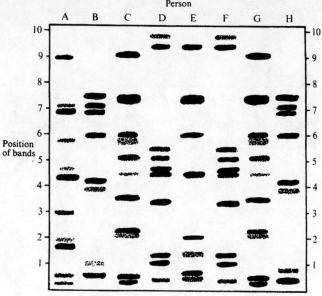

(i)   Person A has 11 bands. How many bands has person F? *(P)(1)*
(ii) Suggest reasons why some bands appear larger or darker than others. *(P)(2)*
(iii) There are three pairs of identical twins shown in the diagram.
      Identify the pairs of identical twins, giving reasons for your answer. *(P)(3)*

LEAG, Biology (Human), Paper 3, 1991

6 The diagram below shows **four** generations of a family which has a history of haemophilia. This disease is inherited as a sex-linked recessive gene on the X chromosome.

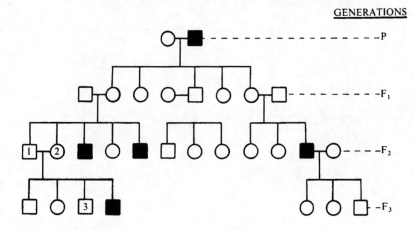

KEY
◯ = NORMAL FEMALE
☐ = NORMAL MALE
■ = HAEMOPHILIC MALE

Use the symbols N = normal and n = haemophilic throughout this question.

(a) How many children did the parent generation give birth to? *(P)(1)*
(b) What is a sex-linked gene? *(K)(2)*
(c) What are the **two** possible genotypes for a phenotypically normal female? *(P)(1)*

NISEAC, Biology (Human), Paper 3, 1990

Answers

Please note that the answers that follow are the author's only and that the various examining groups accept no responsibility for the methods or accuracy of working in the answers given.

THEME 1 MAN'S POSITION IN THE LIVING WORLD

1 (a) **D** (b) **A** (c) **C** (d) **A** (e) **D** (f) **B** (g) **D** (h) **A**

2 (a) 2

   (b) Enzyme 1 acts within a narrower range of pH than enzyme 2.

   Enzyme 1 has a higher rate of reaction than enzyme 2.

3 (a) The action of the enzyme would be speeded up.

   (b) The enzyme, catalase, is contained in the liver. The enzyme breaks down hydrogen peroxide to release oxygen which causes the frothing. More frothing occurred in a pH of 9 than in a pH of 7 or pH of 8.

   (c) Use the same masses of liver in each case. Use the same volume of hydrogen peroxide in each case.

   (d) Increase the range of pH under investigation. Use pH below 7 and above 9.

4

Cell	1 (a)	1 (b)	2 (a)	2 (b)	3 (a)	3 (b)	4 (a)	4 (b)	5 (a)	5 (b)	Name of cell
A	✓			✓			✓				White blood cell
B		✓									Red blood cell
C	✓		✓		✓						Nerve cell
D	✓							✓	✓		Plant palisade cell
E	✓		✓			✓					Sperm cell
F	✓			✓				✓		✓	Cheek cell

5 (a) (i)   J Protoplasm/Cytoplasm
             K Nucleus
             L Cell membrane
      (ii) Cell B
      (iii) B has a cell wall. C is round. B has a nucleus.

   (b) (i)

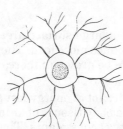

      (ii) An organ is a collection of different tissues. A tissue is a collection of similar cells. A cell is a basic unit that makes up a tissue. In this case the heart is an organ made of muscle, nervous and blood tissues.
            Each of these tissues is made of individual cells.

6

	Human cell	Leaf cell
(i)	No chloroplasts	Chloroplasts present
(ii)	No cell walls	Cell walls present

7 (a) **A** (b) **A** (c) **B** (d) **C**

8 (a) Air spaces under cover slip. Stain on surface of cover slip. Cover slip is not level on the surface of the material.

   (b) (i)   Dirt on the eyepiece lens
      (ii) Incorrect focusing
      (iii) Objective not completely under the tube of the microscope

9 (a)(i)

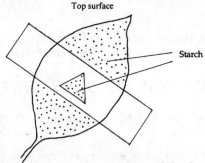

Top surface

Starch

(ii) To prevent light getting to the under surface of the leaf

(b)(i) Photosynthesis

(ii) Carbon dioxide/water

10 Expired air contains carbon dioxide. In A this enters the water and the pond weed uses it for photosynthesis; hence a lot of oxygen produced in A.

In B, the oil prevents any carbon dioxide entering the water. Therefore photosynthesis is not possible and very little oxygen is seen in the tube.

11 (a)(i) The human femur is longer and is less straight.

(ii) The human pelvic cavity is larger.

(b)(i) Both are warm blooded vertebrates with hair and both suckle their young.

(ii) Both have an opposable thumb and index finger. The frontal region of the skull is large to accommodate a large brain.

(c)

	Gorilla	*Man*
(i)	Many lines on palm	Fewer lines on palm
(ii)	Short thumb	Longer thumb
(iii)	Fingers close together	Fingers with spaces between

THEME 2   MAN AND HIS ENVIRONMENT

2.1   Interdependence

1 (a) **A**   (b) **D**   (c)(i) **A**   (ii) **C**   (d) **B**   (e) **C**   (f) **B**   (g) **D**   (h) **D**

2 (a)(i) A Light

B Chemical

C Heat

(ii) Leaves have a large surface area. Palisade cells have a high density of chloroplasts.

(iii) They can produce more food. They can be more productive in less sunny climates. They can therefore be grown in more countries.

(b)(i) 10% of 40% = 4%

(ii) There is such a lot of energy lost as heat between feeding levels in a food chain that the energy in the body tissues of animals is just a small fraction of the radiant energy from the sun that reaches plants. The longer the food chain, the more energy is lost before reaching consumers at the end of the food chain.

3 (a)(i)

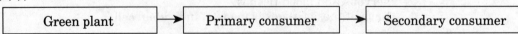

| Green plant | → | Primary consumer | → | Secondary consumer |

(ii) They produce food by converting light energy into chemical energy.

(b)

Organism	*What it feeds on*	*Trophic (feeding) level*
R	V	3rd
S	R	4th
T		1st
V	T	2nd

4 (a)

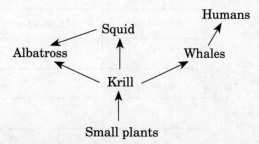

(b)(i) Krill population would decrease.
   (ii) Lack of light prevents small plants photosynthesising. Therefore plant population decreases. Therefore krill population decreases because of lack of food.

(c)(i) Whale population would decrease.
   (ii) Humans would be using part of the food of whales. Therefore there would not be enough food for the whales.

(d) Ban whaling internationally.

5

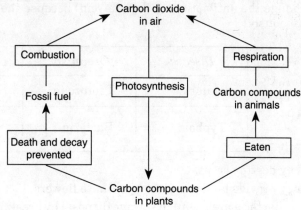

6 (a) A Nitrates
      B Urea
   (b) C Excretion
      D Death
   (c) E Nitrifying
      F Nitrogen-fixing

7 (a)(i) To stop impurities in the air from entering.
      (ii) It will decrease to below 7.
      (iii) Because the bacteria are aerobic and so will need oxygen for respiration.
      (iv) The air reaching the lime water in flask B had so little carbon dioxide that it did not cause the lime water to change colour.
          The air reaching the lime water in flask B had a lot of carbon dioxide from the respiration of bacteria in flask C and so it changed colour.
      (v) The air in flask D would probably have less oxygen than the air in flask B because the bacteria would be using it for respiration.

   (b)(i) On the wood shavings.
      (ii) To give it more time to change the ethanol into acetic acid.
      (iii) It increases the surface for bacterial growth. It also affects the flavour of the vinegar depending on the type of wood.
      (iv) Test the pH.

8 (a)(i) The birth rate remains steady.
      (ii) The death rate shows periods of increase alternating with periods of decrease.
   (b) Phase B
   (c) Stable

9 (a) Country B because there are more people under the age of 20 in the population.
   (b) Country A because there are more people living longer.

10 (a)(i) Extend graph with straight line to give a value of approximately 6 000 million (6 x 10⁹).
      (ii) Increased effectiveness of medical science. Better diet. Agricultural and industrial development.
      (iii) Birth control by natural means. Contraception. Natural disasters, famine and drought.

2.2 Disease

1 (a) **D** (b) **D** (c) **C** (d) **D** (e) **C** (f) **D**

2 (a)

Antibiotic	Diameter of clear area (mm)
1	9
2	35
3	23
4	13
5	30

(b) 2 (spectinomycin)

(c) The clear area around number 2 is smaller than previously.

(d) The bacteria are developing resistance to this antibiotic.

(e) Change the antibiotic to 1 (kanamycin) because the clear area around this is larger than previously.

3 (a)

Disease	Organism	Transmission
Malaria	Protozoan	By a vector
Typhoid	Bacteria	On food/in water

(b) They destroy crops.

(c) They provide honey and they pollinate flowers.

(d) (i) Bacteria are useful in sewage disposal by breaking down organic matter in the digestor used in a sewage works. They also kill and ingest harmful microbes.

(ii) Putrefying bacteria break down organic material. Nitrifying bacteria change ammonium compounds to nitrites, then to nitrates. Denitrifying bacteria change nitrates into nitrogen. Nitrogen fixing bacteria use nitrogen and convert it to a form that can be used by plants.

4 (a) A The bacterium is ingested and broken down by the white blood cell.

B The bacterium makes the white blood cell produce antibodies. These surround the bacterium, immobilising it and making it available for other white blood cells to ingest.

(b) (i) Serum containing antibodies against diphtheria.

(ii) Passive immunity gives short term protection. Active immunity gives long term protection.

(iii) It produced more antibodies because the original supply has been boosted by the second injection.

(iv) 28

(v) The injection is given in an emergency for a fast response. Active immunity takes longer to produce results.

(c) (i) The donor's kidney would not function in the recipient as its tissues would not be compatible.

(ii) The 'foreign' tissue would cause the recipient to produce antibodies. These antibodies would then 'attack' the transplanted kidney.

5 Bacteria enter the damaged dermis of the skin. White blood cells migrate through the wall of the capillary and attack the invading bacteria by either ingesting them directly or by producing antibodies. These surround the bacteria and immobilise them, thus allowing them to be ingested. Platelets break down and begin the clotting process. This forms a protective layer over the wound.

6 (a) (i) Because it obtains its food from its living host and gives nothing in return.

(ii) Hands should always be washed after using the toilet. Food should always be washed before being eaten.

(iii) As a precaution in case other members of the family are infected from the child.

(iv) Bacteria from faeces may enter the broken skin and blood system. They could then be transported around the body in the circulation of blood.

(b) (i) Presence of eggs of head lice. Scalp may be itchy due to the effects of the adult head lice.

(ii) They have six curved claws which grip the hair firmly.

(iii) Use an insecticide such as gamma benzene hexachloride in shampoos. This poisons the head lice.

7 (a) Heart disease, stroke, influenza and pneumonia, cancer, accidents.

(b) It is twice as common in the 1980s.

(c) 550 per 100 000

(d) 50%

(e) A better standard of living due to less overcrowding and a healthier diet.

(f) An increased level of sugar in the diet.

8 (a) (i) France
   (ii) Switzerland
   (iii) No, because the total population of France is much higher than that of Switzerland.
   (iv) A change of sexual habits of AIDS sufferers, e.g. use of condoms. Better sex education making people aware of methods of transmission of AIDS.
   (v) Acquired immune deficiency syndrome
   (vi) A virus

(b) The rate of population growth is likely to decrease because, at present, AIDS is a terminal condition. Therefore the death rate in all populations will increase.

9 (a) (i) Typhoid is spread by food or water being contaminated by bacteria.
   (ii) Malaria is spread by the female Anopheles mosquito carrying the protozoan parasite Plasmodium and transmitting it to humans when it bites them.
   (ii) Influenza is caused by a virus which is spread by droplet infection during sneezing or other close contact between an infected person and a healthy person.

(b) (i) Vaccination prevents the spread of typhoid, together with appropriate food hygiene.
   (ii) The spread of malaria is controlled by killing the vector in the adult or larval stage or by killing the parasite when it is inside the human host with drugs.
   (iii) The prevention of the spread of influenza is brought about by vaccination which may give immunity for 1–2 years. Also contact with infected people should be avoided by an isolation period of at least 7 days.

(c) (i) By mixing of body fluids during sexual intercourse. By blood to blood contact.
   (ii) Use of condoms during sexual intercourse. Avoiding used needles or syringes.

10 (a) Male

(b) Over 65

(c) 2 males:1 female.

(d) They develop it because they live in conditions where the atmosphere is high in tobacco smoke and possibly other air pollutants. Body cells are in an active state of division at this age.

11 (a) (i) Heart attack
   (ii) 9%

(b) More men than women smoke

(c) Fibre

12 (a)

Type of organism	Name of organism	Disease caused
Fungus	Trichophyton	Athlete's foot
Protozoan	Plamodium	Malaria
Bacterium	Salmonella	Food poisoning
Virus	Rubella	German measles

(b) (i) A
   (ii) Mosquito
   (iii) Asexual reproduction
   (iv) It passes out of the liver in the hepatic vein.
   (v) The female Anopheles mosquito feeds on the blood of humans and, in doing so, transmits the parasite from the salivary glands.

2.3 Personal health and hygiene

1 (a) **B**   (b) **D**

2 (a) The four relevant points in the list are that alcohol is quickly absorbed from the stomach; that it slows the passage of a nerve impulse at a synapse; that it affects the cerebellum of the brain so making muscular coordination difficult; that it affects the cerebrum so changing behaviour.

(b) It can cause the bacteria infecting the person to build up a resistance.

3 (a) (i) A
   (ii) There is not so much strain on the vertebral column.
 (b) The head is pushed forward, resulting in a tilted pelvis to maintain balance. Shoulders become very rounded, back muscles are strained and correct breathing is impossible.

4 (a) E280. The acid would preserve the food from bacteria.
 (b) (i) Fruit (in jams)
   (ii) The high content of sugar would tend to dehydrate any micro-organism which settles on it because of osmosis, i.e. water will pass out of the micro-organism into the sugar through the selectively permeable membrane surrounding the cell/cells of the micro-organism.
 (c) (i) The dye with the untreated milk turned white first because of the micro-organisms respiring aerobically and using up oxygen rapidly as they multiplied. Pasteurised milk took longer because it has less micro-organisms in it. These took longer to reach the numbers necessary to cause the colour change. Ultra-heat treated milk contained no living micro-organisms because the heat treatment had killed them. Therefore there was no colour change.
   (ii) Ultra-heat treatment is the most effective treatment for preserving milk.
 (d) Food poisoning due to Salmonella. This bacterium would multiply rapidly when heated.

5 (a) To prevent entry of micro-organisms.
 (b) Sterilisation
 (c) An equal volume of untreated broth in a sterile test tube sealed with sterile cotton wool and tinfoil left in the laboratory at 20 °C.
 (d) A suitable temperature is a condition for all life. Micro-organisms would not reproduce at −4 °C.

6 (a) (i) High-heeled shoes can stunt growth of bones and can cause calluses and misalignment of the bones.
   (ii) Muscles of the leg may be strained during balancing.
   (iii) Because the foot bones are still growing, there must be sufficient room for growth. Shoes which are too small will stunt the growth of bones and cause deformities.
 (b) A slipped disc could result. Sometimes one of the cartilage discs which form immovable joints between the vertebrae is pulled out of alignment as a result of undue strain. In extreme cases pressure can result on spinal nerves or even the spinal cord.

7 (a) Add milk sugar.
 (b) Add black current juice or orange juice to the diet.
 (c) Antibodies from the mother can be present in the milk. These will act against pathogens.
 (d) Some babies become allergic to cows' milk. The high protein of cows' milk can absorb too much acid from the baby's stomach. The acid normally helps digestion and kills bacteria.

8 (a) Some bacteria in milk will survive a temperature of 70 °C and will multiply and cause milk to go sour.
 (b) All bacteria and their spores are killed at this temperature.
 (c) Bacteria do not reproduce at the temperatures at which freezers work but they reproduce slowly at refrigerator temperatures.

2.4 Public health

1 (a) **C**   (b) **D**   (c) **C**   (d) **D**   (e) **B**   (f) **A**

2 (a) (i) 4.44 tonnes per year
   (ii) Mercury can build up in concentration through food chains. Humans could obtain the mercury via fish and could suffer mercuric poisoning.
 (b) (i) 20 522 tonnes per year
   (ii) Fertiliser used in agriculture
   (iii) Use crop rotation methods rather than excess fertiliser. Investigate use of genetic engineering in production of nitrogen-fixing bacteria which can live in crop plants.
 (c) (i) There has been less radioactive liquid discharge from 1979 to 1985.
   (ii) In 1979 it was 4.5 units. In 1985 it was 0.5 units. Therefore it was 9 times more in 1979, i.e. 4.5/0.5.
   (iii) 4 tonnes per year
   (iv) Increased radiation leads to an increase in mutation rate and cancer. Radioactive minerals can be assimilated in plants and enter food chains leading to an effect on humans.
   (v) Storage leading to gradual radioactive decay and loss of radioactivity. Burial in the depths of the earth or at the bottom of the sea. In both cases, the material is in fracture-proof containers.

3 (a) Faeces and urea

(b) Solid coarse materials are trapped in the iron screens.

(c) Fertiliser

(d) The filter bed is filled with coke, clinker and small stones. The effluent is forced up through a vertical pipe in the centre of the bed and out through horizontal side tubes which are perforated with many holes. The side tubes move around in a circle, spraying jets of effluent onto the stones. Anaerobic micro-organisms in the effluent are killed by aeration or by being eaten by useful micro-organisms that grow on the surface of the filter bed stones.

4 (a) (i) Coal, oil and timber

(ii) Oil/coal

(iii) Sulphur dioxide, oxides of nitrogen

(iv) The acid gases, sulphur dioxide and oxides of nitrogen dissolve in water as it condenses and precipitates.

(v) It acidifies lakes/rivers and kills fish and other aquatic life. It acidifies soil, allowing aluminium ions to be available to plant roots. The aluminium is toxic to plants when in high concentration.

(b) Site A. It is upwind of the factory so would not have air pollution from it. It is upstream of the river so would not be affected by chemical discharge into the water. It is still near enough to the factory for access for the employees and near to the town for its amenities.

5 (a) 2500 cm^3

(b) Urination

(c) It would make the urea and salts more concentrated.

(d) During filtration all floating matter and some suspended materials are removed from the water. At this stage, helpful micro-organisms reduce the number of harmful bacteria by eating them. Chlorination kills all remaining bacteria in the water.

(e) To prevent any unwanted materials getting into the water and also to prevent evaporation.

(f) Fluoride strengthens the enamel of teeth.

(g) (i)

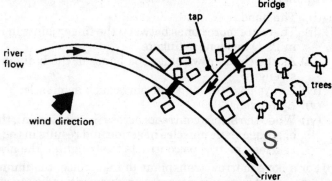

(ii) The sewage treatment plant should be downstream of the village water supply to avoid contamination of the water. It should also avoid the prevailing wind if odours are to be kept from the village.

6 (a) Chlorine kills bacteria and by chlorinating water many waterborne diseases have been controlled. Therefore fewer people die from these and the population increases.

(b) Improved agricultural methods have led to maximum production from crops and domesticated animals. This has led to more available food for the developing world with a consequent increase in population.

7 (a) 27 tonnes

(b) Mercury, lead, copper, zinc, nitrates, phosphates, chlorine, ammonium salts

(c) Plants obtain their nitrogen to make proteins in the form of nitrate.

(d) Ecologically dead means that there are very few or no living organisms in the river. Lack of oxygen has been the main cause for this.

THEME 3 HUMAN STRUCTURE AND FUNCTION

3.1 The skeleton and movement

1 (a) **C** (b) **B** (c) **A** (d) **D** (e) **C** (f) **D**

2 (a) (i) A Ligament

B Synovial membrane

C Synovial fluid

D Ulna

(ii) Smooth cartilage and lubricating synovial fluid

(iii) The biceps contracts, the triceps relaxes. This antagonistic action across a joint, with the muscles firmly attached by tendons, causes the bending action.

(iv) Ligaments attach bones together.

(b) (i)

Key	Letter
Controls	B
Bones in acid for 1 day	A
Bones in acid for 2 days	D
Bones in acid for 3 days	C

(ii) Y because it appears to bend more than X

(iii) Organic material was unchanged and held the bone together.

(iv) Calcium carbonate

(v) It reduces its rigidity.

(vi) Collagen

3 (a) (i) X Ball-and-socket. Y Hinge.

(ii) The head of the humerus fits into the socket of the shoulder blade.
Muscles attached to the bones allow rotation in all directions.

(b) (i) Sphincters are not attached to bones. They do not work in antagonistic pairs.

(ii) The exit of the stomach

(iii) Controls the flow of digested food out of the stomach

4 A Cartilage
B Bone
C Synovial fluid
D Ligament

5 (a) (i) The hand

(ii) There are more bones between the finger joints in P. There seem to be more wrist bones in P. Q has longer fingers.

(iii) As the child grows older the bones of the individual fingers fuse together for greater strength.

(iv) X rays pass through soft parts such as muscle.

(v) By tendons

(vi) When the biceps contracts across the elbow joint, the triceps relaxes. This is an example of antagonistic muscles in action and results in the bending of the arm. When the biceps relaxes, the triceps contracts to straighten the arm.

(b) For a bone marrow transplant to take place, the immune system of the recipient must be suppressed so that it does not produce antibodies to reject the donor's marrow.

(c) (i) and (ii)

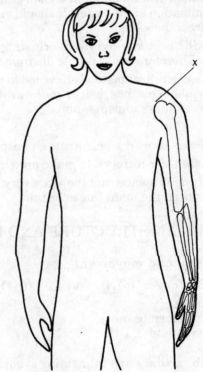

(d)(i) The techniques and materials used for joint replacements have improved since they were first carried out.

(ii) Young children would still be growing; therefore an artificial hip replacement would be of limited value in terms of time.

6 (a) A contracts and B relaxes.

(b) They both relax.

(c)

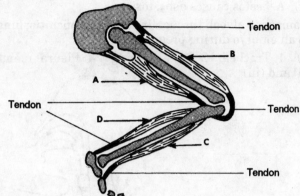

3.2 The respiratory system

1 (a) **C**   (b) **D**   (c) **C**   (d) **B**   (e) **C**   (f) **D**

2 (a)

Structure	What happens
Lung	expands
Rib	raised
Diaphragm muscle	contracts
Diaphragm	lowered
Thorax	volume increases

(b) Volume of carbon dioxide $= 15 - 14.4 \text{ cm}^3 = 0.6 \text{ cm}^3$
Volume of carbon dioxide + oxygen $= 15 - 12 \text{ cm}^3 = 3 \text{ cm}^3$
Volume of oxygen $= 3 - 0.6 = 2.4 \text{ cm}^3$
% oxygen $= 2.4/15 \times 100/1 = 16\%$
% of carbon dioxide $= 0.6/15 \times 100/1 = 4\%$

(c) (i) Sodium hydroxide
(ii) Alkaline pyrogallol
(iii) The normal amount of oxygen in atmospheric air is about 20% and the carbon dioxide is about 0.04%.

3 (a) Energy

(b)(i) A bronchiole
B alveolus
(ii) They have a large, total surface area.

4 (a)(i)

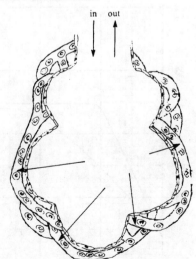

(ii) Carbon dioxide
(iii) Diffusion
(b)(i) 20%
(ii) 16%
(iii) 18%
(iv) B because less oxygen had diffused into the blood supply of the lungs
(v) Asbestos causes asbestosis.
(c) Damage to alveoli through irritation; bronchitis; lung cancer; reduction of oxygen available to an embryo during pregnancy

5 (a)(i) 1 Trachea 2 Rib 3 Lung 4 Pleural membrane 5 Alveolus
(ii) and (iii)

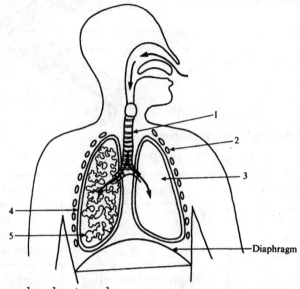

(iv) It moves upward and outward.
(v) 5

3.3 Food and nutrition

1 (a) **B** (b) **D** (c) **A** (d) **B** (e) **C** (f) **C**
2 (a)(i) Cellulose cell wall
(ii) Much of the energy is in the form of cellulose which is a carbohydrate that cannot be digested with human enzymes. Cellulose makes up the bulk of the fibre which is egested.
(iii) Sunlight
(iv) Starch is the insoluble storage product and is contained in the cereal grain. Sugar is soluble and also used as a direct source of energy.
(v) Starch
(b)(i) 2.5%
(ii) An increase in concentration does not increase the rate of digestion—it remains constant. The reason is that all of the starch molecules available have been saturated with enzyme and they are all used.
(iii)

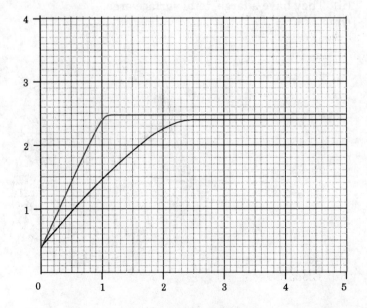

(c) Add equal volumes of 0.2% starch to six test tubes. To each test tube add an equal volume of amylase as follows

Test tube	1	2	3	4	5	6
Amylase %	1.0	1.5	2.0	2.5	3.0	3.5

Place the tubes in a water bath at a constant temperature of 15 °C. Test a sample of each tube at 1 minute intervals with iodine. Digestion of starch is seen when the iodine no longer changes colour.

(d) Approximately pH7

3 (a)

	Letter
Bread	C
Fish	A
Cabbage	D
Butter	B

(b) In **C** there is 1 g in 100 g, therefore 2 g in 200 g.

In **B** there is 0.4 g in 100 g, therefore 0.2 g in 50 g.

Therefore the total protein in the snack is 2.2 g.

4 (a)

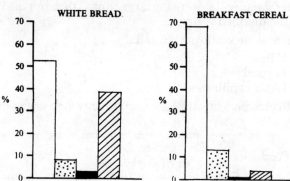

(b) Mix some finely ground breakfast cereal in water, then add an equal volume of Benedict's reagent and heat strongly in a water bath. If there is a colour change from blue to green to yellowish brown or reddish brown, a simple sugar like glucose is present.

5 (a) (i) Milk

(ii) Rice

(b) Mung beans, wheat flour

(c) Protein

(d) Growth and repair

6 (a) **C** (b) **D** (c) **D** (d) **A**

3.4 The digestive system

1 (a) **A** (b) **C** (c) **D** (d) **A** (e) **B** (f) **C**

2 (a) (i) and (ii)

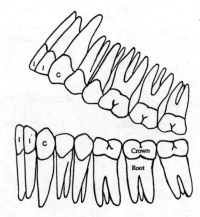

(iii) 32

(iv) Blood vessels and nerves

(b)(i) Food remaining between teeth decays as a result of bacteria feeding on it. The bacteria convert sugar into acid as a waste product. The acid dissolves away the enamel and dentine resulting in tooth decay.

(ii) In 2 and 3, the decay has reached the pulp cavity which contains the nerves. When the nerves are affected, the person feels pain.

(c)(i) More children have decayed teeth in Northern Ireland than in Great Britain. As children get older, more of their teeth decay.

(ii) Add flouride to drinking water. Encourage children to brush their teeth more often. Change children's eating habits, i.e. reduce sugar intake.

(d) Bacteria in the mouth of person B have more time to act on food and produce an acid pH. This will probably lead to more tooth decay. The pH of person B's mouth is rarely neutral and is acid for a much longer period than person A's mouth.

3 (a) A Bile
   B Urea/glucose/protein
   C Glucose

(b) Alcohol

4 (a)(i) A pipette
   (ii) Add an equal volume of Benedict's reagent and boil in a water bath. If the colour changes from blue to green to reddish brown, a simple sugar solution like glucose would be present.

(b) The molecules of protein are too large to pass through the visking tubing.

5 (a) The protein had been digested to smaller molecules (probably peptones). Therefore no proteins would be left in the visking tubing and the protein molecules would have been too big to pass through the visking tubing into the distilled water.

(b) The glucose molecules were small enough to pass through the visking tubing into the water.

(c) The fat molecules were too large to pass through the visking tubing and so no fat was detected in the distilled water.

(d) There is no vitamin C in milk.

6 (a) A Villus
   B Lacteal
   C Blood capillaries

(b) Villi present a much larger surface area for absorption of digested food than a smooth surface.

(c)

Food	Enzyme involved in digestion	Product of digestion	Carried away in
Carbohydrate	Carbohydrase	Reducing sugar	Blood vessels
Fats, oils	Lipase	Glycerol and fatty acids	Lacteals
Protein	Protease	Amino acids	Blood vessels

7 (a) Set up both tubes at the same time. Use equal volumes of pepsin. Keep the tubes at a constant temperature. Set up a control tube with the same volume of egg white, same volume of dilute acid and same volume of boiled, cooled pepsin. Keep the control tube at the same temperature as the others.

(b) Violet

3.5 The circulatory system

1 (a) **C** (b) **B** (c) **C** (d) **A** (e) **C** (f) **C**

2 (a) and (b)

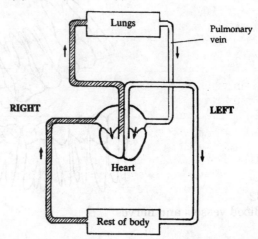

3

4 (a)(i)   1 Aorta   2 Pulmonary vein
   (ii) To stop the heart valves from turning inside out when they close.
   (iii) They close when the left ventricle fills with blood from the left atrium and open when the left ventricle contracts to send blood into the aorta. They prevent back flow of blood into the left ventricle.
   (iv)

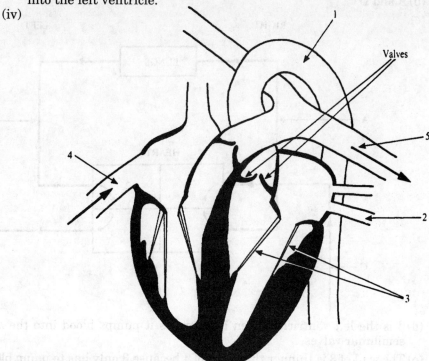

   (b)(i)   4 times
   (ii) Too much fat in the diet
   (c)(i)   21 and 49
   (ii) The blood cholesterol is higher in men than in women between 25 and 45.
   (iii) 4 units
   (iv) High cholesterol is not the only cause of coronary heart disease.
   (d) X is cholesterol lining the inside of the artery. Y are blood cells in the process of clotting. Once a clot has formed in the coronary artery then blood supply to the heart muscle is restricted. The heart muscle will then cease to function without an adequate supply of oxygen and glucose.

5 (a)(i)   32 mm
   (ii) 70 g
   (b)(i)   42 mm
   (ii) 80 g
   (c)(i)

	Length of blood vessel in mm	
	Main artery	*Main vein*
Before the first weight added	17	17
After all the weights were removed	21	30

   (ii) Main artery
   (iii) Main artery
   (iv) (I)   The results of Test 1 are confirmed by the drawing which shows that the artery has a tougher outer non-elastic coat which resists the change in length due to the addition of weight.
   (II)   The results of Test 2 are confirmed by the drawing which shows a thicker layer of muscle and elastic fibres. This allows the artery to be more elastic.
   (III) The artery is best suited to cope with blood at high pressure.

6 (a) Take two samples of enzyme A and B. A is in solution containing 100 units of enzyme per 100 cm³ of liquid. B is 100 units as a powder. Keep A and B in a refrigerator at 4 °C for 15 days. Add both enzymes to the same mass of blood fibrin (clot) in the same volume of distilled water and place both tubes in a water bath at 35 °C for 5 minutes. The active enzyme would have dissolved the fibrin.

(b) Easier storage as a powder. Safer than keeping glass containers. No danger of bacterial contamination.

7 (a) 2 is the left atrium. 3 is the right ventricle.

(b) A and D

(c)

(d) 4 is the left ventricle. When it contracts it pumps blood into the aorta, D, through the semilunar valves.

(e) The wall of 3 is thinner than that of 4 because 3 only has to pump blood to the lungs but 4 has to pump blood all around the body and is therefore more muscular.

8 (a) (i) Lymphocyte
(ii) Antibodies are produced as a response to antigens on the surface of invading pathogens. They surround the pathogen and immobilise it so that phagocytes can ingest the pathogen.
(iii) Phagocytes surround and engulf pathogens. Then they destroy and digest the pathogen.

(b) When the skin is cut, substances released by the platelets cause an enzyme to be activated. This enzyme changes a soluble protein called fibrinogen into fibrin, which is insoluble. A network of threads is formed and red blood cells become trapped in this network and dry to form a clot.

(c) Blood groups are often incompatible because one group may contain antigens which react with antibodies of another group. This causes blood cells to clump together and is called agglutination.

3.6 Regulation/homeostasis

1 (a) **A** (b) **A** (c) **C** (d) **D** (e) **A** (f) **C**

2 (a) A Kidney
B Ureter
C Bladder

(b) Water, glucose

3 (a) (i) Renal artery B.   Ureter D.
(ii) Blood in the renal artery has more oxygen and more urea than the blood in the renal vein.

(b) (i) Because protein molecules are too big to pass through the capillaries (glomerulus) in the Bowman's capsule.
(ii) Diabetes mellitus
(iii) Because it is all reabsorbed into the blood supply of the tubules.

4 (a) (i) 5
(ii) Temperature
(iii) If the stimulus is a cold temperature the erector muscles attached to the hairs will contract and raise the hairs to trap a layer of insulating air.
(iv) The nerve endings in the hair are below the level at which the hair is cut.

(b)(i)

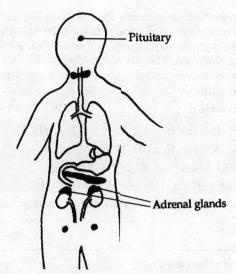

(ii) The pancreas does not secrete insulin until the level of glucose rises above normal. If there is danger of the level falling below normal, glycogen is changed to glucose again.

(iii) Control of glucose is brought about by insulin which is secreted from the pancreas directly into the blood stream. Digestive enzymes have to pass through the pancreatic duct to reach the duodenum.

5 (a) It enables them to colonise a wide range of habitats from the Arctic to the tropics. It allows them to be active throughout the year without hibernating in winter.

(b)(i) There is a decrease during the night and an increase during the day reaching a maximum at 12 noon and beginning to fall at about 8 p.m .

(ii) Between 12 noon and 4 p.m.

(iii) When sweat forms on the surface of the skin it evaporates and the body loses heat by the latent heat of evaporation. As sweat evaporates it carries heat from the skin capillaries.

(c) Sweating makes the body lose water. If urine production continued at the same rate then the body would lose too much water and would dehydrate.

6 (a)(i) A kidney   B ureter

(ii) It carries urine from the kidney to the bladder.

(b)(i)

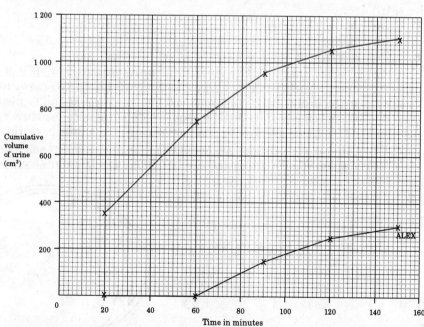

(ii) The presence of salt in the water drunk by Alex caused him to re-absorb more water into the blood supply of the tubules than Chris.

(iii) Chris could have had more to drink than Chris before the beginning of the investigation.

7 (a)(i) X Ureter   Y Renal vein   Z Bladder

(ii) It retains urine until the person is ready to urinate. It can do this because it is a muscular sac which can expand and then contract, forcing urine through its exit because a ring-like sphincter muscle relaxes under a learned conscious control.

(iii) Urea

(b)(i) Because they are too large to pass through the dialysis membrane.

(ii) The solution surrounding the dialysis tubing is continually being replaced. Waste material which has molecules small enough to pass through the tubing will be carried away, e.g. urea. Because there is glucose outside as well as inside the tubing, there is no net loss of glucose or other salts from the blood. The glucose and salts will pass in and out of the tubing at equal rates.

(iii) It only allows small molecules to pass through.

(iv) The glomerulus

3.7 Coordination

1 (a) **B** (b) **B** (c) **B** (d) **C** (e) **D** (f) **D**

2 (a) **D** (b) **A** (c) **E** (d) **B**

3 (a) Ifan (b) Mari (c) Mari (d) Nia

4 (a) They both rely on a stimulus to start the reaction. They both may affect muscles.

(b) The endocrine system relies on the blood system to carry hormones.

5

	Name of chemical(s)
Produced by the pancreas	Insulin, Glucagon
Are hormones	Adrenaline, Insulin, Glucagon
Cause glucose to be stored in the liver	Insulin
Cause glucose to be released by the liver	Adrenaline, Glucagon
Is the stored form of glucose	Glycogen

6 (a) 84%, 75%

(b) There are less normal sighted children in the older age group.
There are more short sighted children in the older age group.
There are more long sighted children in the older age group.

(c) Red–green colour blindness is caused by a sex-linked gene on the X chromosome. It is inherited from the female parent and is much more common in boys than in girls. The fact that it does not develop with age explains why the same percentage of 'other faults' occurs for the younger and older age groups of children on the graph.

(d) (i) **C**
(ii) **A**
(iii) **B**

7 (a) (i) A Iris B Suspensory ligament C Optic nerve
(ii) X is the light sensitive layer of the eye consisting of rods and cones which convert light energy into chemical energy and then into electrical energy which is sent as an impulse to the brain. Y acts as a fine focusing adjustment and focuses the light rays as near to the fovea centralis (yellow spot) which is the most sensitive part of the retina.
(iii) Tears have a very powerful bactericide which kills bacteria on the surface of the eye.

(b) (i) The rays of light are not brought to focus at a sharp point on the retina.
(ii) An abnormally elongated eye ball along the horizontal axis.
(iii)

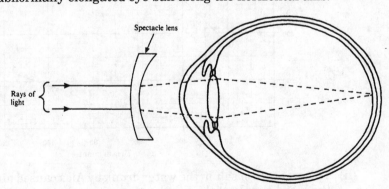

Spectacle lens

Rays of light

8 (a)

Name	*One function*
Cerebral hemisphere	Controls all conscious activity
Cerebellum	Control of balance
Medulla	Controls heart beat/breathing rate
Spinal cord	Takes sensory information to brain

(b)

Statement	Nervous system	Endocrine (hormone) system
Uses motor neurones	✓	
Includes the adrenal glands		✓
Acts more quickly	✓	
Puts substances into the blood system		✓
Uses electrical impulses	✓	
Usually has a long lasting effect		✓

9 (a) A reflex action is a rapid response to a stimulus which does not involve a conscious effort and may not require the use of the brain.

(b) This reflex allows the baby to find the nipple of the mammary gland for feeding.

(c) The stimulus is a sharp tap on the patellar tendon. This initiates a nervous impulse which passes along the sensory nerve, along the dorsal root to the spinal nerve. Here it forms a synapse with the relay nerve in the grey matter which carries the impulse to another synapse with the motor nerve. This carries the impulse along the ventral root to the thigh muscle which contracts.

(d) (i) They dilated.
(ii) Left
(iii) Because the right side of the body is controlled by the left side of the brain and the left side of the body is controlled by the right side of the brain.

10 (a) (i) 0.3 seconds
(ii) 0.5 seconds

(b) 0.5 seconds

(c) B

(d) Liver damage. Brain damage.

THEME 4 HUMAN REPRODUCTION AND THE CONTINUITY OF LIFE

4.1 Human reproduction and development

1 (a) **D**   (b) **B**   (c) **C**   (d) **D**   (e) **A**   (f) **C**

2 (a) (i)   31 days
(ii) 7

(b) Progesterone

(c) Low levels of both progesterone and oestrogen

3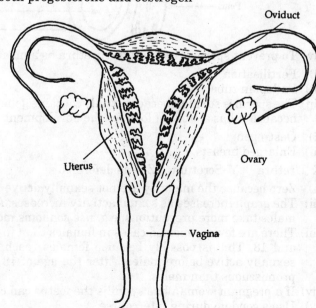

4 (a) A Fallopian tube
       B Ovary
       C Cervix
       D Vagina
       E Uterus
   (b)

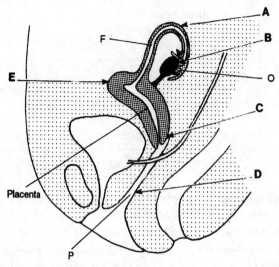

5 (a) A Placenta   B Umbilical cord   C Amnion
   (b) An artery and a vein
   (c) The placenta may act as a barrier for certain bacteria as they will not pass from the mother's blood. Also, maternal and foetal blood groups may be incompatible. The placenta acts as a barrier and will prevent mixing.

6 (a) (i) 1 Seminal vesicles   2 Vas deferens   3 Testis· 4 Scrotum
       (ii) To store urine until the person is ready to urinate.
       (iii) To deposit sperms near the cervix during intercourse. To carry urine through the urethra to the outside.
   (b) (i), (ii), (iii)

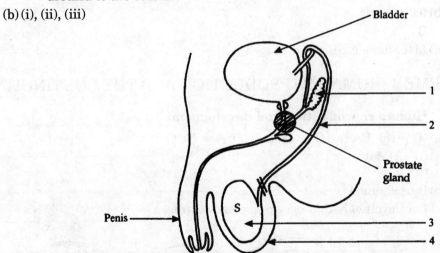

       (iv) To prevent sperms reaching the urethra as a means of contraception.

7 (a) (i) Fertilisation
       (ii) Fallopian tube
       (iii) The sperm is so small because it only contains genetic material whereas the egg is large because it has a store of food for the development of the zygote.
   (b) (i) Oestrogen
       (ii) Enlarged breasts

8 (a) X Urethra   Y Scrotum   Z Vas deferens
   (b) (i) Zero because the majority are not sexually active
       (ii) The graph increases as sexual activity increases. After the age of 20 it is possible that males take more precautions, e.g. use condoms more frequently.
       (iii) There are fewer reported cases in females than in males over 18 but more between 14 and 18. This is possibly because females reach puberty before males and become sexually active before males. After the age of 18 it is possible that females are less promiscuous than males.
       (iv) If a pregnant woman has syphilis the foetus can contract it via the placenta.
       (v) Use a condom during intercourse.

9 (a) (i) The embryos are passed through the cervix into the uterus with a syringe.

   (ii) More than one embryo is introduced because the survival rate is relatively low.

   (iii) This is the normal temperature of the human body and after two days division will have occurred and the embryo will be in a more advanced stage of development and will have a better chance of survival.

(b) (i) Birth control is the regulation of numbers of children produced with the aid of contraception or prevention of fertilisation.

   (ii) Female sterilisation

   (iii) The pill prevents eggs being released whereas the IUD is a barrier which may fail to prevent the egg becoming implanted in the uterine lining.

   (iv) 100. If 20 out of 1 000 become pregnant, $20 \times 5 = 100$ will become pregnant out of 5 000.

(c) (i) 36.75 °C

   (ii) 6

   (iii) Mark ovulation on the time axis of the graph between 12.5 and 16 days.

   (iv) If the woman knows when she is ovulating and wants to become pregnant, she will know when to have intercourse.

4.2   Genetics

1 (a) **D** (b) **B** (c) **C** (d) **A**

2 (a)

Difference	Type A division	Type B division
1	2 cells produced	4 cells produced
2	cells are all diploid	cells produced are haploid

(b) 1 and 3. 4 and 2

(c) In ovaries or testes

3 (a)

	Dominant	Recessive	Co-dominant (incompletely dominant)
Allele O is		✓	
Allele A is			✓
Allele B is			✓

(b)

Woman's gametes	Man's gametes	
	A	O
A	AA	AO
B	AB	BO

(c) 50%

4 (a) (i) Ff free ear lobes.   ff attached ear lobes.

   (ii)

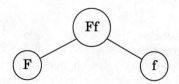

(iii)

Woman's gametes	Man's gametes	
	F	f
F	FF	Ff
F	FF	Ff

(iv) All have free ear lobes

(b)(i) Female

(ii) Male skin cell XY. Female liver cell XX.

5 (a)(i) There is no DNA in a red blood cell because a red blood cell does not have a nucleus (which contains DNA). White blood cells have nuclei.

(ii) A sperm cell has half the number of chromosomes that a cheek cell has; therefore it has half the DNA.

(iii) In the cell at the beginning of mitosis the chromosomes have doubled and hence the DNA has doubled.

(b)(i) 10

(ii) Enzymes vary in their ability to split DNA because the structure of DNA varies according to the bases it possesses.

(iii) The twins are C and G; B and H; D and F. They have the same number of bands and they are in the same positions.

6 (a) 5

(b) A sex-linked gene is one that occurs on the non-pairing segment of an X chromosome.

(c) $X^N X^N$ or $X^N X^n$

EXPERIMENTAL SKILLS AND COURSEWORK

GCSE syllabuses in Human Biology include 'coursework' as part of the assessment. There are certain skills which are best tested via continuous assessment of coursework over a long period of time. Indeed, skills such as handling apparatus and setting up experiments in the laboratory cannot be judged by any other means. Some possible benefits of coursework are:

1 Coursework can be fairer to you if you are hard-working and never receive proper credit in formal examinations because of nervousness.

2 You may also suffer because of difficulty in understanding and expressing yourself in written English. Discussion with your teacher may give a clearer picture of your understanding than a written answer.

3 Coursework can stimulate a sense of investigation and discovery through experiments in the laboratory.

4 Coursework will help your understanding of the role that Human Biology plays in the everyday world, its links with other subjects and its relevance to your life. Examination questions which test knowledge of the applications of Human Biology may be unfair because they depend on knowledge 'outside the syllabus'. If you are encouraged to find facts from various sources, this kind of understanding can be tested. You will be able to learn by using up-to-date information on social and technological issues during coursework.

Guidelines for Coursework

General points to remember:

1 Your coursework assessment will account for at least 20% of your final mark in the examination.

2 You must always carry out practical work with due regard to safety.

3 Practical work will be assessed during coursework over two years but there will not be formal practical tests.

4 Your practical assessment will cover the following skills:
(a) observation and recording
(b) measurement
(c) procedure
(d) handling apparatus
(e) formulation of hypotheses and experimental design

5 Each of the skills (a)–(d) will be assessed on widely separated occasions, using different experiments.

6 In many exercises, there may be an overlap in the skills to be assessed, e.g. observing and measuring a biological structure may be assessed by means of a scale drawing. In this case, skill (b)(measurement) and skill (a) (observation and recording) overlap.

7 Assessments will be based on the principle of positive achievement. You will be given opportunities to show what you understand and *can* do.

8 Evidence of the actual practical work that you have undertaken and on which you have been assessed, must be kept. This could include practical work sheets, drawings, etc., because the examination group for which you have entered the examination, will want to see samples of the work to maintain national standards.

The Assessment of Skills via Coursework Practicals

OBSERVATION AND RECORDING

These skills will be assessed in the context of the following:
(a) Observing and recording changes during an experiment, e.g. colour change; changes in volume or change of state of matter.
(b) Observing and recording similarities and differences between two specimens or photographs.
(c) Observing and recording correct proportions and size of objects.

Practical work suitable for assessing these skills

Comparison of sections through an artery and a vein.
Observation of the colour changes during food tests.
Production of carbon dioxide during breathing.
Comparison of teeth.
Identification of specimens using a simple key.

199

Suggested allocation of marks

1, 2 or 3 marks could be given for the skill tested in accordance with the following guidelines:

3 marks If you observe very accurately and give the complete sequence of changes in an experiment.
OR
If you can observe a minimum of three structural differences or similarities.
OR
If you can make an accurate drawing showing all features in the correct proportion.

2 marks If you observe more than one, but not the complete sequence of changes in an experiment.
OR
If you observe two structural differences or similarities.
OR
If you make a clear drawing showing most features: some drawn to the correct proportion.

1 mark If you show poor observational and recording skills, e.g. if you observe one change only in an experiment.
OR
If you observe only one structural similarity or difference.
OR
If you make a drawing with only some features drawn with only some resemblance to the specimen.

MEASUREMENT

You will be assessed on your ability to measure accurately, length, volume, time, temperature and mass.

Suitable practical work

Release of energy from a sample of food.
Breathing rate or pulse rate.
Determination of vitamin C in a food sample.
Making scale drawings.

Suggested allocation of marks

3 marks All measurements accurate to within ± 1.0 mm, 1.0 cm^3, 1 sec, 1 °C, 1.0 g.
2 marks At least two measurements accurate within the limits shown.
1 mark One measurement accurate within the limits shown.

PROCEDURE

You will be assessed on your ability to follow instructions given in written, diagrammatic, or oral form.

Suitable practical work

Comparison of the amount of carbon dioxide in inhaled and exhaled air.
Preparation of a temporary stained microscope slide.
Investigation of the structure of a sheep's heart, bull's eye, or lamb's kidney.
Use of visking tubing as a model gut lining.
Investigations with enzymes.

Suggested allocation of marks

3 marks You are competent in carrying out procedure in accordance with instructions without prompting.
2 marks You are able to carry out procedures with some prompting.
1 mark You can only partly complete a task even with continuous prompting.

HANDLING APPARATUS

You will be assessed on your ability to handle, assemble and use apparatus and/or materials correctly and safely.

Suitable practical work (see the section entitled 'Procedure')

Suggested allocation of marks

3 marks You can handle apparatus and/or materials correctly and safely without help.
2 marks You can handle apparatus and/or materials correctly and safely with some help.
1 mark You can handle apparatus and/or materials correctly and safely only with considerable help.

FORMULATION AND TESTING OF HYPOTHESES

Given a relevant piece of information, you must think of an explanation for it and design and carry out an experiment to test your explanation.

Suitable practical work

(a) Milk kept in a fridge stays fresh longer than milk kept at room temperature. Suggest a possible explanation for this. Design and conduct an experiment to find out if your explanation is correct.

(b) A person's pulse rate at rest is 70 beats per minute. After running around the school field it was 120. Suggest a possible explanation for this. Design and conduct an experiment to find out if your explanation is correct.

(c) Cake is more fattening than bread. Suggest a possible explanation for this. Design and conduct an experiment to find out if your explanation is correct.

Suggested allocation of marks

3 marks You can formulate the explanation and design and conduct an experiment which tests it without help.

2 marks EITHER

You are unable to suggest an explanation, but given the explanation, you can design and conduct an experiment which tests it without help.

OR

You can suggest an explanation and can design and conduct an experiment to test it with some help.

1 mark EITHER

You are unable to suggest an explanation, but given the explanation, you can design and conduct an experiment which tests it only with considerable help.

OR

You can suggest an explanation but cannot design and conduct an experiment to test it even with considerable help.

Examiners assess candidates by awarding a percentage mark based on certain standards:

1 The ability to show theoretical knowledge and understanding of factual information, relevant to the subject.
2 The ability to record information in a concise form with a balanced and logical arrangement.
3 The ability to handle information in a variety of forms and make deductions from it.
4 The ability to solve problems based on biological data.
5 The ability to use investigatory and experimental skills in a laboratory based situation.

All those who have had experience of marking examination scripts know that the majority of candidates could have improved their performance had they followed some simple rules of technique:

(a) Check that the correct exam paper has been received. This may sound obvious, but in an examination room, where several examinations are going on at the same time, mistakes could be made. Also GCSE examinations often involve a choice of differentiated papers. The choice will have been made before you enter the examination room and so it is essential that you know which paper you have chosen and that you receive the correct paper.

(b) Read the instructions at the top of the paper carefully. Look at the number of questions that are to be attempted and whether any of them are compulsory.

(c) If there is a choice, read all of the questions before deciding which to answer.

(d) Having read all the questions and selected the ones you wish to answer (if there is a choice), consider which ones can be answered by direct recall with the least amount of reasoning. These are the questions which usually can be answered in the shortest time (provided you know the facts).

The reason for choosing questions which require the shortest time to answer is a sound one. Time gained at the beginning of the examination will be of great value later when it can be used for those questions which need skills of reasoning and understanding.

It is common practice to include an indication of the number of marks carried by each part of the questions set in GCSE examinations. The breakdown of marks is usually given in the right-hand margin after each question. Candidates are advised to take special notice of this mark allocation because it shows the maximum mark available for a specific part of a question. There should be a direct relationship between this mark and the time taken to answer the question. For example, if a question is divided into three parts, carrying 5, 5, and 10 marks, respectively, it would be pointless to spend more time on either part 1 or 2 than on part 3. A moment spent on planning just how long to take on each part of a question in relation to the allocation of marks is a sensible use of time.

Carefully judge the relevance of your answers. No marks are awarded for irrelevant material, even though it might be accurate. Each question will have an objective mark scheme which is used by all the examiners marking that particular paper. Include only that information which is vital to answer the question. Also it is essential to make your meaning clear. Examiners are not mind readers and will give no credit to the candidate whose statements are obscure and not intelligible. Make no attempt to pad or fill out answers with flowery language. Always write directly to the point and as concisely as possible. If diagrams are specifically requested in a question, they too will have objective mark schemes. Marks will be awarded for accuracy of proportions, clear lines and clear arrangements of labelling arrows. An untidy sketch will not gain marks and is merely a waste of your valuable time. In order not to smudge and make unclear an otherwise good diagram, it is advisable to use pencil rather than ink. Diagrams should be large enough to show all the necessary details and should be fully labelled. Unless a question specifically asks for a diagram, give due consideration to the relevance of labelled drawings or graphs during the initial planning of the answer. Where diagrams would be useful, again at the planning stage, decide which to use and where in your answer to use them.

Sometimes candidates find difficulty in understanding the meaning of instructions given in questions. The following table contains a list of common terms which often introduce questions on examination papers, together with an explanation of each.

Instruction in question	Meaning
Describe/give a description of . . .	Explain, by the use of prose and diagrams, the nature, form or function of a particular object or concept
Give an account of . . .	Write an explanatory description
Discuss . . .	Give an account of the various views on a topic
Compare . . .	Put side by side, one or more similarities
Contrast . . .	Put side by side, one or more differences

Instruction in question	Meaning
Distinguish between . . .	State the essential features of objects which make each different from others. A combination of 'compare' and 'contrast'.
Explain/Account for . . .	Make known in detail, make understood
Indicate/Show . . .	Point out, make known, make understood
State . . .	Present in a form of a concise statement
Define . . .	State precisely and concisely what is meant by
List . . .	Write, one after another, in the form of a catalogue
Summarize . . .	Give a brief account of
Survey/Outline	Give a general (as opposed to detailed) account of
Write an essay on . . .	Write a full account, subdivided into paragraphs, of the subject
Comment on . . .	Make explanatory remarks or criticisms upon
Illustrate by reference to . . .	Use named examples to demonstrate the idea or principle

After completing an answer, read through it immediately. Check carefully that, as a result of writing at high speed, no words have been omitted, particularly any which might alter the sense of a sentence or passage.

INDEX

Page numbers in bold type indicate the main references for those entries.